KU-347-078

A Publication Distributed by Heron Books

WASHINGTON SQUARE

THE PENSION BEAUREPAS

A BUNDLE OF LETTERS

HENRY JAMES

1843–1916

WASHINGTON SQUARE

THE PENSION BEAUREPAS

A BUNDLE OF LETTERS

BY

HENRY JAMES

DISTRIBUTED BY HERON BOOKS

I.S.B.N. for complete set of ten volumes:
0 86225 187 7
I.S.B.N. for this title:
0 86225 196 6

WASHINGTON SQUARE

WASHINGTON SQUARE.

I.

During a portion of the first half of the present century, and more particularly during the latter part of it, there flourished and practised in the city of New York a physician who enjoyed perhaps an exceptional share of the consideration which, in the United States, has always been bestowed upon distinguished members of the medical profession. This profession in America has constantly been held in honour, and more successfully than elsewhere has put forward a claim to the epithet of "liberal." In a country in which, to play a social part, you must either earn your income or make believe that you earn it, the healing art has appeared in a high degree to combine two recognised sources of credit. It belongs to the realm of the practical, which in the United States is a great recommendation; and it is touched by the light of science—a merit appreciated in a community in which the love of knowledge has not always been accompanied by leisure and opportunity. It was an element in Dr. Sloper's reputation that his learning and his skill were very evenly balanced; he was what you might call a scholarly doctor, and yet there was nothing abstract in his remedies—he always ordered you to take something. Though he was felt to be extremely thorough, he was not uncomfortably theoretic, and if he sometimes explained matters rather more minutely than might seem of use to the patinet, he never went so far (like some practitioners one has heard of) as to trust to the explanation alone, but always left behind him an inscrutable prescription. There were some doctors that left the prescription without offering any explanation at all; and he did not belong to that class either, which was after all the most vulgar. It will be seen that I am describing a clever man; and this is really the reason why Dr. Sloper had become a local celebrity. At the time at which we are chiefly concerned with him, he was some fifty years of age, and his popularity was at its height. He was very witty, and he passed in the best society of New York for a man of the world—which, indeed, he was, in a very sufficient degree. I hasten to add, to anticipate possible misconception, that he was not the least of a charlatan. He was a thoroughly honest man—honest in a degree of which he had perhaps lacked the opportunity to give the complete measure; and, putting aside the great good-nature of the circle in which he practised, which was rather fond of boasting that it possessed the "brightest" doctor in the country, he daily justified his claim to the talents attributed to him by the popular voice. He was an observer, even a philosopher, and to be bright was so natural to him, and (as the popular voice said) came so easily, that he never aimed at mere effect, and had none of the little tricks and pretensions of second-rate reputations. It must be confessed that fortune had favoured him, and that he had found the path to prosperity very soft to his tread. He had married at the age of twenty-seven, for love, a very charming girl, Miss Catherine Harrington, of New York, who, in addition to her charms, had brought him a solid dowry. Mrs. Sloper was amiable, graceful, accomplished, elegant, and in 1820 she had been one of the pretty girls of the small but promising capital which clustered about the Battery and overlooked the Bay, and of which the uppermost boundary was indicated by the grassy waysides of Canal Street. Even at the age of twenty-seven Austin Sloper had made his mark sufficiently to mitigate the anomaly of his having been chosen among a dozen suitors by a young woman of high fashion, who had ten thousand dollars of income and the most charming eyes in the island of Manhattan. These eyes, and some of their accompaniments, were for about five years a source of extreme satisfaction to the young physician, who was both a devoted and a very happy husband. The fact of his having married a rich woman made no difference in the line he had traced for himself, and he cultivated his profession with as definite a purpose as if he still had no other resources than his fraction of the modest patrimony which on his father's death he had shared with his brothers and sisters. This purpose had not been preponderantly to make money—it had been rather to learn something and to do something. To learn something interesting, and to do something useful—this was, roughly speaking, the programme he had sketched, and of which the accident of his wife having an income appeared to him in no degree to modify the validity. He was fond of his practice, and of exercising a skill of which he was agreeably conscious, and it was so patent a truth that if he were not a doctor there was nothing else he could be, that a doctor he persisted in being, in the best possible conditions. Of course his easy domestic situation saved him a good deal of drudgery, and his wife's affiliation to the "best people" brought him a good many of those patients whose symptoms are, if not more interesting in themselves than those of the lower orders, at least more consistently displayed. He desired experience, and in the course of twenty years he got a great deal. It must be added that it came to him in some forms which, whatever might have been their intrinsic value, made it the reverse of welcome. His first child, a little boy of extraordinary promise, as the Doctor, who was not addicted to easy enthusiasms, firmly believed, died at three years of age, in spite of everything that the mother's tenderness and the father's science could invent to save him. Two years later Mrs. Sloper gave birth to a second infant—an infant of a sex which rendered the poor child, to the Doctor's sense, an inadequate substitute for his lamented first-born, of whom he had promised himself to make an admirable man. The little girl was a disappointment; but this was not the worst. A week after her birth the young mother, who, as the phrase is, had been doing well, suddenly betrayed alarming symptoms, and before another week had elapsed Austin Sloper was a widower.

For a man whose trade was to keep people alive

he had certainly done poorly in his own family; and a bright doctor who within three years loses his wife and his little boy should perhaps be prepared to see either his skill or his affection impugned. Our friend, however, escaped criticism: that is, he escaped all criticism but his own, which was much the most competent and most formidable. He walked under the weight of this very private censure for the rest of his days, and bore for ever the scars of a castigation to which the strongest hand he knew had treated him on the night that followed his wife's death. The world, which, as I have said, appreciated him, pitied him too much to be ironical; his misfortune made him more interesting, and even helped him to be the fashion. It was observed that even medical families cannot escape the more insidious forms of disease, and that, after all, Dr. Sloper had lost other patients beside the two I have mentioned; which constituted an honourable precedent. His little girl remained to him, and though she was not what he had desired, he proposed to himself to make the best of her. He had on hand a stock of unexpended authority, by which the child, in its early years, profited largely. She had been named, as a matter of course, after her poor mother, and even in her most diminutive babyhood the Doctor never called her anything but Catherine. She grew up a very robust and healthy child, and her father, as he looked at her, often said to himself that, such as she was, he at least need have no fear of losing her. I say "such as she was," because, to tell the truth—— But this is a truth of which I will defer the telling.

II.

WHEN the child was about ten years old, he invited his sister, Mrs. Penniman, to come and stay with him. The Miss Slopers had been but two in number, and both of them had married early in life. The younger, Mrs. Almond by name, was the wife of a prosperous merchant and the mother of a blooming family. She bloomed herself, indeed, and was a comely, comfortable, reasonable woman, and a favourite with her clever brother, who, in the matter of women, even when they were nearly related to him, was a man of distinct preferences. He preferred Mrs. Almond to his sister Lavinia, who had married a poor clergyman, of a sickly constitution and a flowery style of eloquence, and then, at the age of thirty-three, had been left a widow, without children, without fortune—with nothing but the memory of Mr. Penniman's flowers of speech, a certain vague aroma of which hovered about her own conversation. Nevertheless, he had offered her a home under his own roof, which Lavinia accepted with the alacrity of a woman who had spent the ten years of her married life in the town of Poughkeepsie. The Doctor had not proposed to Mrs. Penniman to come and live with him indefinitely; he had suggested that she should make an asylum of his house while she looked about for unfurnished lodgings. It is uncertain whether Mrs. Penniman ever instituted a search for unfurnished lodgings, but it is beyond dispute that she never found them. She settled herself with her brother and never went away, and when Catherine was twenty years old her Aunt Lavinia was still one of the most striking features of her immediate *entourage*. Mrs. Penniman's own account of the matter was that she had remained to take charge of her niece's education. She had given this account, at least, to every one but the Doctor, who never asked for explanations which he could entertain himself any day with inventing. Mrs. Penniman, moreover, though she had a good deal of a certain sort of artificial assurance, shrank, for indefinable reasons, from presenting herself to her brother as a fountain of instruction. She had not a high sense of humour, but she had enough to prevent her from making this mistake; and her brother, on his side, had enough to excuse her, in her situation, for laying him under contribution during a considerable part of a lifetime. He therefore assented tacitly to the proposition which Mrs. Penniman had tacitly laid down, that it was of importance that the poor motherless girl should have a brilliant woman near her. His assent could only be tacit, for he had never been dazzled by his sister's intellectual lustre. Save when he fell in love with Catherine Harrington, he had never been dazzled, indeed, by any feminine characteristics whatever; and though he was to a certain extent what is called a ladies' doctor, his private opinion of the more complicated sex was not exalted. He regarded its complications as more curious than edifying, and he had an idea of the beauty of *reason*, which was on the whole meagrely gratified by what he observed in his female patients. His wife had been a reasonable woman, but she was a bright exception; among several things that he was sure of, this was perhaps the principal. Such a conviction, of course, did little either to mitigate or to abbreviate his widowhood; and it set a limit to his recognition, at the best, of Catherine's possibilities and of Mrs. Penniman's ministrations. He, nevertheless, at the end of six months, accepted his sister's permanent presence as an accomplished fact, and as Catherine grew older perceived that there were in effect good reasons why she should have a companion of her own imperfect sex. He was extremely polite to Lavinia, scrupulously, formally polite; and she had never seen him in anger but once in her life, when he lost his temper in a theological discussion with her late husband. With her he never discussed theology, nor, indeed, discussed anything; he contented himself with making known, very distinctly, in the form of a lucid ultimatum, his wishes with regard to Catherine.

Once, when the girl was about twelve years old, he had said to her—

"Try and make a clever women of her, Lavinia; I should like her to be a clever woman."

Mrs. Penniman, at this, looked thoughtful a moment. "My dear Austin," she then inquired, "do you think it is better to be clever than to be good?"

"Good for what?" asked the Doctor. "You are good for nothing unless you are clever."

From this assertion Mrs. Penniman saw no reason to dissent; she possibly reflected that her own great use in the world was owing to her aptitude for many things.

"Of course I wish Catherine to be good," the Doctor said next day; "but she won't be any the less virtuous for not being a fool. I am not afraid of her being wicked; she will never have the salt of malice in her character. She is as good as good bread, as the French say; but six years hence I don't want to have to compare her to good bread and butter."

"Are you afraid she will be insipid? My dear brother, it is I who supply the butter; so you needn't fear!" said Mrs. Penniman, who had taken in hand the child's accomplishments, overlooking her at the piano, where Catherine displayed a certain talent, and going with her to the dancing-class, where it must be confessed that she made but a modest figure.

Mrs. Penniman was a tall, thin, fair, rather faded woman, with a perfectly amiable disposition, a high standard of gentility, a taste for light literature, and a certain foolish indirectness and obliquity of character. She was romantic, she was sentimental, she had a passion for little secrets and mysteries—a very innocent passion, for her secrets had hitherto always been as unpractical as addled eggs. She was not absolutely veracious; but this defect was of no great consequence, for she had never had anything to conceal. She would have liked to have a lover, and to correspond with him under an assumed name in letters left at a shop; I am bound to say that her imagination never carried the intimacy farther than this. Mrs. Penniman had never had a lover, but her brother, who was very shrewd, understood her turn of mind. "When Catherine is about seventeen," he said to himself, "Lavinia will try and persuade her that some young man with a moustache is in love with her. It will be quite untrue; no young man, with a moustache or without, will ever be in love with Catherine. But Lavinia will take it up, and talk to her about it; perhaps, even, if her taste for clandestine operations doesn't prevail with her, she will talk to me about it. Catherine won't see it, and won't believe it, fortunately for her peace of mind; poor Catherine isn't romantic."

She was a healthy well-grown child, without a trace of her mother's beauty. She was not ugly; she had simply a plain, dull, gentle countenance. The most that had ever been said for her was that she had a "nice" face, and, though she was an heiress, no one had ever thought of regarding her as a belle. Her father's opinion of her moral purity was abundantly justified; she was excellently, imperturbably good; affectionate, docile, obedient, and much addicted to speaking the truth. In her younger years she was a good deal of a romp, and, though it is an awkward confession to make about one's heroine, I must add that she was something of a glutton. She never, that I know of, stole raisins out of the pantry; but she devoted her pocket-money to the purchase of cream-cakes. As regards this, however, a critical attitude would be inconsistent with a candid reference to the early annals of any biographer. Catherine was decidedly not clever; she was not quick with her book, nor, indeed, with anything else. She was not abnormally deficient, and she mustered learning enough to acquit herself respectably in conversation with her contemporaries, among whom it must be avowed, however, that she occupied a secondary place. It is well known that in New York it is possible for a young girl to occupy a primary one. Catherine, who was extremely modest, had no desire to shine, and on most social occasions, as they are called, you would have found her lurking in the background. She was extremely fond of her father and very much afraid of him; she thought him the cleverest and handsomest and most celebrated of men. The poor girl found her account so completely in the exercise of her affections that the little tremor of fear that mixed itself with her filial passion gave the thing an extra relish rather than blunted its edge. Her deepest desire was to please him, and her conception of happiness was to know that she had succeeded in pleasing him. She had never succeeded beyond a certain point. Though on the whole he was very kind to her, she was perfectly aware of this, and to go beyond the point in question seemed to her really something to live for. What she could not know, of course, was that she disappointed him, though on three or four occasions the Doctor had been almost frank about it. She grew up peacefully and prosperously, but at the age of eighteen Mrs. Penniman had not made a clever woman of her. Dr. Sloper would have liked to be proud of his daughter; but there was nothing to be proud of in poor Catherine. There was nothing, of course, to be ashamed of; but this was not enough for the Doctor, who was a proud man and would have enjoyed being able to think of his daughter as an unusual girl. There would have been a fitness in her being pretty and graceful, intelligent and distinguished; for her mother had been the most charming woman of her little day, and as regards her father, of course he knew his own value. He had moments of irritation at having produced a commonplace child, and he even went so far at times as to take a certain satisfaction in the thought that his wife had not lived to find her out. He was naturally slow in making this discovery himself, and it was not till Catherine had become a young lady grown that he regarded the matter as settled. He gave her the benefit of a great many doubts; he was in no haste to conclude. Mrs. Penniman frequently assured him that his daughter had a delightful nature; but he knew how to interpret this assurance. It meant, to his sense, that Catherine was not wise enough to discover that her aunt was a goose—a limitation of mind that could not fail to be agreeable to Mrs. Penniman. Both she and her brother, however, exaggerated the young girl's limitations; for Catherine, though she was very fond of her aunt, and conscious of the gratitude she owed her, regarded her without a particle of that gentle dread which gave its stamp to her admiration of her father. To her mind there was nothing of the infinite about Mrs. Penniman; Catherine saw her all at once, as it were, and was not dazzled by the apparition; whereas her father's great faculties seemed, as they stretched away, to lose themselves in a sort of luminous vagueness, which indicated, not that they stopped, but that Catherine's own mind ceased to follow them.

It must not be supposed that Dr. Sloper visited his disappointment upon the poor girl, or ever let her suspect that she had played him a trick. On the contrary, for fear of being unjust to her, he did his duty with exemplary zeal, and recognised that she was a faithful and affectionate child. Besides, he was a philosopher; he smoked a good many cigars over his disappointment, and in the fulness of time he got used to it. He satisfied himself that he had expected nothing, though, indeed, with a certain oddity of reasoning. "I expect nothing," he said to himself, "so that if she gives me a surprise, it will be all clear gain. If she doesn't, it will be no loss." This was about the time Catherine had reached her eighteenth year; so that it will be seen her father had not been precipitate. At this time she seemed not only incapable of giving surprises; it was almost a question whether she could have received one—she was so quiet and irresponsive. People who expressed themselves roughly called her stolid. But she was irresponsive because she was shy, uncomfortably, painfully shy. This was not always understood, and she sometimes produced an impression of insensibility. In reality she was the softest creature in the world.

III.

As a child she had promised to be tall, but when she was sixteen she ceased to grow, and her stature, like most other points in her composition, was not unusual. She was strong, however, and properly made, and, fortunately, her health was excellent. It has been noted that the Doctor was a philosopher, but I would not have answered for his philosophy if the poor girl had proved a sickly and suffering person. Her appearance of health constituted her principal claim to beauty, and her clear, fresh complexion, in which white and red were very equally distributed, was, indeed, an excellent thing to see. Her eye was small and quiet, her features were rather thick, her tresses brown and smooth. A dull, plain girl she was called by rigorous critics—a quiet, ladylike girl, by those of the more imaginative sort; but by neither class was she very elaborately discussed. When it had been duly impressed upon her that she was a young lady—it was a good while before she could believe it—she suddenly developed a lively taste for dress: a lively taste is quite the expression to use. I feel as if I ought to write it very small, her judgment in this matter was by no means infallible; it was liable to confusions and embarrassments. Her great indulgence of it was really the desire of a rather inarticulate nature to manifest itself; she sought to be eloquent in her garments, and to make up for her diffidence of speech by a fine frankness of costume. But if she expressed herself in her clothes it is certain that people were not to blame for not thinking her a witty person. It must be added that though she had the expectation of a fortune—Dr. Sloper for a long time had been making twenty thousand dollars a year by his profession and laying aside the half of it—the amount of money at her disposal was not greater than the allowance made to many poorer girls. In those days in New York there were still a few altar-fires flickering in the temple of Republican simplicity, and Dr. Sloper would have been glad to see his daughter present herself, with a classic grace, as a priestess of this mild faith. It made him fairly grimace, in private, to think that a child of his should be both ugly and overdressed. For himself, he was fond of the good things of life, and he made a considerable use of them; but he had a dread of vulgarity and even a theory that it was increasing in the society that surrounded him. Moreover, the standard of luxury in the United States thirty years ago was carried by no means so high as at present, and Catherine's clever father took the old-fashioned view of the education of young persons. He had no particular theory on the subject; it had scarcely as yet become a necessity of self-defence to have a collection of theories. It simply appeared to him proper and reasonable that a well-bred young woman should not carry half her fortune on her back. Catherine's back was a broad one, and would have carried a good deal; but to the weight of the paternal displeasure she never ventured to expose it, and our heroine was twenty years old before she treated herself, for evening wear, to a red satin gown trimmed with gold fringe; though this was an article which, for many years, she had coveted in secret. It made her look, when she sported it, like a woman of thirty; but oddly enough, in spite of her taste for fine clothes, she had not a grain of coquetry, and her anxiety when she put them on was as to whether they, and not she, would look well. It is a point on which history has not been explicit, but the assumption is warrantable; it was in the royal raiment just mentioned that she presented herself at a little entertainment given by her aunt, Mrs. Almond. The girl was at this time in her twenty-first year, and Mrs. Almond's party was the beginning of something very important.

Some three or four years before this, Dr. Sloper had moved his household gods up town, as they say in New York. He had been living ever since his marriage in an edifice of red brick, with granite copings and an enormous fanlight over the door, standing in a street within five minutes' walk of the City Hall, which saw its best days (from the social point of view) about 1820. After this, the tide of fashion began to set steadily northward, as, indeed, in New York, thanks to the narrow channel in which it flows, it is obliged to do, and the great hum of traffic rolled farther to the right and left of Broadway. By the time the Doctor changed his residence, the murmur of trade had become a mighty uproar, which was music in the ears of all good citizens interested in the commercial development, as they delighted to call it, of their fortunate isle. Dr. Sloper's interest in this phenomenon was only indirect—though, seeing that, as the years went on, half his patients came to be over-worked men of business, it might have been more immediate—and when most of his neighbours' dwellings (also ornamented with granite copings and large fanlights) had been converted into offices, warehouses, and shipping agencies, and otherwise applied to the base uses of commerce, he determined to look out for a quieter home. The ideal of quiet and of genteel retirement, in 1835, was found in Washington Square, where the doctor built himself a handsome, modern, wide-fronted house, with a big balcony before the drawing-room windows, and a flight of white marble steps ascending to a portal which was also faced with white marble. This structure, and many of its neighbours, which it exactly resembled, were supposed, forty years ago, to embody the last results of architectural science, and they remain to this day very solid and honourable dwellings. In front of them was the square, containing a considerable quantity of inexpensive vegetation, enclosed by a wooden paling, which increased its rural and accessible appearance; and round the corner was the more august precinct of the Fifth Avenue, taking its origin at this point with a spacious and confident air which already marked it for high destinies. I know not whether it is owing to the tenderness of early associations, but this portion of New York appears to many persons the most delectable. It has a kind of established repose which is not of frequent occurrence in other quarters of the long, shrill city; it has a riper, richer, more honourable look than any of the upper ramifications of the great longitudinal thoroughfare—the look of having had something of a social history. It was here, as you might have been informed on good authority, that you had come into a world which appeared to offer a variety of sources of interest; it was here that your grandmother lived, in venerable solitude, and dispensed a hospitality which commended itself alike to the infant imagination and the infant palate, it was here that you took your first walks abroad; following the nursery-maid with unequal step and sniffing up the strange odour of the ailantus-trees which at that time formed the principal umbrage of the square, and diffused an aroma that you were not yet critical enough to dislike as it deserved; it was here, finally, that your first school, kept by a broad-bosomed, broad-based old lady with a ferule, who was always having tea in a blue cup, with a saucer that didn't match, enlarged the circle both of your observations and your sensations. It was here, at any rate, that my heroine spent many years of her life; which is my excuse for this topographical parenthesis.

Mrs. Almond lived much farther up town, in an embryonic street with a high number—a region where the extension of the city began to assume a theoretic air, where poplars grew beside the pavement (when there was one), and mingled their shade with the steep roofs of desultory Dutch houses, and where pigs and chickens disported themselves in the gutter. These elements of rural picturesqueness have now wholly departed from New York street scenery; but they were to be found within the memory of middle-aged persons, in quarters which now would blush to be reminded of them. Catherine had a great many cousins, and with her Aunt Almond's children, who ended by being nine in number, she lived on terms of considerable intimacy. When she was younger, they had been rather afraid of her; she was believed, as the phrase is, to be highly educated, and a person who lived in the intimacy of their Aunt Penniman had something of reflected grandeur. Mrs. Penniman, among the little Almonds, was an object of more admiration than sympathy. Her manners were strange and formidable, and her mourning robes—she dressed in black for twenty years after her husband's death, and then suddenly appeared, one morning, with pink roses in her cap—were complicated in odd, unexpected places with buckles, bugles, and pins, which discouraged familiarity She took children too hard, both for good and for evil, and had an oppressive air of expecting subtle things of them; so that going to see her was a good deal like being taken to church and made to sit in a front pew. It was discovered after a while, however, that Aunt Penniman was but an accident in Catherine's existence, and not a part of its essence, and that when the girl came to spend a Saturday with her cousins, she was available for "follow-my-master," and even for leap-frog. On this basis an understanding was easily arrived at, and for several years Catherine fraternised with her young kinsmen.

I say young kinsmen, because seven of the little Almonds were boys, and Catherine had a preference for those games which are most conveniently played in trousers. By degrees, however, the little Almonds' trousers began to lengthen, and the wearers to disperse and settle themselves in life. The elder children were older than Catherine, and the boys were sent to college or placed in counting-rooms. Of the girls, one married very punctually, and the other as punctually became engaged. It was to celebrate this latter event that Mrs. Almond gave the little party I have mentioned. Her daughter was to marry a stout young stockbroker, a boy of twenty; it was thought a very good thing.

IV.

Mrs. Penniman, with more buckles and bangles than ever, came of course to the entertainment, accompanied by her niece; the Doctor, too, had promised to look in later in the evening. There was to be a good deal of dancing, and before it had gone very far, Marian Almond came up to Catherine, in company with a tall young man. She introduced the young man as a person who had a great desire to make our heroine's acquaintance, and as a cousin of Arthur Townsend, her own intended.

Marian Almond was a pretty little person of seventeen, with a very small figure and a very big sash, to the elegance of whose manners matrimony had nothing to add. She already had all the airs of a hostess, receiving the company, shaking her fan, saying that with so many people to attend to she should have no time to dance. She made a long speech about Mr. Townsend's cousin, to whom she administered a tap with her fan before turning away to other cares. Catherine had not understood all that she said; her attention was given to enjoying Marian's ease of manner and flow of ideas, and to looking at the young man, who was remarkably handsome. She had succeeded, however, as she often failed to do when people were presented to her, in catching his name, which appeared to be the same as that of Marian's little stockbroker. Catherine was always agitated by an introduction; it seemed a difficult moment, and she wondered that some people—her new acquaintance at this moment, for instance—should mind it so little. She wondered what she ought to say, and what would be the consequences of her saying nothing. The consequences at present were very agreeable. Mr. Townsend, leaving her no time for embarrassment, began to talk with an easy smile, as if he had known her for a year.

"What a delightful party! What a charming house! What an interesting family! What a pretty girl your cousin is!"

These observations, in themselves of no great profundity, Mr. Townsend seemed to offer for what they were worth, and as a contribution to an acquaintance. He looked straight into Catherine's eyes. She answered nothing; she only listened, and looked at him; and he, as if he expected no particular reply, went on to say many other things in the same comfortable and natural manner. Catherine, though she felt tongue-tied, was conscious of no embarrassment; it seemed proper that he should talk, and that she should simply look at him. What made it natural was that he was so handsome, or rather, as she phrased it to herself, so beautiful. The music had been silent for a while, but it suddenly began again; and then he asked her, with a deeper, intenser, smile, if she would do him the honour of dancing with them. Even to this inquiry she gave no audible assent; she simply let him put his arm round her waist—as she did so it occurred to her more vividly than it had ever done before, that this was a singular place for a gentleman's arm to be—and in a moment he was guiding her round the room in the harmonious rotation of the polka. When they paused, she felt that she was red; and then, for some moments, she stopped looking at him. She fanned herself, and looked at the flowers that were painted on her fan. He asked her if she would begin again, and she hesitated to answer, still looking at the flowers.

"Does it make you dizzy?" he asked, in a tone of great kindness.

Then Catherine looked up at him; he was certainly beautiful, and not at all red. "Yes," she said; she hardly knew why, for dancing had never made her dizzy.

"Ah, well, in that case," said Mr. Townsend, "we will sit still and talk. I will find a good place to sit."

He found a good place—a charming place; a little sofa that seemed meant only for two persons. The rooms by this time were very full; the dancers increased in number, and people stood close in front of them, turning their backs, so that Catherine and her companion seemed secluded and unobserved. "*We* will talk," the young man had said; but he still did all the talking. Catherine leaned back in her place, with her eyes fixed upon him, smiling and thinking him very clever. He had features like young men in pictures; Catherine had never seen such features—so delicate, so chiselled and finished—among the young New Yorkers whom she passed in the streets and met at parties. He was tall and slim, but he looked extremely strong. Catherine thought he looked like a statue. But a statue would not talk like that, and, above all, would not have eyes of so rare a colour. He had never been at Mrs. Almond's before; he felt very much like a stranger; and it was very kind of Catherine to take pity on him. He was Arthur Townsend's cousin—not very near; several times removed—and Arthur had brought him to present him to the family. In fact, he was a great stranger in New York. It was his native place; but he had not been there for many years. He had been knocking about the world, and living in far-away lands; he had only come back a month or two before. New York was very pleasant, only he felt lonely.

"You see, people forget you," he said, smiling at Catherine with his delightful gaze, while he leaned forward obliquely, turning towards her, with his elbows on his knees.

It seemed to Catherine that no one who had once seen him would ever forget him; but though she made this reflection she kept it to herself, almost as you would keep something precious.

They sat there for some time. He was very amusing. He asked her about the people that were near them; he tried to guess who some of them were, and he made the most laughable mistakes. He criticised them very freely, in a positive, off-hand way. Catherine had never heard any one—especially any young man—talk just like that. It was the way a young man might talk in a novel; or better still, in a play, on the stage, close before the footlights, looking at the audience, and with every one looking at him, so that you wondered at his presence of mind. And yet Mr. Townsend was not like an actor; he seemed so sincere, so natural. This was very interesting; but in the midst of it, Marian Almond came pushing through the crowd, with a little ironical cry, when she found these young people still together, which made every one turn round, and cost Catherine a conscious blush. Marian broke up their talk, and told Mr. Townsend—whom she treated as if she were already married, and he had become her cousin—to run away to her mother, who had been wishing for the last half-hour to introduce him to Mr. Almond.

"We shall meet again!" he said to Catherine as he left her, and Catherine thought it a very original speech.

Her cousin took her by the arm, and made her walk about. "I needn't ask you what you think of Morris!" the young girl exclaimed.

"Is that his name?"

"I don't ask you what you think of his name, but what you think of himself," said Marian.

"Oh, nothing particular!" Catherine answered, dissembling for the first time in her life.

"I have half a mind to tell him that!" cried Marian. "It will do him good. He's so terribly conceited."

"Conceited?" said Catherine, staring.

"So Arthur says, and Arthur knows about him."

"Oh, don't tell him!" Catherine murmured imploringly.

"Don't tell him he's conceited? I have told him so a dozen times."

At this profession of audacity, Catherine looked

down at her little companion in amazement. She supposed it was because Marian was going to be married that she took so much on herself; but she wondered too, whether, when she herself should become engaged, such exploits would be expected of her.

Half an hour later she saw her aunt Penniman sitting in the embrasure of a window, with her head a little on one side, and her gold eye-glass raised to her eyes, which were wandering about the room. In front of her was a gentleman, bending forward a little, with his back turned to Catherine. She knew his back immediately, though she had never seen it; for when he left her, at Marian's instigation, he had retreated in the best order, without turning round. Morris Townsend—the name had already become very familiar to her, as if some one had been repeating it in her ear for the last half hour—Morris Townsend was giving his impressions of the company to her aunt, as he had done to herself; he was saying clever things, and Mrs. Penniman was smiling, as if she approved of them. As soon as Catherine had perceived this she moved away; she would not have liked him to turn round and see her. But it gave her pleasure—the whole thing. That he should talk with Mrs. Penniman, with whom she lived and whom she saw and talked with every day—that seemed to keep him near her, and to make him even easier to contemplate than if she herself had been the object of his civilities; and that Aunt Lavinia should like him, should not be shocked or startled by what he said, this also appeared to the girl a personal gain; for Aunt Lavinia's standard was extremely high, planted as it was over the grave of her late husband, in which, as she had convinced every one, the very genius of conversation was buried. One of the Almond boys, as Catherine called him, invited our heroine to dance a quadrille, and for a quarter of an hour her feet at least were occupied. This time she was not dizzy; her head was very clear. Just when the dance was over, she found herself in the crowd face to face with her father. Dr. Sloper had usually a little smile, never a very big one, and with his little smile playing in his clear eyes and on his neatly-shaved lips, he looked at his daughter's crimson gown.

"Is it possible that this magnificent person is my child?" he said.

You would have surprised him if you had told him so; but it is a literal fact that he almost never addressed his daughter save in the ironical form. Whenever he addressed her he gave her pleasure; but she had to cut her pleasure out of the piece, as it were. There were portions left over, light remnants and snippets of irony, which she never knew what to do with, which seemed too delicate for her own use; and yet Catherine, lamenting the limitations of her understanding, felt that they were too valuable to waste, and had a belief that if they passed over her head they yet contributed to the general sum of human wisdom.

"I am not magnificent," she said, mildly, wishing that she had put on another dress.

"You are sumptuous, opulent, expensive," her father rejoined. "You look as if you had eighty thousand a year."

"Well, so long as I haven't——" said Catherine illogically. Her conception of her prospective wealth was as yet very indefinite.

"So long as you haven't you shouldn't look as if you had. Have you enjoyed your party?"

Catherine hesitated a moment; and then, looking away, "I am rather tired," she murmured. I have said that this entertainment was the beginning of something important for Catherine. For the second time in her life she made an indirect answer; and the beginning of a period of dissimulation is certainly a significant date. Catherine was not so easily tired as that.

Nevertheless, in the carriage, as they drove home, she was as quiet as if fatigue had been her portion. Dr. Sloper's manner of addressing his sister Lavinia had a good deal of resemblance to the tone he had adopted towards Catherine.

"Who was the young man that was making love to you?" he presently asked.

"Oh, my good brother!" murmured Mrs. Penniman, in deprecation.

"He seemed uncommonly tender. Whenever I looked at you, for half an hour, he had the most devoted air."

"The devotion was not to me," said Mrs. Penniman. "It was to Catherine; he talked to me of her."

Catherine had been listening with all her ears. "Oh, Aunt Penniman!" she exclaimed faintly.

"He is very handsome; he is very clever; he expressed himself with a great deal—a great deal of felicity," her aunt went on.

"He is in love with this regal creature, then?" the Doctor inquired humorously.

"Oh, father," cried the girl, still more faintly, devoutly thankful the carriage was dark.

"I don't know that; but he admired her dress."

Catherine did not say to herself in the dark, "My dress only?" Mrs. Penniman's announcement struck her by its richness, not by its meagreness.

"You see," said her father, "he thinks you have eighty thousand a year."

"I don't believe he thinks of that," said Mrs. Penniman; "he is too refined."

"He must be tremendously refined not to think of that!"

"Well, he is!" Catherine exclaimed, before she knew it.

"I thought you had gone to sleep," her father answered. "The hour has come!" he added to himself. "Lavinia is going to get up a romance for Catherine. It's a shame to play such tricks on the girl. What is the gentleman's name?" he went on, aloud.

"I didn't catch it, and I didn't like to ask him. He asked to be introduced to me," said Mrs. Penniman, with a certain grandeur; "but you know how indistinctly Jefferson speaks." Jefferson was Mr. Almond. "Catherine, dear, what was the gentleman's name?"

For a minute, if it had not been for the rumbling of the carriage, you might have heard a pin drop.

"I don't know, Aunt Lavinia," said Catherine, very softly. And, with all his irony, her father believed her.

V.

HE learned what he had asked some three or four days later, after Morris Townsend, with his cousin, had called in Washington Square. Mrs. Penniman did not tell her brother, on the drive home, that she had intimated to this agreeable young man, whose name she did not know, that, with her niece, she should be very glad to see him; but she was greatly pleased, and even a little flattered, when, late on a Sunday afternoon, the two gentlemen made their appearance. His coming with Arthur Townsend made it more natural and easy; the latter young man was on the point of becoming connected with the family, and Mrs. Penniman had remarked to Catherine that, as he was going to marry Marian, it would be polite in him to call. These events came to pass late in the autumn, and Catherine and her aunt had been sitting together in the closing dusk, by the firelight, in the high back-parlour.

Arthur Townsend fell to Catherine's portion, while his companion placed himself on the sofa, beside Mrs. Penniman. Catherine had hitherto not been a harsh critic; she was easy to please—she liked to talk with young men. But Marian's betrothed, this evening, made her feel vaguely fastidious; he sat looking at the fire and rubbing his knees with his hands. As for Catherine, she scarcely even pretended to keep up the conversation; her attention had fixed itself on the other side of the room; she was listening to what went on between the other Mr. Townsend and her aunt. Every now and then he looked over at Catherine herself and smiled, as if to show that what he said was for her benefit too. Catherine would have liked to change her place, to go and sit near them, where she might see and hear him better. But she was afraid of seeming bold—of looking eager; and, besides, it would not have been polite to Marian's little suitor. She wondered why the other gentleman had picked out her aunt—how he came to have so much to say to Mrs. Penniman, to whom, usually, young men were not especially devoted. She was not at all jealous of Aunt Lavinia, but she was a little envious, and above all she wondered; for Morris Townsend was an object on which she found that her imagination could exercise itself indefinitely. His cousin had been describing a house that he had taken in view of his union with Marian, and the domestic conveniences he meant to introduce into it; how Marian wanted a larger one, and Mrs. Almond recommended a smaller one, and how he himself was convinced that he had got the neatest house in New York.

"It doesn't matter," he said; "it's only for three or four years. At the end of three or four years we'll move. That's the way to live in New York—to move every three or four years. Then you always get the last thing. It's because the city's growing so quick—you've got to keep up with it. It's going straight up town—that's where New York's going. If I wasn't afraid Marian would be lonely, I'd go up there—right up to the top—and wait for it. Only have to wait ten years—they'd all come up after you. But Marian says she wants some neighbours—she doesn't want to be a pioneer. She says that if she's got to be the first settler she had better go out to Minnesota. I guess we'll move up little by little; when we get tired of one street we'll go higher. So you see we'll always have a new house; it's a great advantage to have a new house; you get all the latest improvements. They invent everything all over again about every five years, and it's a great thing to keep up with the new things. I always try and keep up with the new things of every kind. Don't you think that's a good motto for a young couple—to keep 'going higher?' That's the name of that piece of poetry—what do they call it?—*Excelsior!*"

Catherine bestowed on her junior visitor only just enough attention to feel that this was not the way Mr. Morris Townsend had talked the other night, or that he was talking now to her fortunate aunt. But suddenly his aspiring kinsman became more interesting. He seemed to have become conscious that she was affected by his companion's presence, and he thought it proper to explain it.

"My cousin asked me to bring him, or I shouldn't have taken the liberty. He seemed to want very much to come; you know he's awfully sociable. I told him I wanted to ask you first, but he said Mrs. Penniman had invited him. He isn't particular what he says when he wants to come somewhere! But Mrs. Penniman seems to think it's all right."

"We are very glad to see him," said Catherine. And she wished to talk more about him; but she hardly knew what to say. "I never saw him before," she went on presently.

Arthur Townsend stared.

"Why, he told me he talked with you for over half an hour the other night."

"I mean before the other night. That was the first time."

"Oh, he has been away from New York—he has been all round the world. He doesn't know many people here, but he's very sociable, and he wants to know every one."

"Every one?" said Catherine.

"Well, I mean all the good ones. All the pretty young ladies—like Mrs. Penniman!" And Arthur Townsend gave a private laugh.

"My aunt likes him very much," said Catherine.

"Most people like him—he's so brilliant."

"He's more like a foreigner," Catherine suggested.

"Well, I never knew a foreigner!" said young Townsend, in a tone which seemed to indicate that his ignorance had been optional.

"Neither have I," Catherine confessed, with more humility. "They say they are generally brilliant," she added, vaguely.

"Well, the people of this city are clever enough for me. I know some of them that think they are too clever for me; but they ain't!"

"I suppose you can't be too clever," said Catherine, still with humility.

"I don't know. I know some people that call my cousin too clever."

Catherine listened to this statement with extreme interest, and a feeling that if Morris Townsend had a fault it would naturally be that one. But she did not commit herself, and in a moment she asked: —"Now that he has come back, will he stay here always?"

"Ah," said Arthur, "if he can get something to do."

"Something to do?"

"Some place or other; some business."

"Hasn't he got any?" said Catherine, who had never heard of a young man—of the upper class—in this situation.

"No; he's looking round. But he can't find anything."

"I am very sorry," Catherine permitted herself to observe.

"Oh, he doesn't mind," said young Townsend. "He takes it easy—he isn't in a hurry. He is very particular."

Catherine thought he naturally would be, and gave herself up for some moments to the contemplation of this idea, in several of its bearings.

"Won't his father take him into his business—his office?" she at last inquired.

"He hasn't got any father—he has only got a sister. Your sister can't help you much."

It seemed to Catherine that if she were his sister she would disprove this axiom. "Is she—is she pleasant?" she asked in a moment.

"I don't know—I believe she's very respectable,"

said young Townsend. And then he looked across to his cousin and began to laugh. "Look here, we are talking about you," he added.

Morris Townsend paused in his conversation with Mrs. Penniman, and stared, with a little smile. Then he got up, as if he were going.

"As far as you are concerned, I can't return the compliment," he said to Catherine's companion. "But as regards Miss Sloper, it's another affair."

Catherine thought this little speech wonderfully well turned; but she was embarrassed by it, and she also got up. Morris Townsend stood looking at her and smiling; he put out his hand for farewell. He was going, without having said anything to her; but even on these terms she was glad to have seen him.

"I will tell her what you have said—when you go!" said Mrs. Penniman, with an insinuating laugh.

Catherine blushed, for she felt almost as if they were making sport of her. What in the world could this beautiful young man have said? He looked at her still, in spite of her blush; but very kindly and respectfully.

"I have had no talk with you," he said, "and that was what I came for. But it will be a good reason for coming another time; a little pretext—if I am obliged to give one. I am not afraid of what your aunt will say when I go."

With this the two young men took their departure; after which Catherine, with her blush still lingering, directed a serious and interrogative eye to Mrs. Penniman. She was incapable of elaborate artifice, and she resorted to no jocular device—to no affectation of the belief that she had been maligned—to learn what she desired.

"What did you say you would tell me?" she asked.

Mrs. Penniman came up to her, smiling and nodding a little, looked at her all over, and gave a twist to the knot of ribbon in her neck. "It's a great secret, my dear child; but he is coming a-courting!"

Catherine was serious still. "Is that what he told you!"

"He didn't say so exactly. But he left me to guess it. I'm a good guesser."

"Do you mean a-courting me?"

"Not me, certainly, miss; though I must say he is a hundred times more polite to a person who has no longer extreme youth to recommend her than most of the young men. He is thinking of some one else." And Mrs. Penniman gave her niece a delicate little kiss. "You must be very gracious to him."

Catherine stared—she was bewildered. "I don't understand you," she said; "he doesn't know me."

"Oh yes, he does; more than you think. I have told him all about you."

"Oh, Aunt Penniman!" murmured Catherine, as if this had been a breach of trust. "He is a perfect stranger—we don't know him." There was infinite modesty in the poor girl's "we."

Aunt Penniman, however, took no account of it; she spoke even with a touch of acrimony. "My dear Catherine, you know very well that you admire him!"

"Oh, Aunt Penniman!" Catherine could only murmur again. It might very well be that she admired him—though this did not seem to her a thing to talk about. But that this brilliant stranger—this sudden apparition, who had barely heard the sound of her voice—took that sort of interest in her that was expressed by the romantic phrase of which Mrs. Penniman had just made use: this could only be a figment of the restless brain of Aunt Lavinia, whom every one knew to be a woman of powerful imagination.

VI.

Mrs. Penniman even took for granted at times that other people had as much imagination as herself; so that when, half an hour later, her brother came in, she addressed him quite on this principle.

"He has just been here, Austin; it's such a pity you missed him."

"Whom in the world have I missed?" asked the Doctor.

"Mr. Morris Townsend; he has made us such a delightful visit."

"And who in the world is Mr. Morris Townsend?"

"Aunt Penniman means the gentleman—the gentleman whose name I couldn't remember," said Catherine.

"The gentleman at Elizabeth's party who was so struck with Catherine," Mrs. Penniman added.

"Oh, his name is Morris Townsend, is it? And did he come here to propose to you?"

"Oh, father," murmured the girl for all answer, turning away to the window, where the dusk had deepened to darkness.

"I hope he won't do that without your permission," said Mrs. Penniman, very graciously.

"After all, my dear, he seems to have yours," her brother answered.

Lavinia simpered, as if this might not be quite enough, and Catherine, with her forehead touching the window-panes, listened to this exchange of epigrams as reservedly as if they had not each been a pin-prick in her own destiny.

"The next time he comes," the Doctor added, "you had better call me. He might like to see me."

Morris Townsend came again, some five days afterwards; but Dr. Sloper was not called, as he was absent from home at the time. Catherine was with her aunt when the young man's name was brought in, and Mrs. Penniman, effacing herself and protesting, made a great point of her niece's going into the drawing-room alone.

"This time it's for you—for you only," she said. "Before, when he talked to me, it was only preliminary—it was to gain my confidence. Literally, my dear, I should not have the *courage* to show myself to-day."

And this was perfectly true. Mrs. Penniman was not a brave woman, and Morris Townsend had struck her as a young man of great force of character, and of remarkable powers of satire; a keen, resolute, brilliant nature, with which one must exercise a great deal of tact. She said to herself that he was "imperious," and she liked the word and the idea. She was not the least jealous of her niece, and she had been perfectly happy with Mr. Penniman, but in the bottom of her heart she permitted herself the observation: "That's the sort of husband I should have had!" He was certainly much more imperious—she ended by calling it imperial—than Mr. Penniman.

So Catherine saw Mr. Townsend alone, and her aunt did not come in even at the end of the visit. The visit was a long one; he sat there—in the front parlour, in the biggest arm-chair—for more than an hour. He seemed more at home this time—more familiar; lounging a little in the chair, slapping a cushion that was near him with his stick, and looking round the room a good deal, and at the objects it contained, as well as at Catherine; whom, however, he also contemplated freely. There was a smile of respectful devotion in his handsome eyes which seemed to Catherine almost solemnly beautiful; it made her think of a young knight in a poem. His talk, however, was not particularly knightly; it was light and easy and friendly; it took a practical turn, and he asked a number of questions about herself—what were her tastes—if she liked this and that—what were her habits. He said to her, with his charming smile, "Tell me about yourself; give me a little sketch." Catherine had very little to tell, and she had no talent for sketching; but before he went she had confided to him that she had a secret passion for the theatre, which had been but scantily gratified, and a taste for operatic music—that of Bellini and Donizetti, in especial (it must be remembered in extenuation of this primitive young woman that she held these opinions in an age of general darkness)—which she rarely had an occasion to hear, except on the hand-organ. She confessed that she was not particularly fond of literature. Morris Townsend agreed with her that books were tiresome things; only, as he said, you had to read a good many before you found it out. He had been to places that people had written books about, and they were not a bit like the descriptions. To see for yourself—that was the great thing; he always tried to see for himself. He had seen all the principal actors—he had been to all the best theatres in London and Paris. But the actors were always like the authors—they always exaggerated. He liked everything to be natural. Suddenly he stopped, looking at Catherine with his smile.

"That's what I like you for; you are so natural! Excuse me," he added; "you see I am natural myself!"

And before she had time to think whether she excused him or not—which afterwards, at leisure, she became conscious that she did—he began to talk about music, and to say that it was his greatest pleasure in life. He had heard all the great singers in Paris and London—Pasta and Rubini and Lablache—and when you had done that, you could say that you knew what singing was.

"I sing a little myself," he said; "some day I will show you. Not to-day, but some other time."

And then he got up to go; he had omitted, by accident, to say that he would sing to her if she would play to him. He thought of this after he got into the street; but he might have spared his compunction, for Catherine had not noticed the lapse. She was thinking only that "some other time" had a delightful sound; it seemed to spread itself over the future.

This was all the more reason, however, though she was ashamed and uncomfortable, why she should tell her father that Mr. Morris Townsend had called again. She announced the fact abruptly, almost violently, as soon as the Doctor came into the house; and having done so—it was her duty—she took measures to leave the room. But she could not leave it fast enough; her father stopped her just as she reached the door.

"Well, my dear, did he propose to you to-day?" the Doctor asked.

This was just what she had been afraid he would say; and yet she had no answer ready. Of course she would have liked to take it as a joke—as her father must have meant it; and yet she would have liked, also, in denying it, to be a little positive, a little sharp; so that he would perhaps not ask the question again. She didn't like it—it made her unhappy. But Catherine could never be sharp; and for a moment she only stood, with her hand on the door-knob, looking at her satiric parent, and giving a little laugh.

"Decidedly," said the Doctor to himself, "my daughter is not brilliant!"

But he had no sooner made this reflection than Catherine found something; she had decided on the whole to take the thing as a joke.

"Perhaps he will do it the next time!" she exclaimed, with a repetition of her laugh. And she quickly got out of the room.

The Doctor stood staring; he wondered whether his daughter were serious. Catherine went straight to her own room, and by the time she reached it she bethought herself that there was something else—something better—she might have said. She almost wished, now, that her father would ask his question again, so that she might reply:—"Oh yes, Mr. Morris Townsend proposed to me, and I refused him!"

The Doctor, however, began to put his questions elsewhere; it naturally having occurred to him that he ought to inform himself properly about this handsome young man who had formed the habit of running in and out of his house. He addressed himself to the elder of his sisters, Mrs. Almond—not going to her for the purpose; there was no such hurry as that—but having made a note of the matter for the first opportunity. The Doctor was never eager, never impatient nor nervous; but he made notes of everything, and he regularly consulted his notes. Among them the information he obtained from Mrs. Almond about Morris Townsend took its place.

"Lavinia has already been to ask me," she said. "Lavinia is most excited; I don't understand it. It's not, after all, Lavinia that the young man is supposed to have designs upon. She is very peculiar."

"Ah, my dear," the Doctor replied, "she has not lived with me these twelve years without my finding it out!"

"She has got such an artificial mind," said Mrs. Almond, who always enjoyed an opportunity to discuss Lavinia's peculiarities with her brother. "She didn't want me to tell you that she had asked me about Mr. Townsend; but I told her I would. She always wants to conceal everything."

"And yet at moments no one blurts things out with such crudity. She is like a revolving lighthouse; pitch darkness alternating with a dazzling brilliancy! But what did you tell her?" the Doctor asked.

"What I tell you; that I know very little of him."

"Lavinia must have been disappointed at that," said the Doctor; "she would prefer him to have been guilty of some romantic crime. However, we must make the best of people. They tell me our gentleman is the cousin of the little boy to whom you are about to entrust the future of your little girl."

"Arthur is not a little boy; he is a very old man; you and I will never be so old. He is a distant relation of Lavinia's *protégé*. The name is the same, but I am given to understand that there are Townsends and Townsends. So Arthur's mother tells me; she talked about 'branches'—younger branches, elder branches, inferior branches—as if it were a royal house. Arthur, it appears, is of the reigning line, but poor Lavinia's young man is not. Beyond this, Arthur's mother knows very little about him; she has only a vague story that he has been 'wild.' But I know his sister a little, and she is a very nice woman. Her name is Mrs. Montgomery; she is a widow, with a little property and five children. She lives in the Second Avenue."

"What does Mrs. Montgomery say about him?"

"That he has talents by which he might distinguish himself."

"Only he is lazy, eh?"

"She doesn't say so."

"That's family pride," said the Doctor. "What is his profession?"

"He hasn't got any; he is looking for something. I believe he was once in the Navy."

"Once? What is his age?"

"I suppose he is upwards of thirty. He must have gone into the Navy very young. I think Arthur told me that he inherited a small property —which was perhaps the cause of his leaving the Navy—and that he spent it all in a few years. He travelled all over the world, lived abroad, amused himself. I believe it was a kind of system, a theory he had. He has lately come back to America, with the intention, as he tells Arthur, of beginning life in earnest."

"Is he in earnest about Catherine, then?"

"I don't see why you should be incredulous," said Mrs. Almond. "It seems to me that you have never done Catherine justice. You must remember that she has the prospect of thirty thousand a year."

The Doctor looked at his sister a moment, and then, with the slightest touch of bitterness:—"You at least appreciate her," he said.

Mrs. Almond blushed.

"I don't mean that is her only merit; I simply mean that it is a great one. A great many young men think so; and you appear to me never to have been properly aware of that. You have always had a little way of alluding to her as an unmarriageable girl."

"My allusions are as kind as yours, Elizabeth," said the Doctor, frankly. "How many suitors has Catherine had, with all her expectations—how much attention has she ever received? Catherine is not unmarriageable, but she is absolutely unattractive. What other reason is there for Lavinia being so charmed with the idea that there is a lover in the house? There has never been one before, and Lavinia, with her sensitive, sympathetic nature, is not used to the idea. It affects her imagination. I must do the young men of New York the justice to say that they strike me as very disinterested. They prefer pretty girls—lively girls—girls like your own. Catherine is neither pretty nor lively."

"Catherine does very well; she has a style of her own—which is more than my poor Marian has, who has no style at all," said Mrs. Almond. "The reason Catherine has received so little attention is that she seems to all the young men to be older than themselves. She is so large, and she dresses—so richly. They are rather afraid of her, I think; she looks as if she had been married already, and you know they don't like married women. And if our young men appear disinterested," the Doctor's wiser sister went on, "it is because they marry, as a general thing, so young, before twenty-five, at the age of innocence and sincerity, before the age of calculation. If they only waited a little, Catherine would fare better."

"As a calculation? Thank you very much," said the Doctor.

"Wait till some intelligent man of forty comes along, and he will be delighted with Catherine," Mrs. Almond continued.

"Mr. Townsend is not old enough, then; his motives may be pure."

"It is very possible that his motives are pure; I should be very sorry to take the contrary for granted. Lavinia is sure of it, and, as he is a very prepossessing youth, you might give him the benefit of the doubt."

Dr. Sloper reflected a moment.

"What are his present means of subsistence?"

"I have no idea. He lives, as I say, with his sister."

"A widow, with five children? Do you mean he lives *upon* her?"

Mrs. Almond got up, and with a certain impatience: "Had you not better ask Mrs. Montgomery herself?" she inquired.

"Perhaps I may come to that," said the Doctor. "Did you say the Second Avenue?" He made a note of the Second Avenue.

VII.

He was, however, by no means so much in earnest as this might seem to indicate; and, indeed, he was more than anything else amused with the whole situation. He was not in the least in a state of tension or of vigilance, with regard to Catherine's prospects; he was even on his guard against the ridicule that might attach itself to the spectacle of a house thrown into agitation by its daughter and heiress receiving attentions unprecedented in its annals. More than this, he went so far as to promise himself some entertainment from the little drama—if drama it was—of which Mrs. Penniman desired to represent the ingenious Mr. Townsend as the hero. He had no intention, as yet, of regulating the *dénouement*. He was perfectly willing, as Elizabeth had suggested, to give the young man the benefit of every doubt. There was no great danger in it; for Catherine, at the age of twenty-two, was after all a rather mature blossom, such as could be plucked from the stem only by a vigorous jerk. The fact that Morris Townsend was poor—was not of necessity against him; the Doctor had never made up his mind that his daughter should marry a rich man. The fortune she would inherit struck him as a very sufficient provision for two reasonable persons, and if a penniless swain who could give a good account of himself should enter the lists, he should be judged quite upon his personal merits. There were other things besides. The Doctor thought it very vulgar to be precipitate in accusing people of mercenary motives, inasmuch as his door had as yet not been in the least besieged by fortune-hunters; and, lastly, he was very curious to see whether Catherine might really be loved for her moral worth. He smiled as he reflected that poor Mr. Townsend had been only twice to the house, and he said to Mrs. Penniman that the next time he should come she must ask him to dinner.

He came very soon again, and Mrs. Penniman had of course great pleasure in executing this mission. Morris Townsend accepted her invitation with equal good grace, and the dinner took place a few days later. The Doctor had said to himself, justly enough, that they must not have the young man alone; this would partake too much of the nature of encouragement. So two or three other persons were invited; but Morris Townsend, though he was by no means the ostensible, was the real, occasion of the feast. There is every reason to suppose that he desired to make a good impression; and if he fell short of this result, it was not for want of a good deal of intelligent effort. The Doctor talked to him very little during dinner; but he observed him attentively, and after the ladies had gone out he pushed him the wine and asked him several questions. Morris was not a young man who needed to be pressed, and he found quite enough encouragement in the superior quality of the claret. The Doctor's wine was admirable, and it may be communicated to the reader that while he sipped it Morris reflected that a cellar-full of good liquor—there was evidently a cellar-full here—would be a most attractive idiosyncrasy in a father-in-law. The Doctor was struck with his appreciative guest; he saw that he was not a commonplace young man. "He has ability," said Catherine's father, "decided ability; he has a very good head if he chooses to use it. And he is uncommonly well turned out; quite the sort of figure that pleases the ladies. But I don't think I like him." The Doctor, however, kept his reflections to himself, and talked to his visitors about foreign lands, concerning which Morris offered him more information than he was ready, as he mentally phrased it, to swallow. Dr. Sloper had travelled but little, and he took the liberty of not believing everything this anecdotical idler narrated. He prided himself on being something of a physiognomist, and while the young man, chatting with easy assurance, puffed his cigar and filled his glass again, the Doctor sat with his eyes quietly fixed on his bright, expressive face. "He has the assurance of the devil himself," said Morris's host; "I don't think I ever saw such assurance. And his powers of invention are most remarkable. He is very knowing; they were not so knowing as that in my time. And a good head, did I say? I should think so—after a bottle of Madeira, and a bottle and a half of claret?"

After dinner Morris Townsend went and stood before Catherine, who was standing before the fire in her red satin gown.

"He doesn't like me—he doesn't like me at all!" said the young man.

"Who doesn't like you?" asked Catherine.

"Your father; extraordinary man!"

"I don't see how you know," said Catherine, blushing.

"I feel; I am very quick to feel."

"Perhaps you are mistaken."

"Ah, well; you ask him and you will see."

"I would rather not ask him, if there is any danger of his saying what you think."

Morris looked at her with an air of mock melancholy.

"It wouldn't give you any pleasure to contradict him?"

"I never contradict him," said Catherine.

"Will you hear me abused without opening your lips in my defence?"

"My father won't abuse you. He doesn't know you enough."

Morris Townsend gave a loud laugh, and Catherine began to blush again.

"I shall never mention you," she said, to take refuge from her confusion.

"That is very well; but it is not quite what I should have liked you to say. I should have liked you to say: 'If my father doesn't think well of you, what does it matter?'"

"Ah, but it would matter; I couldn't say that!" the girl exclaimed.

He looked at her for a moment, smiling a little; and the Doctor, if he had been watching him just then, would have seen a gleam of fine impatience in the sociable softness of his eye. But there was no impatience in his rejoinder—none, at least, save what was expressed in a little appealing sigh. "Ah, well, then, I must not give up the hope of bringing him round!"

He expressed it more frankly to Mrs. Penniman, later in the evening. But before that he sang two or three songs at Catherine's timid request; not that he flattered himself that this would help to bring her father round. He had a sweet, light tenor voice, and when he had finished, every one made some exclamation—every one, that is, save Catherine, who remained intensely silent. Mrs. Penniman declared that his manner of singing was "most artistic," and Dr. Sloper said it was "very taking—very taking indeed;" speaking loudly and distinctly, but with a certain dryness.

"He doesn't like me—he doesn't like me at all," said Morris Townsend, addressing the aunt in the same manner as he had done the niece. "He thinks I'm all wrong."

Unlike her niece, Mrs. Penniman asked for no explanation. She only smiled very sweetly, as if she understood everything; and, unlike Catherine too, she made no attempt to contradict him. "Pray, what does it matter?" she murmured softly.

"Ah, you say the right thing!" said Morris, greatly to the gratification of Mrs. Penniman, who prided herself on always saying the right thing.

The Doctor, the next time he saw his sister Elizabeth, let her know that he had made the acquaintance of Lavinia's *protégé.*

"Physically," he said, "he's uncommonly well

set up. As an anatomist, it is really a pleasure to me to see such a beautiful structure; although, if people were all like him, I suppose there would be very little need for doctors."

"Don't you see anything in people but their bones?" Mrs. Almond rejoined. "What do you think of him as a father?"

"As a father? Thank Heaven I am not his father!"

"No; but you are Catherine's. Lavinia tells me she is in love."

"She must get over it. He is not a gentleman."

"Ah, take care! Remember that he is a branch of the Townsends."

"He is not what I call a gentleman. He has not the soul of one. He is extremely insinuating; but it's a vulgar nature. I saw through it in a minute. He is altogether too familiar—I hate familiarity. He is a plausible coxcomb."

"Ah, well," said Mrs. Almond; "if you make up your mind so easily, it's a great advantage."

"I don't make up my mind easily. What I tell you is the result of thirty years of observation; and in order to be able to form that judgment in a single evening, I have had to spend a lifetime in study."

"Very possibly you are right. But the thing is for Catherine to see it."

"I will present her with a pair of spectacles!" said the Doctor.

VIII.

If it were true that she was in love, she was certainly very quiet about it; but the Doctor was of course prepared to admit that her quietness might mean volumes. She had told Morris Townsend that she would not mention him to her father, and she saw no reason to retract this vow of discretion. It was no more than decently civil, of course, that after having dined in Washington Square, Morris should call there again; and it was no more than natural that, having been kindly received on this occasion, he should continue to present himself. He had had plenty of leisure on his hands; and thirty years ago, in New York, a young man of leisure had reason to be thankful for aids to self-oblivion. Catherine said nothing to her father about these visits, though they had rapidly become the most important, the most absorbing thing in her life. The girl was very happy. She knew not as yet what would come of it; but the present had suddenly grown rich and solemn. If she had been told she was in love, she would have been a good deal surprised; for she had an idea that love was an eager and exacting passion, and her own heart was filled in these days with the inpulse of self-effacement and sacrifice. Whenever Morris Townsend had left the house, her imagination projected itself, with all its strength, into the idea of his soon coming back; but if she had been told at such a moment that he would not return for a year, or even that he would never return, she would not have complained nor rebelled, but would have humbly accepted the decree, and sought for consolation in thinking over the times she had already seen him, the words he had spoken, the sound of his voice, of his tread, the expression of his face. Love demands certain things as a right; but Catherine had no sense of her rights; she had only a consciousness of immense and unexpected favours. Her very gratitude for these things had hushed itself; for it seemed to her that there would be something of impudence in making a festival of her secret. Her father suspected Morris Townsend's visits, and noted her reserve. She seemed to beg pardon for it; she looked at him constantly in silence, as if she meant to say that she said nothing because she was afraid of irritating him. But the poor girl's dumb eloquence irritated him more than anything else would have done, and he caught himself murmuring more than once that it was a grievous pity his only child was a simpleton. His murmurs, however, were inaudible; and for a while he said nothing to any one. He would have liked to know exactly how often young Townsend came; but he had determined to ask no questions of the girl herself—to say nothing more to her that would show that he watched her. The Doctor had a great idea of being largely just: he wished to leave his daughter her liberty, and interfere only when the danger should be proved. It was not in his manner to obtain information by indirect methods, and it never even occurred to him to question the servants. As for Lavinia, he hated to talk to her about the matter; she annoyed him with her mock romanticism. But he had to come to this. Mrs. Penniman's convictions as regards the relations of her niece and the clever young visitor who saved appearances by coming ostensibly for both the ladies —Mrs. Penniman's convictions had passed into a riper and richer phase. There was to be no crudity in Mrs. Penniman's treatment of the situation; she had become as uncommunicative as Catherine herself. She was tasting of the sweets of concealment; she had taken up the line of mystery. "She would be enchanted to be able to prove to herself that she is persecuted," said the Doctor; and when at last he questioned her, he was sure she would contrive to extract from his words a pretext for this belief.

"Be so good as to let me know what is going on in the house," he said to her, in a tone which, under the circumstances, he himself deemed genial.

"Going on, Austin?" Mrs. Penniman exclaimed. "Why, I am sure I don't know! I believe that last night the old gray cat had kittens?"

"At her age?" said the Doctor. "The idea is startling—almost shocking. Be so good as to see that they are all drowned. But what else has happened?"

"Ah, the dear little kittens!" cried Mrs. Penniman. "I wouldn't have them drowned for the world!"

Her brother puffed his cigar a few moments in silence. "Your sympathy with kittens, Lavinia," he presently resumed, "arises from a feline element in your own character."

"Cats are very graceful, and very clean," said Mrs. Penniman, smiling.

"And very stealthy. You are the embodiment both of grace and of neatness; but you are wanting in frankness."

"You certainly are not, dear brother."

"I don't pretend to be graceful, though I try to be neat. Why haven't you let me know that Mr. Morris Townsend is coming to the house four times a week?"

Mrs. Penniman lifted her eyebrows. "Four times a week?"

"Five times, if you prefer it. I am away all day, and I see nothing. But when such things happen, you should let me know."

Mrs. Penniman, with her eyebrows still raised, reflected intently. "Dear Austin," she said at last, "I am incapable of betraying a confidence. I would rather suffer anything."

"Never fear; you shall not suffer. To whose confidence is it you allude? Has Catherine made you take a vow of eternal secrecy?"

"By no means. Catherine has not told me as much as she might. She has not been very trustful."

"It is the young man, then, who has made you his confidant? Allow me to say that it is extremely indiscreet of you to form secret alliances with young men. You don't know where they may lead you."

"I don't know what you mean by an alliance," said Mrs. Penniman. "I take a great interest in Mr. Townsend; I won't conceal that. But that's all."

"Under the circumstances, that is quite enough. What is the source of your interest in Mr. Townsend?"

"Why," said Mrs. Penniman, musing, and then breaking into her smile, "that he is so interesting!"

The Doctor felt that he had need of his patience. "And what makes him interesting?—his good looks?"

"His misfortunes, Austin."

"Ah, he has had misfortunes? That, of course, is always interesting. Are you at liberty to mention a few of Mr. Townsend's?"

"I don't know that he would like it," said Mrs. Penniman. "He has told me a great deal about himself—he has told me, in fact, his whole history. But I don't think I ought to repeat those things. He would tell them to you, I am sure, if he thought you would listen to him kindly. With kindness you may do anything with him."

The Doctor gave a laugh. "I shall request him very kindly, then, to leave Catherine alone."

"Ah!" said Mrs. Penniman, shaking her forefinger at her brother, with her little finger turned out, "Catherine has probably said something to him kinder than that!"

"Said that she loved him? Do you mean that?"

Mrs. Penniman fixed her eyes on the floor. "As I tell you, Austin, she doesn't confide in me."

"You have an opinion, I suppose, all the same. It is that I ask you for; though I don't conceal from you that I shall not regard it as conclusive."

Mrs. Penniman's gaze continued to rest on the carpet; but at last she lifted it, and then her brother thought it very expressive. "I think Catherine is very happy; that is all I can say."

"Townsend is trying to marry her—is that what you mean?"

"He is greatly interested in her."

"He finds her such an attractive girl?"

"Catherine has a lovely nature, Austin," said Mrs. Penniman, "and Mr. Townsend has had the intelligence to discover that."

"With a little help from you, I suppose. My dear Lavinia," cried the Doctor, "you are an admirable aunt!"

"So Mr. Townsend says," observed Lavinia, smiling.

"Do you think he is sincere?" asked her brother.

"In saying that?"

"No; that's of course. But in his admiration for Catherine?"

"Deeply sincere. He has said to me the most appreciative, the most charming things about her. He would say them to you, if he were sure you would listen to him—gently."

"I doubt whether I can undertake it. He appears to require a great deal of gentleness."

"He is a sympathetic, sensitive nature," said Mrs. Penniman.

Her brother puffed his cigar again in silence. "These delicate qualities have survived his vicissitudes, eh? All this while you haven't told me about his misfortunes."

"It is a long story," said Mrs. Penniman, "and I regard it as a sacred trust. But I suppose there is no objection to my saying that he has been wild—he frankly confesses that. But he has paid for it."

"That's what has impoverished him, eh?"

"I don't mean simply in money. He is very much alone in the world."

"Do you mean that he has behaved so badly that his friends have given him up?"

"He has had false friends, who have deceived and betrayed him."

"He seems to have some good ones too. He has a devoted sister, and half a dozen nephews and nieces."

Mrs. Penniman was silent a minute. "The nephews and nieces are children, and the sister is not a very attractive person."

"I hope he doesn't abuse her to you," said the Doctor; "for I am told he lives upon her."

"Lives upon her?"

"Lives with her, and does nothing for himself; it is about the same thing."

"He is looking for a position—most earnestly," said Mrs. Penniman. "He hopes every day to find one."

"Precisely. He is looking for it here—over there in the front parlour. The position of husband of a weak-minded woman with a large fortune would suit him to perfection!"

Mrs. Penniman was truly amiable, but she now gave signs of temper. She rose with much animation, and stood for a moment looking at her brother. "My dear Austin," she remarked, "if you regard Catherine as a weak-minded woman, you are particularly mistaken!' And with this she moved majestically away.

IX.

It was a regular custom with the family in Washington Square to go and spend Sunday evening at Mrs. Almond's. On the Sunday after the conversation I have just narrated, this custom was not intermitted; and on this occasion, towards the middle of the evening, Dr. Sloper found reason to withdraw to the library, with his brother-in-law, to talk over a matter of business. He was absent some twenty minutes, and when he came back into the circle, which was enlivened by the presence of several friends of the family, he saw that Morris Townsend had come in and had lost as little time as possible in seating himself on a small sofa, beside Catherine. In the large room, where several different groups had been formed, and the hum of voices and of laughter was loud, these two young persons might confabulate, as the Doctor phrased it to himself, without attracting attention. He saw in a moment, however, that his daughter was painfully conscious of his own observation. She sat motionless, with her eyes bent down, staring at her open fan, deeply flushed, shrinking together as if to minimise the indiscretion of which she confessed herself guilty.

The Doctor almost pitied her. Poor Catherine

was not defiant; she had no genius for bravado; and as she felt that her father viewed her companion's attentions with an unsympathising eye, there was nothing but discomfort for her in the accident of seeming to challenge him. The Doctor felt, indeed, so sorry for her that he turned away, to spare her the sense of being watched; and he was so intelligent a man that, in his thoughts, he rendered a sort of poetic justice to her situation.

"It must be deucedly pleasant for a plain, inanimate girl like that to have a beautiful young fellow come and sit down beside her and whisper to her that he is her slave—if that is what this one whispers. No wonder she likes it, and that she thinks me a cruel tyrant; which of course she does, though she is afraid—she hasn't the animation necessary—to admit it to herself. Poor old Catherine!" mused the Doctor; "I verily believe she is capable of defending me when Townsend abuses me!"

And the force of this reflection, for the moment, was such in making him feel the natural opposition between his point of view and that of an infatuated child, that he said to himself that he was perhaps after all taking things too hard and crying out before he was hurt. He must not condemn Morris Townsend unheard. He had a great aversion to taking things too hard; he thought that half the discomfort and many of the disappointments of life come from it; and for an instant he asked himself whether, possibly, he did not appear ridiculous to this intelligent young man, whose private perception of incongruities he suspected of being keen. At the end of a quarter of an hour Catherine had got rid of him, and Townsend was now standing before the fireplace in conversation with Mrs. Almond.

"We will try him again," said the Doctor. And he crossed the room and joined his sister and her companion, making her a sign that she should leave the young man to him. She presently did so, while Morris looked at him, smiling, without a sign of evasiveness in his affable eye.

"He's amazingly conceited!" thought the Doctor; and then he said aloud: "I am told you are looking out for a position."

"Oh, a position is more than I should presume to call it," Morris Townsend answered. "That sounds so fine. I should like some quiet work—something to turn an honest penny."

"What sort of thing should you prefer?"

"Do you mean what am I fit for? Very little, I am afraid. I have nothing but my good right arm, as they say in the melodramas."

"You are too modest," said the Doctor. "In addition to your good right arm, you have your subtle brain. I know nothing of you but what I see; but I see by your physiognomy that you are extremely intelligent."

"Ah," Townsend murmured, "I don't know what to answer when you say that! You advise me, then, not to despair?"

And he looked at his interlocutor as if the question might have a double meaning. The Doctor caught the look and weighed it a moment before he replied. "I should be very sorry to admit that a robust and well-disposed young man need ever despair. If he doesn't succeed in one thing, he can try another. Only, I should add, he should choose his line with discretion."

"Ah, yes, with discretion," Morris Townsend repeated, sympathetically. "Well, I have been indiscreet, formerly; but I think I have got over it. I am very steady now." And he stood a moment, looking down at his remarkably neat shoes. Then at last, "Were you kindly intending to propose something for my advantage?" he inquired, looking up and smiling.

"Damn his impudence!" the Doctor exclaimed, privately. But in a moment he reflected that he himself had, after all, touched first upon this delicate point, and that his words might have been construed as an offer of assistance. "I have no particular proposal to make," he presently said; "but it occurred to me to let you know that I have you in my mind. Sometimes one hears of opportunities. For instance—should you object to leaving New York—to going to a distance?"

"I am afraid I shouldn't be able to manage that. I must seek my fortune here or nowhere. You see," added Morris Townsend, "I have ties—I have responsibilities here. I have a sister, a widow, from whom I have been separated for a long time, and to whom I am almost everything. I shouldn't like to say to her that I must leave her. She rather depends upon me, you see."

"Ah, that's very proper; family feeling is very proper," said Dr. Sloper. "I often think there is not enough of it in our city. I think I have heard of your sister."

"It is possible, but I rather doubt it; she lives so very quietly."

"As quietly, you mean," the Doctor went on, with a short laugh, "as a lady may do who has several young children."

"Ah, my little nephews and nieces—that's the very point! I am helping to bring them up," said Morris Townsend. "I am a kind of amateur tutor; I give them lessons."

"That's very proper, as I say; but it is hardly a career."

"It won't make my fortune!" the young man confessed.

"You must not be too much bent on a fortune," said the Doctor. "But I assure you I will keep you in mind; I won't lose sight of you!"

"If my situation becomes desperate I shall perhaps take the liberty of reminding you!" Morris rejoined, raising his voice a little, with a brighter smile, as his interlocutor turned away.

Before he left the house the Doctor had a few words with Mrs. Almond.

"I should like to see his sister," he said. "What do you call her? Mrs. Montgomery. I should like to have a little talk with her."

"I will try and manage it," Mrs. Almond responded. "I will take the first opportunity of inviting her, and you shall come and meet her. Unless, indeed," Mrs. Almond added, "she first takes it into her head to be sick and to send for you."

"Ah no, not that; she must have trouble enough without that. But it would have its advantages, for then I should see the children. I should like very much to see the children."

"You are very thorough. Do you want to catechise them about their uncle?"

"Precisely. Their uncle tells me he has charge of their education, that he saves their mother the expense of school-bills. I should like to ask them a few questions in the commoner branches."

"He certainly has not the cut of a schoolmaster!" Mrs. Almond said to herself a short time afterwards, as she saw Morris Townsend in a corner bending over her niece, who was seated.

And there was, indeed, nothing in the young man's discourse at this moment that savoured of the pedagogue.

"Will you meet me somewhere to-morrow or next day?" he said, in a low tone, to Catherine.

"Meet you?" she asked, lifting her frightened eyes.

"I have something particular to say to you—very particular."

"Can't you come to the house? Can't you say it there?"

Townsend shook his head gloomily. "I can't enter your doors again!"

"Oh, Mr. Townsend!" murmured Catherine. She trembled as she wondered what had happened, whether her father had forbidden it.

"I can't in self-respect," said the young man. "Your father has insulted me."

"Insulted you?"

"He has taunted me with my poverty."

"Oh, you are mistaken—you misunderstood

him!" Catherine spoke with energy, getting up from her chair.

"Perhaps I am too proud—too sensitive. But would you have me otherwise?" he asked, tenderly.

"Where my father is concerned, you must not be sure. He is full of goodness," said Catherine.

"He laughed at me for having no position! I took it quietly; but only because he belongs to you."

"I don't know," said Catherine; "I don't know what he thinks. I am sure he means to be kind. You must not be too proud."

"I will be proud only of you," Morris answered. "Will you meet me in the Square in the afternoon?"

A great blush on Catherine's part had been the answer to the declaration I have just quoted. She turned away, heedless of his question.

"Will you meet me?" he repeated. "It is very quiet there; no one need see us—toward dusk?"

"It is you who are unkind, it is you who laugh, when you say such things as that."

"My dear girl!" the young man murmured.

"You know how little there is in me to be proud of I am ugly and stupid."

Morris greeted this remark with an ardent murmur, in which she recognised nothing articulate but an assurance that she was his own dearest.

But she went on. "I am not even—I am not even——" And she paused a moment.

"You are not what?"

"I am not even brave."

"Ah, then, if you are afraid, what shall we do?"

She hesitated awhile; then at last—"You must come to the house," she said; "I am not afraid of that."

"I would rather it were in the Square," the young man urged. "You know how empty it is, often. No one will see us."

"I don't care who sees us! But leave me now."

He left her resignedly; he had got what he wanted. Fortunately he was ignorant that half an hour later, going home with her father and feeling him near, the poor girl, in spite of her sudden declaration of courage, began to tremble again. Her father said nothing; but she had an idea his eyes were fixed upon her in the darkness. Mrs. Penniman also was silent; Morris Townsend had told her that her niece preferred, unromantically, an interview in a chintz-covered parlour to a sentimental tryst beside a fountain sheeted with dead leaves, and she was lost in wonderment at the oddity—almost the perversity—of the choice.

X.

CATHERINE received the young man the next day on the ground she had chosen—amid the chaste upholstery of a New York drawing-room furnished in the fashion of fifty years ago. Morris had swallowed his pride and made the effort necessary to cross the threshold of her too derisive parent—an act of magnanimity which could not fail to render him doubly interesting.

"We must settle something—we must take a line," he declared, passing his hand through his hair and giving a glance at the long narrow mirror which adorned the space between the two windows, and which had at its base a little gilded bracket covered by a thin slab of white marble, supporting in its turn a backgammon board folded together in the shape of two volumes, two shining folios inscribed in letters of greenish gilt, *History of England*. If Morris had been pleased to describe the master of the house as a heartless scoffer, it is because he thought him too much on his guard, and this was the easiest way to express his own dissatisfaction—a dissatisfaction which he had made a point of concealing from the Doctor. It will probably seem to the reader, however, that the Doctor's vigilance was by no means excessive, and that these two young people had an open field. Their intimacy was now considerable, and it may appear that for a shrinking and retiring person our heroine had been liberal of her favours. The young man, within a few days, had made her listen to things for which she had not supposed that she was prepared; having a lively foreboding of difficulties, he proceeded to gain as much ground as possible in the present. He remembered that fortune favours the brave, and even if he had forgotten it, Mrs. Penniman would have remembered it for him. Mrs. Penniman delighted of all things in a drama, and she flattered herself that a drama would now be enacted. Combining as she did the zeal of the prompter with the impatience of the spectator, she had long since done her utmost to pull up the curtain. She, too, expected to figure in the performance—to be the confidant, the Chorus, to speak the epilogue. It may even be said that there were times when she lost sight altogether of the modest heroine of the play, in the contemplation of certain great passages which would naturally occur between the hero and herself.

What Morris had told Catherine at last was simply that he loved her, or rather adored her. Virtually, he had made known as much already—his visits had been a series of eloquent intimations of it. But now he had affirmed it in lover's vows, and, as a memorable sign of it, he had passed his arm round the girl's waist and taken a kiss. This happy certitude had come sooner than Catherine expected, and she had regarded it, very naturally, as a priceless treasure. It may even be doubted whether she had ever definitely expected to possess it; she had not been waiting for it, and she had never said to herself that at a given moment it must come. As I have tried to explain, she was not eager and exacting; she took what was given her from day to day; and if the delightful custom of her lover's visits, which yielded her a happiness in which confidence and timidity were strangely blended, had suddenly come to an end, she would not only not have spoken of herself as one of the forsaken, but she would not have thought of herself as one of the disappointed. After Morris had kissed her, the last time he was with her, as a ripe assurance of his devotion, she begged him to go away, to leave her alone, to let her think. Morris went away, taking another kiss first. But Catherine's meditations had lacked a certain coherence. She felt his kisses on her lips and on her cheeks for a long time afterwards; the sensation was rather an obstacle than an aid to reflection. She would have liked to see her situation all clearly before her, to make up her mind what she should do if, as she feared, her father should tell her that he disapproved of Morris Townsend. But all that she could see with any vividness was that it was terribly strange that any one should disapprove of him; that there must in that case be some mistake, some mystery, which in a little while would be set at rest. She put off deciding and choosing; before the vision of a conflict with her father she dropped her eyes and sat motionless, holding her breath and waiting. It made her heart beat, it was intensely painful.

When Morris kissed her and said these things—that also made her heart beat; but this was worse, and it frightened her. Nevertheless, to-day, when the young man spoke of settling something, taking a line, she felt that it was the truth, and she answered very simply and without hesitating.

"We must do our duty," she said; "we must speak to my father. I will do it to-night; you must do it to-morrow."

"It is very good of you to do it first," Morris answered. "The young man—the happy lover—generally does that. But just as you please!"

It pleased Catherine to think that she should be brave for his sake, and in her satisfaction she even gave a little smile. "Women have more tact," she said; "they ought to do it first. They are more conciliating; they can persuade better."

"You will need all your powers of persuasion. But after all," Morris added, "you are irresistible."

"Please don't speak that way—and promise me this. To-morrow, when you talk with father, you will be very gentle and respectful."

"As much so as possible," Morris promised. "It won't be much use, but I shall try. I certainly would rather have you easily than have to fight for you."

"Don't talk about fighting; we shall not fight."

"Ah, we must be prepared," Morris rejoined; "you especially, because for you it must come hardest. Do you know the first thing your father will say to you?"

"No, Morris; please tell me."

"He will tell you I am mercenary."

"Mercenary?"

"It's a big word; but it means a low thing. It means that I am after your money."

"Oh!" murmured Catherine, softly.

The exclamation was so deprecating and touching that Morris indulged in another little demonstration of affection. "But he will be sure to say it," he added.

"It will be easy to be prepared for that," Catherine said. "I shall simply say that he is mistaken—that other men may be that way, but that you are not."

"You must make a great point of that, for it will be his own great point."

Catherine looked at her lover a minute, and then she said, "I shall persuade him. But I am glad we shall be rich," she added.

Morris turned away, looking into the crown of his hat. "No, it's a misfortune," he said at last. "It is from that our difficulty will come."

"Well, if it is the worst misfortune, we are not so unhappy. Many people would not think it so bad. I will persuade him, and after that we shall be very glad we have money.

Morris Townsend listened to this robust logic in silence. "I will leave my defence to you; it's a charge that a man has to stoop to defend himself from."

Catherine on her side was silent for a while; she was looking at him while he looked, with a good deal of fixedness, out of the window. "Morris," she said, abruptly, "are you very sure you love me?"

He turned round, and in a moment he was

bending over her. "My own dearest, can you doubt it?"

"I have only known it five days," she said; "but now it seems to me as if I could never do without it."

"You will never be called upon to try!" And he gave a little tender, reassuring laugh. Then, in a moment, he added, "There is something you must tell me, too." She had closed her eyes after the last word she uttered, and kept them closed; and at this she nodded her head, without opening them. "You must tell me," he went on, "that if your father is dead against me, if he absolutely forbids our marriage, you will still be faithful."

Catherine opened her eyes, gazing at him, and she could give no better promise than what he read there.

"You will cleave to me?" said Morris. "You know you are your own mistress—you are of age."

"Ah, Morris!" she murmured, for all answer. Or rather not for all; for she put her hand into his own. He kept it awhile, and presently he kissed her again. This is all that need be recorded of their conversation; but Mrs. Penniman, if she had been present, would probably have admitted that it was as well it had not taken place beside the fountain in Washington Square.

XI.

CATHERINE listened for her father when he came in that evening, and she heard him go to his study. She sat quiet, though her heart was beating fast, for nearly half an hour; then she went and knocked at his door—a ceremony without which she never crossed the threshold of this apartment. On entering it now she found him in his chair beside the fire, entertaining himself with a cigar and the evening paper.

"I have something to say to you," she began very gently; and she sat down in the first place that offered.

"I shall be very happy to hear it, my dear," said her father. He waited—waited, looking at her, while she stared, in a long silence, at the fire. He was curious and impatient, for he was sure she was going to speak of Morris Townsend; but he let her take her own time, for he was determined to be very mild.

"I am engaged to be married!" Catherine announced at last, still staring at the fire.

The Doctor was startled; the accomplished fact was more than he had expected. But he betrayed no surprise. "You do right to tell me," he simply said. "And who is the happy mortal whom you have honoured with your choice?"

"Mr. Morris Townsend." And as she pronounced her lover's name, Catherine looked at him. What she saw was her father's still gray eye and his clear-cut, definite smile. She contemplated these objects for a moment, and then she looked back at the fire; it was much warmer.

"When was this arrangement made?" the Doctor asked.

"This afternoon—two hours ago."

"Was Mr. Townsend here?"

"Yes, father; in the front parlour." She was very glad that she was not obliged to tell him that the ceremony of their betrothal had taken place out there under the bare ailantus-trees.

"Is it serious?" said the Doctor.

"Very serious, father."

Her father was silent a moment. "Mr. Townsend ought to have told me."

"He means to tell you to-morrow."

"After I know all about it from you? He ought to have told me before. Does he think I didn't care—because I left you so much liberty?"

"Oh, no," said Catherine; "he knew you would care. And we have been so much obliged to you for—for the liberty."

The Doctor gave a short laugh. "You might have made a better use of it, Catherine."

"Please don't say that, father," the girl urged, softly, fixing her dull and gentle eyes upon him.

He puffed his cigar awhile, meditatively. "You have gone very fast," he said at last.

"Yes," Catherine answered simply; "I think we have."

Her father glanced at her an instant, removing his eyes from the fire. "I don't wonder Mr. Townsend likes you. You are so simple and so good."

"I don't know why it is—but he *does* like me. I am sure of that."

"And are you very fond of Mr. Townsend?"

"I like him very much, of course—or I shouldn't consent to marry him."

"But you have known him a very short time, my dear."

"Oh," said Catherine, with some eagerness, "it doesn't take long to like a person—when once you begin."

"You must have begun very quickly. Was it the first time you saw him—that night at your aunt's party?"

"I don't know, father," the girl answered. "I can't tell you about that."

"Of course; that's your own affair. You will have observed that I have acted on that principle. I have not interfered, I have left you your liberty, I have remembered that you are no longer a little girl—that you have arrived at years of discretion."

"I feel very old—and very wise," said Catherine, smiling faintly.

"I am afraid that before long you will feel older and wiser yet. I don't like your engagement."

"Ah!" Catherine exclaimed, softly, getting up from her chair.

"No, my dear. I am sorry to give you pain; but I don't like it. You should have consulted me before you settled it. I have been too easy with you, and I feel as if you had taken advantage of my indulgence. Most decidedly, you should have spoken to me first."

Catherine hesitated a moment, and then—" It was because I was afraid you wouldn't like it!" she confessed.

"Ah, there it is! You had a bad conscience."

"No, I have not a bad conscience, father!" the girl cried out, with considerable energy. "Please don't accuse me of anything so dreadful." These words, in fact, represented to her imagination something very terrible indeed, something base and cruel, which she associated with malefactors and prisoners. "It was because I was afraid—afraid——" she went on.

"If you were afraid, it was because you had been foolish!"

"I was afraid you didn't like Mr. Townsend."

"You were quite right. I don't like him."

"Dear father, you don't know him," said Catherine, in a voice so timidly argumentative that it might have touched him.

"Very true; I don't know him intimately. But I know him enough. I have my impression of him. You don't know him either."

She stood before the fire, with her hands lightly clasped in front of her; and her father, leaning back in his chair and looking up at her, made this remark with a placidity that might have been irritating.

I doubt, however, whether Catherine was irritated, though she broke into a vehement protest. "I don't know him?" she cried. "Why, I know him—better than I have ever known any one!"

"You know a part of him—what he has chosen to show you. But you don't know the rest."

"The rest? What is the rest?"

"Whatever it may be. There is sure to be plenty of it."

"I know what you mean," said Catherine, remembering how Morris had forewarned her. "You mean that he is mercenary."

Her father looked up at her still, with his cold, quiet, reasonable eye. "If I meant it, my dear, I should say it! But there is an error I wish particularly to avoid—that of rendering Mr. Townsend more interesting to you by saying hard things about him."

"I won't think them hard, if they are true," said Catherine.

"If you don't, you will be a remarkably sensible young woman!"

"They will be your reasons, at any rate, and you will want me to hear your reasons."

The Doctor smiled a little. "Very true. You have a perfect right to ask for them." And he puffed his cigar a few moments. "Very well, then, without accusing Mr. Townsend of being in love only with your fortune—and with the fortune that you justly expect—I will say that there is every reason to suppose that these good things have entered into his calculation more largely than a tender solicitude for your happiness strictly requires. There is, of course, nothing impossible in an intelligent young man entertaining a disinterested affection for you. You are an honest, amiable girl, and an intelligent young man might easily find it out. But the principal thing that we know about this young man—

who is, indeed, very intelligent—leads us to suppose that, however much he may value your personal merits, he values your money more. The principal thing we know about him is that he has led a life of dissipation, and has spent a fortune of his own in doing so. That is enough for me, my dear. I wish you to marry a young man with other antecedents —a young man who could give positive guarantees. If Morris Townsend has spent his own fortune in amusing himself, there is every reason to believe that he would spend yours."

The Doctor delivered himself of these remarks slowly, deliberately, with occasional pauses and prolongations of accent, which made no great allowance for poor Catherine's suspense as to his conclusion. She sat down at last, with her head bent and her eyes still fixed upon him; and strangely enough—I hardly know how to tell it—even while she felt that what he said went so terribly against her, she admired his neatness and nobleness of expression. There was something hopeless and oppressive in having to argue with her father; but she too, on her side, must try to be clear. He was so quiet; he was not at all angry; and she, too, must be quiet. But her very effort to be quiet made her tremble.

"That is not the principal thing we know about him," she said; and there was a touch of her tremor in her voice. "There are other things—many other things. He has very high abilities—he wants so much to do something. He is kind, and generous, and true," said poor Catherine, who had not suspected hitherto the resources of her eloquence.

"And his fortune—his fortune that he spent—was very small!"

"All the more reason he shouldn't have spent it," cried the Doctor, getting up with a laugh. Then as Catherine, who had also risen to her feet again, stood there in her rather angular earnestness, wishing so much and expressing so little, he drew her towards him and kissed her. "You won't think me cruel?" he said, holding her a moment.

This question was not reassuring; it seemed to Catherine, on the contrary, to suggest possibilities which made her feel sick. But she answered coherently enough—"No, dear father; because if you knew how I feel—and you must know, you know everything—you would be so kind, so gentle."

"Yes, I think I know how you feel," the Doctor said. "I will be very kind—be sure of that. And I will see Mr. Townsend to-morrow. Meanwhile, and for the present, be so good as to mention to no one that you are engaged."

XII.

On the morrow, in the afternoon, he stayed at home, awaiting Mr. Townsend's call—a proceeding by which it appeared to him (justly perhaps, for he was a very busy man) that he paid Catherine's suitor great honour, and gave both these young people so much the less to complain of. Morris presented himself with a countenance sufficiently serene—he appeared to have forgotten the "insult" for which he had solicited Catherine's sympathy two evenings before, and Dr. Sloper lost no time in letting him know that he had been prepared for his visit.

"Catherine told me yesterday what has been going on between you," he said. "You must allow me to say that it would have been becoming of you to give me notice of your intentions before they had gone so far."

"I should have done so," Morris answered, "if you had not had so much the appearance of leaving your daughter at liberty. She seems to me quite her own mistress."

"Literally, she is. But she has not emancipated herself morally quite so far, I trust, as to choose a husband without consulting me. I have left her at liberty, but I have not been in the least indifferent.

The truth is that your little affair has come to a head with a rapidity that surprises me. It was only the other day that Catherine made your acquaintance."

"It was not long ago, certainly," said Morris, with great gravity. "I admit that we have not been slow to—to arrive at an understanding. But that was very natural, from the moment we were sure of ourselves—and of each other. My interest in Miss Sloper began the first time I saw her."

"Did it not by chance precede your first meeting?" the Doctor asked.

Morris looked at him an instant. "I certainly had already heard that she was a charming girl."

"A charming girl—that's what you think her?"

"Assuredly. Otherwise I should not be sitting here."

The Doctor meditated a moment. "My dear young man," he said at last, "you must be very susceptible. As Catherine's father, I have, I trust, a just and tender appreciation of her many good qualities; but I don't mind telling you that I have never thought of her as a charming girl, and never expected any one else to do so."

Morris Townsend received this statement with a smile that was not wholly devoid of deference. "I don't know what I might think of her if I were her father. I can't put myself in that place. I speak from my own point of view."

"You speak very well," said the Doctor; "but that is not all that is necessary. I told Catherine yesterday that I disapproved of her engagement."

"She let me know as much, and I was very

sorry to hear it. I am greatly disappointed." And Morris sat in silence awhile, looking at the floor.

"Did you really expect I would say I was delighted, and throw my daughter into your arms?"

"Oh, no; I had an idea you didn't like me."

"What gave you the idea?"

"The fact that I am poor."

"That has a harsh sound," said the Doctor, "but it is about the truth—speaking of you strictly as a son-in-law. Your absence of means, of a profession, of visible resources or prospects, places you in a category from which it would be imprudent for me to select a husband for my daughter, who is a weak young woman with a large fortune. In any other capacity I am perfectly prepared to like you. As a son-in-law, I abominate you!"

Morris Townsend listened respectfully. "I don't think Miss Sloper is a weak woman," he presently said.

"Of course you must defend her—it's the least you can do. But I have known my child twenty years, and you have known her six weeks. Even if she were not weak, however, you would still be a penniless man."

"Ah, yes; that is *my* weakness! And therefore, you mean, I am mercenary—I only want your daughter's money."

"I don't say that. I am not obliged to say it; and to say it, save under stress of compulsion, would be very bad taste. I say simply that you belong to the wrong category."

"But your daughter doesn't marry a category," Townsend urged, with his handsome smile. "She marries an individual—an individual whom she is so good as to say she loves."

"An individual who offers so little in return!"

"Is it possible to offer more than the most tender affection and a lifelong devotion?" the young man demanded.

"It depends how we take it. It is possible to offer a few other things besides, and not only it is possible, but it's usual. A lifelong devotion is measured after the fact; and meanwhile it is customary in these cases to give a few material securities. What are yours? A very handsome face and figure, and a very good manner. They are excellent as far as they go, but they don't go far enough."

"There is one thing you should add to them," said Morris; "the word of a gentleman!"

"The word of a gentleman that you will always love Catherine? You must be a very fine gentleman to be sure of that."

"The word of a gentleman that I am not mercenary; that my affection for Miss Sloper is as pure and disinterested a sentiment as was ever lodged in a human breast! I care no more for her fortune than for the ashes in that grate."

"I take note—I take note," said the Doctor. "But having done so, I turn to our category again. Even with that solemn vow on your lips, you take your place in it. There is nothing against you but an accident, if you will; but with my thirty years' medical practice, I have seen that accidents may have far-reaching consequences."

Morris smoothed his hat—it was already remarkably glossy—and continued to display a self-control which, as the Doctor was obliged to admit, was extremely creditable to him. But his disappointment was evidently keen.

"Is there nothing I can do to make you believe in me?"

"If there were I should be sorry to suggest it, for—don't you see?—I don't want to believe in you!" said the Doctor, smiling.

"I would go and dig in the fields."

"That would be foolish."

"I will take the first work that offers, to-morrow."

"Do so by all means—but for your own sake, not for mine."

"I see; you think I am an idler!" Morris exclaimed, a little too much in the tone of a man who has made a discovery. But he saw his error immediately and blushed.

"It doesn't matter what I think, when once I have told you I don't think of you as a son-in-law."

But Morris persisted. "You think I would squander her money."

The Doctor smiled. "It doesn't matter, as I say; but I plead guilty to that."

"That's because I spent my own, I suppose," said Morris. "I frankly confess that. I have been wild. I have been foolish. I will tell you every crazy thing I ever did, if you like. There were some great follies among the number—I have never concealed that. But I have sown my wild oats. Isn't there some proverb about a reformed rake? I was not a rake, but I assure you I have reformed.

It is better to have amused oneself for a while and have done with it. Your daughter would never care for a milksop; and I will take the liberty of saying that you would like one quite as little. Besides, between my money and hers there is a great difference. I spent my own; it was because it was my own that I spent it. And I made no debts; when it was gone I stopped. I don't owe a penny in the world."

"Allow me to inquire what you are living on now—though I admit," the Doctor added, "that the question, on my part, is inconsistent."

"I am living on the remnants of my property," said Morris Townsend.

"Thank you!" the Doctor gravely replied.

Yes, certainly, Morris's self-control was laudable. "Even admitting I attach an undue importance to Miss Sloper's fortune," he went on, "would not that be in itself an assurance that I should take good care of it?"

"That you should take too much care would be quite as bad as that you should take too little. Catherine might suffer as much by your economy as by your extravagance."

"I think you are very unjust!" The young man made this declaration decently, civilly, without violence.

"It is your privilege to think so, and I surrender my reputation to you! I certainly don't flatter myself I gratify you."

"Don't you care a little to gratify your daughter? Do you enjoy the idea of making her miserable?"

"I am perfectly resigned to her thinking me a tyrant for a twelvemonth."

"For a twelvemonth!" exclaimed Morris, with a laugh.

"For a lifetime, then! She may as well be miserable in that way as in the other."

Here at last Morris lost his temper. "Ah, you are not polite, sir!" he cried.

"You push me to it—you argue too much."

"I have a great deal at stake."

"Well, whatever it is," said the Doctor, "you have lost it!"

"Are you sure of that?" asked Morris; "are you sure your daughter will give me up?"

"I mean, of course, you have lost it as far as I am concerned. As for Catherine's giving you up—no, I am not sure of it. But as I shall strongly recommend it, as I have a great fund of respect and affection in my daughter's mind to draw upon, and as she has the sentiment of duty developed in a very high degree, I think it extremely possible."

Morris Townsend began to smooth his hat again. "I, too, have a fund of affection to draw upon!" he observed at last.

The Doctor at this point showed his own first symptoms of irritation. "Do you mean to defy me?"

"Call it what you please, sir! I mean not to give your daughter up."

The Doctor shook his head. "I haven't the least fear of your pining away your life. You are made to enjoy it."

Morris gave a laugh. "Your opposition to my marriage is all the more cruel, then! Do you intend to forbid your daughter to see me again?"

"She is past the age at which people are forbidden, and I am not a father in an old-fashioned novel. But I shall strongly urge her to break with you."

"I don't think she will," said Morris Townsend.

"Perhaps not. But I shall have done what I could."

"She has gone too far," Morris went on.

"To retreat? Then let her stop where she is."

"Too far to stop, I mean."

The Doctor looked at him a moment; Morris had his hand on the door. "There is a great deal of impertinence in your saying it."

"I will say no more, sir!" Morris answered; and, making his bow, he left the room.

XIII.

It may be thought the Doctor was too positive, and Mrs. Almond intimated as much. But as he said, he had his impression; it seemed to him sufficient, and he had no wish to modify it. He had passed his life in estimating people (it was part of the medical trade), and in nineteen cases out of twenty he was right.

"Perhaps Mr. Townsend is the twentieth case," Mrs. Almond suggested.

"Perhaps he is, though he doesn't look to me at all like a twentieth case. But I will give him the benefit of the doubt, and, to make sure, I will go and talk with Mrs. Montgomery. She will almost certainly tell me I have done right; but it is just possible that she will prove to me that I have made the greatest mistake of my life. If she does, I will beg Mr. Townsend's pardon. You needn't invite her to meet me, as you kindly proposed; I will write her a frank letter, telling her how matters stand, and asking leave to come and see her."

"I am afraid the frankness will be chiefly on your side. The poor little woman will stand up for her brother, whatever he may be."

"Whatever he may be? I doubt that. People are not always so fond of their brothers."

"Ah," said Mrs. Almond, "when it's a question of thirty thousand a year coming into a family——"

"If she stands up for him on account of the money, she will be a humbug. If she is a humbug I shall see it. If I see it, I won't waste time with her."

"She is not a humbug—she is an exemplary woman. She will not wish to play her brother a trick simply because he is selfish."

"If she is worth talking to, she will sooner play him a trick than that he should play Catherine one. Has she seen Catherine, by the way—does she know her?"

"Not to my knowledge. Mr. Townsend can have had no particular interest in bringing them together."

"If she is an exemplary woman, no. But we shall see to what extent she answers your description."

"I shall be curious to hear her description of you!" said Mrs. Almond, with a laugh. "And, meanwhile, how is Catherine taking it?"

"As she takes everything—as a matter of course."

"Doesn't she make a noise? Hasn't she made a scene?"

"She is not scenic."

"I thought a love-lorn maiden was always scenic."

"A fantastic widow is more so. Lavinia has made me a speech; she thinks me very arbitrary."

"She has a talent for being in the wrong," said Mrs. Almond. "But I am very sorry for Catherine, all the same."

"So am I. But she will get over it."

"You believe she will give him up?"

"I count upon it. She has such an admiration for her father."

"Oh, we know all about that! But it only makes me pity her the more. It makes her dilemma the more painful, and the effort of choosing between you and her lover almost impossible."

"If she can't choose, all the better."

"Yes, but he will stand there entreating her to choose, and Lavinia will pull on that side."

"I am glad she is not on my side; she is capable of ruining an excellent cause. The day Lavinia gets into your boat it capsizes. But she had better be careful," said the Doctor. "I will have no treason in my house!"

"I suspect she will be careful; for she is at bottom very much afraid of you."

"They are both afraid of me—harmless as I am!" the Doctor answered. "And it is on that that I build—on the salutary terror I inspire!"

XIV.

He wrote his frank letter to Mrs. Montgomery, who punctually answered it, mentioning an hour at which he might present himself in the Second Avenue. She lived in a neat little house of red brick, which had been freshly painted, with the edges of the bricks very sharply marked out in white. It has now disappeared, with its companions, to make room for a row of structures more majestic. There were green shutters upon the windows, without slats, but pierced with little holes, arranged in groups; and before the house was a diminutive yard, ornamented with a bush of mysterious character, and surrounded by a low wooden paling, painted in the same green as the shutters. The place looked like a magnified baby-house, and might have been taken down from a shelf in a toy-shop. Dr. Sloper, when he went to call, said to himself, as he glanced at the objects I have enumerated, that Mrs. Montgomery was evidently a thrifty and self-respecting little person—the modest proportions of her dwelling seemed to indicate that she was of small stature—who took a virtuous satisfaction in keeping herself tidy, and had resolved that, since she might not be splendid, she would at least be immaculate. She received him in a little parlour, which was precisely the parlour he had expected: a small unspeckled bower, ornamented with a desultory foliage of tissue-paper, and with clusters of glass drops, amid which—to carry out the analogy—the temperature of the leafy season was maintained by means of a cast-iron stove, emitting a dry blue flame, and smelling strongly of varnish. The walls were embellished with engravings swathed in pink gauze, and the tables ornamented with volumes of extracts from the poets, usually bound in black cloth stamped with florid designs in jaundiced gilt. The Doctor had time to take cognisance of these details; for Mrs. Montgomery, whose conduct he pronounced under the circumstances inexcusable, kept him waiting some ten minutes before she appeared. At last, however, she rustled in, smoothing down a stiff poplin dress, with a little frightened flush in a gracefully rounded cheek.

She was a small, plump, fair woman, with a bright, clear eye, and an extraordinary air of neatness and briskness. But these qualities were evidently combined with an unaffected humility, and the Doctor gave her his esteem as soon as he had looked at her. A brave little person, with lively perceptions, and yet a disbelief in her own talent for social, as distinguished from practical, affairs—this was his rapid mental *résumé* of Mrs. Montgomery, who, as he saw, was flattered by what she regarded as the honour of his visit. Mrs. Montgomery, in her little red house in the Second Avenue, was a person for whom Dr. Sloper was one of the great men, one of the fine gentlemen of New York; and while she fixed her agitated eyes upon him, while she clasped her mittened hands together in her glossy poplin lap, she had the appearance of saying to herself that he quite answered her idea of what a distinguished guest would naturally be. She apologised for being late; but he interrupted her.

"It doesn't matter," he said; "for while I sat here I had time to think over what I wish to say to you, and to make up my mind how to begin."

"Oh, do begin!" murmured Mrs. Montgomery.

"It is not so easy," said the Doctor, smiling. "You will have gathered from my letter that I wish to ask you a few questions, and you may not find it very comfortable to answer them."

"Yes; I have thought what I should say. It is not very easy."

"But you must understand my situation—my state of mind. Your brother wishes to marry my daughter, and I wish to find out what sort of a young man he is. A good way to do so seemed to be to come and ask you; which I have proceeded to do."

Mrs. Montgomery evidently took the situation very seriously; she was in a state of extreme moral concentration. She kept her pretty eyes, which were illumined by a sort of brilliant modesty, attached to his own countenance, and evidently paid the most earnest attention to each of his words. Her expression indicated that she thought his idea of coming to see her a very superior conception, but that she was really afraid to have opinions on strange subjects.

"I am extremely glad to see you," she said, in a tone which seemed to admit, at the same time, that this had nothing to do with the question.

The doctor took advantage of this admission. "I didn't come to see you for your pleasure; I came to make you say disagreeable things—and you can't like that. What sort of a gentleman is your brother?"

Mrs. Montgomery's illuminated gaze grew vague, and began to wander. She smiled a little, and for some time made no answer, so that the Doctor at last became impatient. And her answer, when it came, was not satisfactory. "It is difficult to talk about one's brother."

"Not when one is fond of him, and when one has plenty of good to say."

"Yes, even then, when a good deal depends on it," said Mrs. Montgomery.

"Nothing depends on it, for you."

"I mean for—for——" and she hesitated.

"For your brother himself. I see!"

"I mean for Miss Sloper," said Mrs. Montgomery.

The Doctor liked this; it had the accent of sincerity. "Exactly; that's the point. If my poor girl should marry your brother, everything—as regards her happiness—would depend on his being a good fellow. She is the best creature in the world, and she could never do him a grain of injury. He, on the other hand, if he should not be all that we desire, might make her very miserable. That is why I want you to throw some light upon his character, you know. Of course, you are not bound to do it. My daughter, whom you have never seen, is nothing to you; and I, possibly, am only an indiscreet and impertinent old man. It is perfectly open to you to tell me that my visit is in very bad taste and that I had better go about my business. But I don't think you will do this; because I think we shall interest you, my poor girl and I. I am sure that if you were to see Catherine, she would interest you very much. I don't mean because she is interesting in the usual sense of the word, but because you would feel sorry for her. She is so soft, so simple-minded, she would be such an easy victim! A bad husband would have remarkable facilities for making her miserable; for she would have neither the intelligence nor the resolution to get the better of him, and yet she would have an exaggerated power of suffering. I see," added the Doctor, with his most insinuating, his most professional laugh, "you are already interested!"

"I have been interested from the moment he told me he was engaged," said Mrs. Montgomery.

"Ah! he says that—he calls it an engagement?"

"Oh, he has told me you didn't like it."

"Did he tell you that I don't like *him?*"

"Yes, he told me that too. I said I couldn't help it!" added Mrs. Montgomery.

"Of course you can't. But what you can do is to tell me I am right—to give me an attestation, as it were." And the Doctor accompanied this remark with another professional smile.

Mrs. Montgomery, however, smiled not at all; it was obvious that she could not take the humorous view of his appeal. "That is a good deal to ask," she said at last.

"There can be no doubt of that; and I must, in conscience, remind you of the advantages a young man marrying my daughter would enjoy. She has an income of ten thousand dollars in her own right, left her by her mother; if she marries a husband I approve, she will come into almost twice as much more at my death."

Mrs. Montgomery listened in great earnestness to this splendid financial statement; she had never heard thousands of dollars so familiarly talked about. She flushed a little with excitement. "Your daughter will be immensely rich," she said softly.

"Precisely—that's the bother of it."

"And if Morris should marry her, he—he——" And she hesitated timidly.

"He would be master of all that money? By no means. He would be master of the ten thousand a year that she has from her mother; but I should leave every penny of my own fortune, earned in the laborious exercise of my profession, to public institutions."

Mrs. Montgomery dropped her eyes at this, and sat for some time gazing at the straw matting which covered her floor.

"I suppose it seems to you," said the Doctor, laughing, "that in so doing I should play your brother a very shabby trick."

"Not at all. That is too much money to get possession of so easily, by marrying. I don't think it would be right."

"It's right to get all one can. But in this case

your brother wouldn't be able. If Catherine marries without my consent, she doesn't get a penny from my own pocket."

"Is that certain?" asked Mrs. Montgomery, looking up.

"As certain as that I sit here!"

"Even if she should pine away?"

"Even if she should pine to a shadow, which isn't probable."

"Does Morris know this?"

"I shall be most happy to inform him!" the Doctor exclaimed.

Mrs. Montgomery resumed her meditations, and her visitor, who was prepared to give time to the affair, asked himself whether, in spite of her little conscientious air, she was not playing into her brother's hands. At the same time he was half ashamed of the ordeal to which he had subjected her, and was touched by the gentleness with which she bore it. "If she were a humbug," he said, "she would get angry; unless she be very deep indeed. It is not probable that she is as deep as that."

"What makes you dislike Morris so much?" she presently asked, emerging from her reflections.

"I don't dislike him in the least as a friend, as a companion. He seems to me a charming fellow, and I should think he would be excellent company. I dislike him, exclusively, as a son-in-law. If the only office of a son-in-law were to dine at the paternal table, I should set a high value upon your brother. He dines capitally. But that is a small part of his function, which, in general, is to be a protector, and care-taker of my child, who is singularly ill-adapted to take care of herself. It is there that he doesn't satisfy me. I confess I have nothing but my impression to go by; but I am in the habit of trusting my impression. Of course you are at liberty to contradict it flat. He strikes me as selfish and shallow."

Mrs. Montgomery's eyes expanded a little, and the Doctor fancied he saw the light of admiration in them. "I wonder you have discovered he is selfish!" she exclaimed.

"Do you think he hides it so well?"

"Very well indeed," said Mrs. Montgomery. "And I think we are all rather selfish," she added quickly.

"I think so too; but I have seen people hide it better than he. You see I am helped by a habit I have of dividing people into classes, into types. I may easily be mistaken about your brother as an individual, but his type is written on his whole person."

"He is very good-looking," said Mrs. Montgomery.

The Doctor eyed her a moment. "You women are all the same! But the type to which your brother belongs was made to be the ruin of you, and you were made to be its handmaids and victims. The sign of the type in question is the determination—sometimes terrible in its quiet intensity—to accept nothing of life but its pleasures, and to secure these pleasures chiefly by the aid of your complaisant sex. Young men of this class never do anything for themselves that they can get other people to do for them, and it is the infatuation, the devotion, the superstition of others, that keeps them going. These others in ninety-nine cases out of a hundred are women. What our young friends chiefly insist upon is that some one else shall suffer for them; and women do that sort of thing, as you must know, wonderfully well." The Doctor paused a moment, and then he added abruptly, "You have suffered immensely for your brother!"

This exclamation was abrupt, as I say, but it was also perfectly calculated. The Doctor had been rather disappointed at not finding his compact and comfortable little hostess surrounded in a more visible degree by the ravages of Morris Townsend's immorality; but he had said to himself that this was not because the young man had spared her, but because she had contrived to plaster up her wounds. They were aching there, behind the varnished stove, the festooned engravings, beneath her own neat little poplin bosom; and if he could only touch the tender spot, she would make a movement that would betray her. The words I have just quoted were an attempt to put his finger suddenly upon the place; and they had some of the success that he looked for. The tears sprang for a moment to Mrs. Montgomery's eyes, and she indulged in a proud little jerk of the head.

"I don't know how you have found that out!" she exclaimed.

"By a philosophic trick—by what they call induction. You know you have always your option of contradicting me. But kindly answer me a question. Don't you give your brother money? I think you ought to answer that."

"Yes, I have given him money," said Mrs. Montgomery.

"And you have not had much to give him?"

She was silent a moment "If you ask me for a confession of poverty, that is easily made. I am very poor."

"One would never suppose it from your—your charming house," said the Doctor. "I learned from my sister that your income was moderate, and your family numerous."

"I have five children," Mrs. Montgomery observed; "but I am happy to say I can bring them up decently."

"Of course you can—accomplished and devoted as you are! But your brother has counted them over, I suppose?"

"Counted them over?"

"He knows there are five, I mean. He tells me it is he that brings them up."

Mrs. Montgomery stared a moment, and then quickly—"Oh, yes; he teaches them——Spanish."

The Doctor laughed out. "That must take a great deal off your hands! Your brother also knows, of course, that you have very little money."

"I have often told him so!" Mrs. Montgomery exclaimed, more unreservedly than she had yet spoken. She was apparently taking some comfort in the Doctor's clairvoyance.

"Which means that you have often occasion to, and that he often sponges on you. Excuse the crudity of my language; I simply express a fact. I don't ask you how much of your money he has had, it is none of my business. I have ascertained what

I suspected—what I wished." And the Doctor got up, gently smoothing his hat. Your brother lives on you," he said as he sood there.

Mrs. Montgomery quickly rose from her chair, following her visitor's movements with a look of fascination. But then, with a certain inconsequence —"I have never complained of him!" she said.

"You needn't protest—you have not betrayed him. But I advise you not to give him any more money."

"Don't you see it is in my interest that he should marry a rich person?" she asked. "If, as you say, he lives on me, I can only wish to get rid of him, and to put obstacles in the way of his marrying is to increase my own difficulties."

"I wish very much you would come to me with your difficulties," said the Doctor. "Certainly, if I throw him back on your hands, the least I can do is to help you to bear the burden. If you will allow me to say so, then, I shall take the liberty of placing in your hands, for the present, a certain fund for your brother's support."

Mrs. Montgomery stared; she evidently thought he was jesting; but she presently saw that he was not, and the complication of her feelings became painful. "It seems to me that I ought to be very much offended with you," she murmured.

"Because I have offered you money? That's a superstition," said the Doctor. "You must let me come and see you again, and we will talk about these things. I suppose that some of your children are girls."

"I have two little girls," said Mrs. Montgomery.

"Well, when they grow up, and begin to think of taking husbands, you will see how anxious you will be about the moral character of these gentlemen. Then you will understand this visit of mine!"

"Ah, you are not to believe that Morris's moral character is bad!"

The Doctor looked at her a little, with folded arms. "There is something I should greatly like—as a moral satisfaction. I should like to hear you say—'He is abominably selfish!'"

The words came out with the grave distinctness of his voice, and they seemed for an instant to create, to poor Mrs. Montgomery's troubled vision, a material image. She gazed at it an instant, and then she turned away. "You distress me, sir!" she exclaimed. "He is, after all, my brother, and his talents, his talents——" On these last words her voice quavered, and before he knew it she had burst into tears.

"His talents are first-rate!" said the Doctor. "We must find the proper field for them!" And he assured her most respectfully of his regret at having so greatly discomposed her. "It's all for my poor Catherine," he went on. "You must know her, and you will see."

Mrs. Montgomery brushed away her tears and blushed at having shed them. "I should like to know your daughter," she answered; and then, in an instant—"Don't let her marry him!"

Dr. Sloper went away with the words gently humming in his ears—"Don't let her marry him!" They gave him the moral satisfaction of which he had just spoken, and their value was the greater that they had evidently cost a pang to poor little Mrs. Montgomery's family pride.

XV.

HE had been puzzled by the way that Catherine carried herself; her attitude at this sentimental crisis seemed to him unnaturally passive. She had not spoken to him again after that scene in the library, the day before his interview with Morris; and a week had elapsed without making any change in her manner. There was nothing in it that appealed for pity, and he was even a little disappointed at her not giving him an opportunity to make up for his harshness by some manifestation of liberality which should operate as a compensation. He thought a little of offering to take her for a tour in Europe; but he was determined to do this only in case she should seem mutely to reproach him. He had an idea that she would display a talent for mute reproaches, and he was surprised at not finding himself exposed to these silent batteries. She said nothing, either tacitly, or explicitly, and as she was never very talkative, there was now no especial eloquence in her reserve. And poor Catherine was not sulky—a style of behaviour for which she had too little histrionic talent; she was simply very patient. Of course she was thinking over her situation, and she was apparently doing so in a deliberate and unimpassioned manner, with a view of making the best of it.

"She will do as I have bidden her," said the Doctor, and he made the further reflection that his daughter was not a woman of a great spirit. I know not whether he had hoped for a little more resistance for the sake of a little more entertainment; but he said to himself, as he had said before, that though it might have its momentary alarms, paternity was, after all, not an exciting vocation.

Catherine meanwhile had made a discovery of a very different sort; it had become vivid to her that there was a great excitement in trying to be a good daughter. She had an entirely new feeling, which may be described as a state of expectant suspense about her own actions. She watched herself as she would have watched another person, and wondered what she would do. It was as if this other person, who was both herself and not herself, had suddenly sprung into being, inspiring her with a natural curiosity as to the performance of untested functions.

"I am glad I have such a good daughter," said her father, kissing her, after the lapse of several days.

"I am trying to be good," she answered, turning away, with a conscience not altogether clear.

"If there is anything you would like to say to me, you know you must not hesitate. You needn't feel obliged to be so quiet. I shouldn't care that Mr. Townsend should be a frequent topic of conversation, but whenever you have anything particular to say about him I shall be very glad to hear it."

"Thank you," said Catherine; "I have nothing particular at present."

He never asked her whether she had seen Morris again, because he was sure that if this had been the case she would tell him. She had in fact not seen him, she had only written him a long letter. The letter at least was long for her; and, it may be added, that it was long for Morris; it consisted of five pages, in a remarkably neat and handsome hand. Catherine's handwriting was beautiful, and she was even a little proud of it; she was extremely fond of copying, and possessed volumes of extracts which testified to this accomplishment; volumes which she had exhibited one day to her lover, when the bliss of feeling that she was important in his eyes was exceptionally keen. She told Morris in writing that her father had expressed the wish that she should not see him again, and that she begged he would not come to the house until she should have "made up her mind." Morris replied with a passionate epistle, in which he asked to what, in Heaven's name, she wished to make up her mind. Had not her mind been made up two weeks before, and could it be possible that she entertained the idea of throwing him off? Did she mean to break down at the very beginning of their ordeal, after all the promises of fidelity she had both given and extracted? And he gave an account of his own interview with her father—an account not identical at all points with that offered in these pages. "He was terribly violent," Morris wrote; "but you know my self-control. I have need of it all when I remember that I have it in my power to break in upon your cruel captivity." Catherine sent him in answer to this, a note of three lines. "I am in great trouble; do not doubt of my affection, but let me wait a little and think." The idea of a struggle with her father, of setting up her will against his own, was heavy on her soul, and it kept her formally submissive, as a great physical weight keeps us motionless. It never entered into her mind to throw her lover off; but from the first she tried to assure herself that there would be a peaceful way out of their difficulty. The assurance was vague, for it contained no element of positive conviction that her father would change his mind. She only had an idea that if she should be very good, the situation would in some mysterious manner improve. To be good, she must be patient, respectful, abstain from judging her father too harshly, and from committing any act of open defiance. He was perhaps right, after all, to think as he did; by which Catherine meant not in the least that his judgment of Morris's motives in seeking to marry her was perhaps a just one, but that it was probably natural and proper that conscientious parents should be suspicious and even unjust. There were probably people in the world as bad as her father supposed Morris to be, and if there were the slightest chance of Morris being one of these sinister persons, the Doctor was right in taking it into account. Of course he could not know what she knew, how the purest love and truth were seated in the young man's eyes; but Heaven, in its time, might appoint a way of bringing him to such knowledge. Catherine expected a good deal of Heaven, and referred to the skies the initiative, as the French say, in dealing with her dilemma. She could not imagine herself imparting any kind of knowledge to her father, there was something superior even in his injustice and absolute in his mistakes. But she could at least be good, and if she were only good enough, Heaven would invent some way of reconciling all things—the dignity of her father's errors and the sweetness of her own confidence, the strict performance of her filial duties and the enjoyment of Morris Townsend's affection. Poor Catherine would have been glad to regard Mrs. Penniman as an illuminating agent, a part which this lady herself indeed was but imperfectly prepared to play. Mrs. Penniman took too much satisfaction in the sentimental shadows of this little drama to have, for the moment, any great interest in dissipating them. She wished the plot to thicken, and the advice that she gave her niece tended, in her own imagination to produce this result. It was rather incoherent counsel, and from one day to another it contradicted itself; but it was pervaded by an earnest desire that Catherine should do something striking. "You must *act*, my dear; in your situation the great thing is to act," said Mrs. Penniman, who found her niece altogether beneath her opportunities. Mrs. Penniman's real hope was that the girl would make a secret marriage, at which she should officiate as brideswoman or duenna. She had a vision of this ceremony being performed in some subterranean chapel—subterranean chapels in New York were not frequent, but Mrs. Penniman's imagination was not chilled by trifles—and of the guilty couple—she liked to think of poor Catherine and her suitor as the guilty couple—being shuffled away in a fast-whirling vehicle to some obscure lodging in the suburbs, where she would pay them (in a thick veil) clandestine visits, where they would endure a period of romantic privation, and where ultimately, after she should have been their earthly providence, their intercessor, their advocate, and their medium of communication with the world, they should be reconciled to her brother in an artistic tableau, in which she herself should be somehow the central figure. She hesitated as yet to recommend this course to Catherine, but she attempted to draw an attractive picture of it to Morris Townsend. She was in daily communication with the young man, whom she kept informed by letters of the state of affairs in Washington Square. As he had been banished, as she said, from the house, she no longer saw him; but she ended by writing to him that she longed for an interview. This interview could take place only on neutral ground, and she bethought herself greatly before selecting a place of meeting. She had an inclination for Greenwood Cemetery, but she gave it up as too distant; she could not absent herself for so long, as she said, without exciting suspicion. Then she thought of the Battery, but that was rather cold and windy, besides one's being exposed to intrusion from the Irish emigrants who at this point alight, with large appetites, in the New World; and at last she fixed upon an oyster saloon in the Seventh Avenue, kept by a negro—an establishment of which she knew nothing save that she had noticed it in passing. She made an appointment with Morris Townsend to meet him there, and she went to the tryst at dusk, enveloped in an impenetrable veil. He kept her waiting for half-an-hour—he had almost the whole width of the city to traverse—but she liked to wait, it seemed to intensify the situation. She ordered a cup of tea, which proved excessively bad, and this gave her a sense that she was suffering in a romantic cause. When Morris at last arrived, they sat together for half-an-hour in the duskiest corner of a back shop; and it is hardly too much to say that this was the happiest half-hour that Mrs. Penniman had known for years. The situation was really thrilling, and it scarcely seemed to her a false note when her companion asked for an oyster-stew, and proceeded to consume it before her eyes. Morris, indeed, needed all the satisfaction that stewed oysters could give him, for it may be intimated to the reader that he regarded Mrs. Penniman in the light of a fifth wheel to his coach. He was in a state of irritation natural to a gentleman of fine parts who had been snubbed in a benevolent attempt to confer a distinction upon a young woman of inferior characteristics, and the insinuating sympathy of this somewhat desiccated matron appeared to offer him no practical relief. He thought her a humbug, and he judged of humbugs with a good deal of confidence. He had listened and made himself agreeable to her at first, in order to get a footing in Washington Square; and at present he needed all his self-command to be decently civil. It would have gratified him to tell her that she was a fantastic old woman, and that he should like to put her into an omnibus and send her home. We know, however, that Morris possessed the virtue of self-control, and he had moreover the constant habit of seeking to be agreeable; so that, although Mrs. Penniman's demeanour only exasperated his already unquiet nerves, he listened to her with a sombre deference in which she found much to admire.

XVI.

THEY had of course immediately spoken of Catherine. "Did she send me a message, or—or anything?" Morris asked. He appeared to think that she might have sent him a trinket or a lock of her hair.

Mrs. Penniman was slightly embarrassed, for she had not told her niece of her intended expedition. "Not exactly a message," she said; "I didn't ask her for one, because I was afraid to—to excite her."

"I am afraid she is not very excitable!" And Morris gave a smile of some bitterness.

"She is better than that. She is steadfast—she is true!"

"Do you think she will hold fast then?"

"To the death!"

"Oh, I hope it won't come to that," said Morris.

"We must be prepared for the worst, and that is what I wish to speak to you about."

"What do you call the worst?"

"Well," said Mrs. Penniman, "my brother's hard, intellectual nature."

"Oh, the devil!"

"He is impervious to pity," Mrs. Penniman added, by way of explanation.

"Do you mean that he won't come round?"

"He will never be vanquished by argument. I

have studied him. He will be vanquished only by the accomplished fact."

"The accomplished fact?"

"He will come round afterwards," said Mrs. Penniman, with extreme significance. "He cares for nothing but facts; he must be met by facts!"

"Well," rejoined Morris, "it is a fact that I wish to marry his daughter. I met him with that the other day, but he was not at all vanquished."

Mrs. Penniman was silent a little, and her smile beneath the shadow of her capacious bonnet, on the edge of which her black veil was arranged curtainwise, fixed itself upon Morris's face with a still more tender brilliancy. "Marry Catherine first and meet him afterwards!" she exclaimed.

"Do you recommend that?" asked the young man, frowning heavily.

She was a little frightened, but she went on with considerable boldness. "That is the way I see it: a private marriage—a private marriage." She repeated the phrase because she liked it.

"Do you mean that I should carry Catherine off? What do they call it—elope with her?"

"It is not a crime when you are driven to it," said Mrs. Penniman. "My husband, as I have told you, was a distinguished clergyman; one of the most eloquent men of his day. He once married a young couple that had fled from the house of the young lady's father. He was so interested in their story. He had no hesitation, and everything came out beautifully. The father was afterwards reconciled, and thought everything of the young man. Mr. Penniman married them in the evening, about seven o'clock. The church was so dark, you could scarcely see; and Mr. Penniman was intensely agitated; he was so sympathetic. I don't believe he could have done it again."

"Unfortunately Catherine and I have not Mr. Penniman to marry us," said Morris.

"No, but you have me!" rejoined Mrs. Penniman, expressively. "I can't perform the ceremony, but I can help you. I can watch."

"The woman's an idiot," thought Morris; but he was obliged to say something different. It was not, however, materially more civil. "Was it in order to tell me this that you requested I would meet you here?"

Mrs. Penniman had been conscious of a certain vagueness in her errand, and of not being able to offer him any very tangible reward for his long walk. "I thought perhaps you would like to see one who is so near to Catherine," she observed with considerable majesty. "And also," she added, "that you would value an opportunity of sending her something."

Morris extended his empty hands with a melancholy smile. "I am greatly obliged to you, but I have nothing to send."

"Haven't you a *word?*" asked his companion, with her suggestive smile coming back.

Morris frowned again. "Tell her to hold fast," he said, rather curtly.

"That is a good word—a noble word. It will make her happy for many days. She is very touching, very brave," Mrs. Penniman went on, arranging her mantle and preparing to depart. While she was so engaged she had an inspiration. She found the phrase that she could boldly offer as a vindication of the step she had taken. "If you marry Catherine at all risks," she said, "you will give my brother a proof of your being what he pretends to doubt."

"What he pretends to doubt?"

"Don't you know what that is?" Mrs. Penniman asked, almost playfully.

"It does not concern me to know," said Morris, grandly.

"Of course it makes you angry."

"I despise it," Morris declared.

"Ah, you know what it is, then?" said Mrs. Penniman, shaking her finger at him. "He pretends that you like—you like the money."

Morris hesitated a moment; and then, as if he spoke advisedly—"I *do* like the money!"

"Ah, but not—but not as he means it. You don't like it more than Catherine?"

He leaned his elbows on the table and buried his head in his hands, "You torture me!" he murmured. And, indeed, this was almost the effect of the poor lady's too importunate interest in his situation.

But she insisted on making her point. "If you marry her in spite of him, he will take for granted that you expect nothing of him, and are prepared to do without it. And so he will see that you are disinterested."

Morris raised his head a little, following this argument. "And what shall I gain by that?"

"Why, that he will see that he has been wrong in thinking that you wished to get his money."

"And seeing that I wish he would go to the deuce with it, he will leave it to a hospital. Is that what you mean?" asked Morris.

"No, I don't mean that; though that would be very grand!" Mrs. Penniman quickly added. "I mean that having done you such an injustice, he will think it his duty, at the end, to make some amends."

Morris shook his head, though it must be confessed he was a little struck with this idea. "Do you think he is so sentimental?"

"He is not sentimental," said Mrs. Penniman; "but, to be perfectly fair to him, I think he has, in his own narrow way, a certain sense of duty."

There passed through Morris Townsend's mind a rapid wonder as to what he might, even under a remote contingency, be indebted to from the action of this principle in Dr. Sloper's breast, and the inquiry exhausted itself in his sense of the ludicrous. "Your brother has no duties to me," he said presently, "and I none to him."

"Ah, but he has duties to Catherine."

"Yes, but you see that on that principle Catherine has duties to him as well."

Mrs. Penniman got up, with a melancholy sigh, as if she thought him very unimaginative. "She has always performed them faithfully; and now do you think she has no duties to *you?*" Mrs. Penniman always, even in conversation, italicised her personal pronouns.

"It would sound harsh to say so! I am so grateful for her love," Morris added.

"I will tell her you said that! And now, remember that if you need me, I am there." And Mrs. Penniman, who could think of nothing more to say, nodded vaguely in the direction of Washington Square.

Morris looked some moments at the sanded floor of the shop; he seemed to be disposed to linger a moment. At last, looking up with a certain abruptness, "It is your belief that if she marries me he will cut her off?" he asked.

Mrs. Penniman stared a little, and smiled. "Why, I have explained to you what I think would happen—that in the end it would be the best thing to do."

"You mean that, whatever she does, in the long run she will get the money?"

"It doesn't depend upon her, but upon you. Venture to appear as disinterested as you are!" said Mrs. Penniman ingeniously. Morris dropped his eyes on the sanded floor again, pondering this; and she pursued. "Mr. Penniman and I had nothing, and we were very happy. Catherine, moreover, has her mother's fortune, which, at the time my sister-in-law married, was considered a very handsome one."

"Oh, don't speak of that!" said Morris; and, indeed, it was quite superfluous, for he had contemplated the fact in all its lights.

"Austin married a wife with money—why shouldn't you?"

"Ah! but your brother was a doctor," Morris objected.

"Well, all young men can't be doctors!"

"I should think it an extremely loathsome profession," said Morris, with an air of intellectual independence. Then, in a moment, he went on rather inconsequently, "Do you suppose there is a will already made in Catherine's favour?"

"I suppose so—even doctors must die; and perhaps a little in mine," Mrs. Penniman frankly added.

"And you believe he would certainly change it—as regards Catherine?"

"Yes; and then change it back again."

"Ah, but one can't depend on that!" said Morris.

"Do you want to *depend* on it?" Mrs. Penniman asked.

Morris blushed a little. "Well, I am certainly afraid of being the cause of an injury to Catherine."

"Ah! you must not be afraid. Be afraid of nothing, and everything will go well!"

And then Mrs. Penniman paid for her cup of tea, and Morris paid for his oyster stew, and they went out together into the dimly-lighted wilderness of the Seventh Avenue. The dusk had closed in completely and the street lamps were separated by wide intervals of a pavement in which cavities and fissures played a disproportionate part. An omnibus, emblazoned with strange pictures, went tumbling over the dislocated cobble-stones.

"How will you go home?" Morris asked, following this vehicle with an interested eye. Mrs. Penniman had taken his arm.

She hesitated a moment. "I think this manner would be pleasant," she said; and she continued to let him feel the value of his support.

So he walked with her through the devious ways of the west side of the town, and through the bustle of gathering nightfall in populous streets, to the quiet precinct of Washington Square. They lingered a moment at the foot of Dr. Sloper's white marble steps, above which a spotless white door, adorned with a glittering silver plate, seemed to figure, for Morris, the closed portal of happiness; and then Mrs. Penniman's companion rested a melancholy eye upon a lighted window in the upper part of the house.

"That is my room—my dear little room!" Mrs. Penniman remarked.

Morris started. "Then I needn't come walking round the square to gaze at it."

"That's as you please. But Catherine's is behind; two noble windows on the second floor. I think you can see them from the other street."

"I don't want to see them, ma'am!" And Morris turned his back to the house.

"I will tell her you have been *here*, at any rate," said Mrs. Penniman, pointing to the spot where they stood; "and I will give her your message—that she is to hold fast!"

"Oh, yes! of course. You know I write her all that."

"It seems to say more when it is spoken! And remember, if you need me, that I am *there*;" and Mrs. Penniman glanced at the third floor.

On this they separated, and Morris, left to himself, stood looking at the house a moment; after which he turned away, and took a gloomy walk round the Square, on the opposite side, close to the wooden fence. Then he came back, and paused for a minute in front of Dr. Sloper's dwelling. His eyes travelled over it; they even rested on the ruddy windows of Mrs. Penniman's apartment. He thought it a devilish comfortable house.

XVII.

Mrs. Penniman told Catherine that evening—the two ladies were sitting in the back parlour—that she had had an interview with Morris Townsend; and on receiving this news the girl started with a sense of pain. She felt angry for the moment; it was almost the first time she had ever felt angry. It seemed to her that her aunt was meddlesome; and from this came a vague apprehension that she would spoil something.

"I don't see why you should have seen him. I don't think it was right," Catherine said.

"I was so sorry for him—it seemed to me some one ought to see him."

"No one but I," said Catherine, who felt as if she were making the most presumptuous speech of her life, and yet at the same time had an instinct that she was right in doing so.

"But you wouldn't, my dear," Aunt Lavinia rejoined; "and I didn't know what might have become of him."

"I have not seen him, because my father has forbidden it," Catherine said, very simply.

There was a simplicity in this, indeed, which fairly vexed Mrs. Penniman. "If your father forbade you to go to sleep, I suppose you would keep awake!" she commented.

Catherine looked at her. "I don't understand you. You seem to be very strange."

"Well, my dear, you will understand me some day!" And Mrs. Penniman, who was reading the evening paper, which she perused daily from the first line to the last, resumed her occupation. She wrapped herself in silence; she was determined Catherine should ask her for an account of her interview with Morris. But Catherine was silent for so long, that she almost lost patience; and she was on the point of remarking to her that she was very heartless, when the girl at last spoke.

"What did he say?" she asked.

"He said he is ready to marry you any day, in spite of everything."

Catherine made no answer to this, and Mrs. Penniman almost lost patience again; owing to which she at last volunteered the information that Morris looked very handsome, but terribly haggard.

"Did he seem sad?" asked her niece.

"He was dark under the eyes," said Mrs. Penniman. "So different from when I first saw him; though I am not sure that if I had seen him in this condition the first time, I should not have been even more struck with him. There is something brilliant in his very misery."

This was, to Catherine's sense, a vivid picture, and though she disapproved, she felt herself gazing at it. "Where did you see him?" she asked presently.

"In—in the Bowery; at a confectioner's," said

Mrs. Penniman, who had a general idea that she ought to dissemble a little.

"Whereabouts is the place?" Catherine inquired, after another pause.

"Do you wish to go there, my dear?" said her aunt.

"Oh, no!" And Catherine got up from her seat and went to the fire, where she stood looking awhile at the glowing coals.

"Why are you so dry, Catherine?" Mrs. Penniman said at last.

"So dry?"

"So cold—so irresponsive."

The girl turned, very quickly. "Did *he* say that?"

Mrs. Penniman hesitated a moment. "I will tell you what he said. He said he feared only one thing—that you would be afraid."

"Afraid of what?"

"Afraid of your father."

Catherine turned back to the fire again, and then, after a pause, she said—"I *am* afraid of my father."

Mrs. Penniman got quickly up from her chair and approached her niece. "Do you mean to give him up, then?"

Catherine for some time never moved; she kept her eyes on the coals. At last she raised her head and looked at her aunt. "Why do you push me so?" she asked.

"I don't push you. When have I spoken to you before?"

"It seems to me that you have spoken to me several times."

"I am afraid it is necessary, then, Catherine," said Mrs. Penniman, with a good deal of solemnity. "I am afraid you don't feel the importance——" She paused a little; Catherine was looking at her. "The importance of not disappointing that gallant young heart!" And Mrs. Penniman went back to her chair, by the lamp, and, with a little jerk, picked up the evening paper again.

Catherine stood there before the fire, with her hands behind her, looking at her aunt, to whom it seemed that the girl had never had just this dark fixedness in her gaze. "I don't think you understand—or that you know me," she said.

"If I don't, it is not wonderful; you trust me so little."

Catherine made no attempt to deny this charge, and for sometime more nothing was said. But Mrs. Penniman's imagination was restless, and the evening paper failed on this occasion to enchain it.

"If you succumb to the dread of your father's wrath," she said, "I don't know what will become of us."

"Did *he* tell you to say these things to me?"

"He told me to use my influence."

"You must be mistaken," said Catherine. "He trusts me."

"I hope he may never repent of it!" And Mrs. Penniman gave a little sharp slap to her newspaper. She knew not what to make of her niece, who had suddenly become stern and contradictious.

This tendency on Catherine's part was presently even more apparent. "You had much better not make any more appointments with Mr. Townsend," she said. "I don't think it is right."

Mrs. Penniman rose with considerable majesty. "My poor child, are you jealous of me?" she inquired.

"Oh, Aunt Lavinia!" murmured Catherine blushing.

"I don't think it is your place to teach me what is right."

On this point Catherine made no concession. "It can't be right to deceive."

"I certainly have not deceived *you!*"

"Yes; but I promised my father ——"

"I have no doubt you promised your father. But I have promised him nothing!"

Catherine had to admit this, and she did so in silence. "I don't believe Mr. Townsend himself likes it," she said at last.

"Doesn't like meeting me?"

"Not in secret."

"It was not in secret; the place was full of people."

"But it was a secret place—away off in the Bowery."

Mrs. Penniman flinched a little. "Gentlemen enjoy such things," she remarked, presently. "I know what gentlemen like."

"My father wouldn't like it, if he knew."

"Pray, do you propose to inform him?" Mrs. Penniman inquired.

"No, Aunt Lavinia. But please don't do it again."

"If I do it again, you will inform him: is that

what you mean? I do not share your dread of my brother; I have always known how to defend my own position. But I shall certainly never again take any step on your behalf; you are much too thankless. I knew you were not a spontaneous nature, but I believed you were firm, and I told your father that he would find you so. I am disappointed—but your father will not be!" And with this, Mrs. Penniman offered her niece a brief good-night, and withdrew to her own apartment.

XVIII.

Catherine sat alone by the parlour fire—sat there for more than an hour, lost in her meditations. Her aunt seemed to her aggressive and foolish, and to see it so clearly—to judge Mrs. Penniman so positively—made her feel old and grave. She did not resent the imputation of weakness; it made no impression on her, for she had not the sense of weakness, and she was not hurt at not being appreciated. She had an immense respect for her father, and she felt that to displease him would be a misdemeanour analogous to an act of profanity in a great temple: but her purpose had slowly ripened, and she believed that her prayers had purified it of its violence. The evening advanced, and the lamp burned dim without her noticing it; her eyes were fixed upon her terrible plan. She knew her father was in his study—that he had been there all the evening; from time to time she expected to hear him move. She thought he would perhaps come, as he sometimes came, into the parlour. At last the clock struck eleven, and the house was wrapped in silence; the servants had gone to bed. Catherine got up and went slowly to the door of the library, where she waited a moment, motionless. Then she knocked, and then she waited again. Her father had answered her, but she had not the courage to turn the latch. What she had said to her aunt was true enough—she was afraid of him; and in saying that she had no sense of weakness she meant that she was not afraid of herself. She heard him move within, and he came and opened the door for her.

"What is the matter?" asked the Doctor. "You are standing there like a ghost."

She went into the room, but it was some time before she contrived to say what she had come to say. Her father, who was in his dressing-gown and slippers, had been busy at his writing-table, and after looking at her for some moments, and waiting for her to speak, he went and seated himself at his papers again. His back was turned to her—she began to hear the scratching of his pen. She remained near the door, with her heart thumping beneath her bodice; and she was very glad that his back was turned, for it seemed to her that she could more easily address herself to this portion of his person than to his face. At last she began, watching it while she spoke.

"You told me that if I should have anything more to say about Mr. Townsend you would be glad to listen to it."

"Exactly, my dear," said the Doctor, not turning round, but stopping his pen.

Catherine wished it would go on, but she herself continued. "I thought I would tell you that I have not seen him again, but that I should like to do so."

"To bid him good-bye?" asked the Doctor.

The girl hesitated a moment. "He is not going away."

The Doctor wheeled slowly round in his chair, with a smile that seemed to accuse her of an epigram; but extremes meet, and Catherine had not intended one. "It is not to bid him good-bye, then?" her father said.

"No, father, not that; at least, not for ever. I have not seen him again, but I should like to see him," Catherine repeated.

The Doctor slowly rubbed his under lip with the feather of his quill.

"Have you written to him?"

"Yes, four times."

"You have not dismissed him, then. Once would have done that."

"No," said Catherine; "I have asked him—asked him to wait."

Her father sat looking at her, and she was afraid he was going to break out into wrath; his eyes were so fine and cold.

"You are a dear, faithful child," he said at last. "Come here to your father." And he got up, holding out his hands toward her.

The words were a surprise, and they gave her an exquisite joy. She went to him, and he put his arm round her tenderly, soothingly; and then he kissed her. After this he said—

"Do you wish to make me very happy?"

"I should like to—but I am afraid I can't," Catherine answered.

"You can if you will. It all depends on your will."

"Is it to give him up?" said Catherine.

"Yes, it is to give him up."

And he held her still, with the same tenderness, looking into her face and resting his eyes on her averted eyes. There was a long silence; she wished he would release her.

"You are happier than I, father," she said, at last.

"I have no doubt you are unhappy just now. But it is better to be unhappy for three months and get over it, than for many years and never get over it."

"Yes, if that were so," said Catherine.

"It would be so; I am sure of that." She answered nothing, and he went on. "Have you no faith in my wisdom, in my tenderness, in my solicitude for your future?"

"Oh, father!" murmured the girl.

"Don't you suppose that I know something of men: their vices, their follies, their falsities?"

She detached herself, and turned upon him. "He is not vicious—he is not false!"

Her father kept looking at her with his sharp, pure eye. "You make nothing of my judgment, then?"

"I can't believe that!"

"I don t ask you to believe it, but to take it on trust."

Catherine was far from saying to herself that this was an ingenious sophism; but she met the appeal none the less squarely. "What has he done—what do you know?"

"He has never done anything—he is a selfish idler."

"Oh, father, don't abuse him!" she exclaimed, pleadingly.

"I don't mean to abuse him; it would be a great mistake. You may do as you choose," he added, turning away.

"I may see him again?"

"Just as you choose."

"Will you forgive me?"

"By no means."

"It will only be for once."

"I don't know what you mean by once. You must either give him up or continue the acquaintance."

"I wish to explain—to tell him to wait."

"To wait for what?"

"Till you know him better—till you consent."

"Don't tell him any such nonsense as that. I know him well enough, and I shall never consent."

"But we can wait a long time," said poor Catherine, in a tone which was meant to express the humblest conciliation, but which had upon her father's nerves the effect of an iteration not characterised by tact.

The Doctor answered, however, quietly enough: "Of course you can wait till I die, if you like."

Catherine gave a cry of natural horror.

"Your engagement will have one delightful effect upon you; it will make you extremely impatient for that event."

Catherine stood staring, and the Doctor enjoyed the point he had made. It came to Catherine with the force—or rather with the vague impressiveness—of a logical axiom which it was not in her province to controvert; and yet, though it was a scientific truth, she felt wholly unable to accept it.

"I would rather not marry, if that were true," she said.

"Give me a proof of it, then; for it is beyond a question that by engaging yourself to Morris Townsend you simply wait for my death."

She turned away, feeling sick and faint; and the Doctor went on. "And if you wait for it with impatience, judge, if you please, what *his* eagerness will be!"

Catherine turned it over—her father's words had such an authority for her that her very thoughts were capable of obeying him. There was a dreadful ugliness in it, which seemed to glare at her through the interposing medium of her own feebler reason. Suddenly, however, she had an inspiration—she almost knew it to be an inspiration.

"If I don't marry before your death, I will not after," she said.

To her father, it must be admitted, this seemed only another epigram; and as obstinacy, in unaccomplished minds, does not usually select such a mode of expression, he was the more surprised at this wanton play of a fixed idea.

"Do you mean that for an impertinence?" he inquired; an inquiry of which, as he made it, he quite perceived the grossness.

"An impertinence? Oh father, what terrible things you say!"

"If you don't wait for my death, you might as well marry immediately; there is nothing else to wait for."

For some time Catherine made no answer; but finally she said—

"I think Morris—little by little—might persuade you."

"I shall never let him speak to me again. I dislike him too much."

Catherine gave a long, low sigh; she tried to stifle it, for she had made up her mind that it was wrong to make a parade of her trouble, and to endeavour to act upon her father by the meretricious aid of emotion. Indeed, she even thought it wrong—in the sense of being inconsiderate—to attempt to act upon his feelings at all; her part was to effect some gentle, gradual change in his intellectual perception of poor Morris's character. But the means of effecting such a change were at present shrouded in mystery, and she felt miserably helpless and hopeless. She had exhausted all arguments, all replies. Her father might have pitied her, and in fact he did so; but he was sure he was right.

"There is one thing you can tell Mr. Townsend, when you see him again," he said: "that if you marry without my consent, I don't leave you a farthing of money. That will interest him more than anything else you can tell him."

"That would be very right," Catherine answered. "I ought not in that case have a farthing of your money."

"My dear child," the Doctor observed, laughing, "your simplicity is touching. Make that remark, in that tone, and with that expression of countenance, to Mr. Townsend and take a note of his answer. It won't be polite—it will express irritation; and I shall be glad of that, as it will put me in the right; unless, indeed—which is perfectly possible—you should like him the better for being rude to you."

"He will never be rude to me," said Catherine, gently.

"Tell him what I say, all the same."

She looked at her father, and her quiet eyes filled with tears.

"I think I will see him, then," she murmured, in her timid voice.

"Exactly as you choose!" And he went to the door and opened it for her to go out. The movement gave her a terrible sense of his turning her off.

"It will be only once, for the present," she added, lingering a moment.

"Exactly as you choose," he repeated, standing there with his hand on the door. "I have told you what I think. If you see him, you will be an ungrateful, cruel child; you will have given your old father the greatest pain of his life."

This was more than the poor girl could bear; her tears overflowed, and she moved towards her grimly consistent parent with a pitiful cry. Her hands were raised in supplication, but he sternly evaded this appeal. Instead of letting her sob out her misery on his shoulder, he simply took her by the arm and directed her course across the threshold, closing the door gently but firmly behind her. After he had done so, he remained listening. For a long time there was no sound; he knew that she was standing outside. He was sorry for her, as I have said; but he was so sure he was right.

At last he heard her move away, and then her footstep creaked faintly upon the stairs.

The Doctor took several turns round his study, with his hands in his pockets, and a thin sparkle, possibly of irritation, but partly also of something like humour, in his eye. "By Jove," he said to himself, "I believe she will stick—I believe she will stick!" And this idea of Catherine "sticking" appeared to have a comical side, and to offer a prospect of entertainment. He determined, as he said to himself, to see it out.

XIX.

It was for reasons connected with this determination that on the morrow he sought a few words of private conversation with Mrs. Penniman. He sent for her to the library, and he there informed her that he hoped very much that, as regarded this affair of Catherine's, she would mind her *p*'s and *q*'s.

"I don't know what you mean by such an expression," said his sister. "You speak as if I were learning the alphabet."

"The alphabet of common sense is something you will never learn," the Doctor permitted himself to respond.

"Have you called me here to insult me?" Mrs. Penniman inquired.

"Not at all. Simply to advise you. You have taken up young Townsend; that's your own affair. I have nothing to do with your sentiments, your fancies, your affections, your delusions; but what I request of you is that you will keep these things to yourself. I have explained my views to Catherine; she understands them perfectly, and anything that she does further in the way of encouraging Mr. Townsend's attentions will be in deliberate opposition to my wishes. Anything that you should do in the way of giving her aid and comfort will be—permit me the expression—distinctly treasonable. You know high treason is a capital offence; take care how you incur the penalty."

Mrs. Penniman threw back her head, with a certain expansion of the eye which she occasionally practised. "It seems to me that you talk like a great autocrat."

"I talk like my daughter's father."

"Not like your sister's brother!" cried Lavinia.

"My dear Lavinia," said the Doctor, "I sometimes wonder whether I am your brother. We are so extremely different. In spite of differences, however, we can, at a pinch, understand each other; and that is the essential thing just now. Walk straight with regard to Mr. Townsend; that's all I ask. It is highly probable you have been corresponding with him for the last three weeks—perhaps even seeing him. I don't ask you — you needn't tell me." He had a moral conviction that she would contrive to tell a fib about the matter, which it would disgust him to listen to. "Whatever you have done, stop doing it. That's all I wish."

"Don't you wish also by chance to murder your child?" Mrs. Penniman inquired.

"On the contrary, I wish to make her live and be happy."

"You will kill her; she passed a dreadful night."

"She won't die of one dreadful night, nor of a dozen. Remember that I am a distinguished physician."

Mrs. Penniman hesitated a moment. Then she

risked her retort. "Your being a distinguished physician has not prevented you from already losing *two members* of your family!"

She had risked it, but her brother gave her such a terribly incisive look—a look so like a surgeon's lancet—that she was frightened at her courage. And he answered her in words that corresponded to the look: "It may not prevent me, either, from losing the society of still another."

Mrs. Penniman took herself off, with whatever air of depreciated merit was at her command, and repaired to Catherine's room, where the poor girl was closeted. She knew all about her dreadful night, for the two had met again, the evening before, after Catherine left her father. Mrs. Penniman was on the landing of the second floor when her niece came upstairs. It was not remarkable that a person of so much subtlety should have discovered that Catherine had been shut up with the Doctor. It was still less remarkable that she should have felt an extreme curiosity to learn the result of this interview, and that this sentiment, combined with her great amiability and generosity, should have prompted her to regret the sharp words lately exchanged between her niece and herself. As the unhappy girl came into sight, in the dusky corridor, she made a lively demonstration of sympathy. Catherine's bursting heart was equally oblivious. She only knew that her aunt was taking her into her arms. Mrs. Penniman drew her into Catherine's own room, and the two women sat there together, far into the small hours; the younger one with her head on the other's lap, sobbing and sobbing at first in a soundless, stifled manner, and then at last perfectly still. It gratified Mrs. Penniman to be able to feel conscientiously that this scene virtually removed the interdict which Catherine had placed upon her further communion with Morris Townsend. She was not gratified, however, when, in coming back to her niece's room before breakfast, she found that Catherine had risen and was preparing herself for this meal.

"You should not go to breakfast," she said; "you are not well enough, after your fearful night."

"Yes, I am very well, and I am only afraid of being late."

"I can't understand you!" Mrs. Penniman cried. "You should stay in bed for three days."

"Oh, I could never do that!" said Catherine, to whom this idea presented no attractions.

Mrs. Penniman was in despair, and she noted, with extreme annoyance, that the trace of the night's tears had completely vanished from Catherine's eyes. She had a most impracticable *physique*. "What effect do you expect to have upon your father," her aunt demanded, "if you come plumping down, without a vestige of any sort of feeling, as if nothing in the world had happened?"

"He would not like me to lie in bed," said Catherine, simply.

"All the more reason for your doing it. How else do you expect to move him?"

Catherine thought a little. "I don't know how; but not in that way. I wish to be just as usual." And she finished dressing, and, according to her aunt's expression, went plumping down into the paternal presence. She was really too modest for consistent pathos.

And yet it was perfectly true that she had had a dreadful night. Even after Mrs. Penniman left her she had had no sleep. She lay staring at the uncomforting gloom, with her eyes and ears filled with the movement with which her father had turned her out of his room, and of the words in which he had told her that she was a heartless daughter. Her heart was breaking. She had heart enough for that. At moments it seemed to her that she believed him, and that to do what she was doing, a girl must indeed be bad. She *was* bad; but she couldn't help it. She would try to appear good, even if her heart were perverted; and from time to time she had a fancy that she might accomplish something by ingenious concessions to form, though she should persist in caring for Morris. Catherine's ingenuities were indefinite, and we are not called upon to expose their hollowness. The best of them perhaps showed itself in that freshness of aspect which was so discouraging to Mrs. Penniman, who was amazed at the absence of haggardness in a young woman who for a whole night had lain quivering beneath a father's curse. Poor Catherine was conscious of her freshness; it gave her a feeling about the future which rather added to the weight upon her mind. It seemed a proof that she was strong and solid and dense, and would live to a great age—longer than might be generally convenient; and this idea was depressing, for it appeared to saddle her with a pretension the more, just when the cultivation of any pretension was inconsistent with her doing right. She wrote that day to Morris Townsend, requesting him to come and see her on the morrow; using very few words, and explaining nothing. She would explain everything face to face.

XX.

On the morrow, in the afternoon, she heard his voice at the door, and his step in the hall. She received him in the big, bright front-parlour, and she instructed the servant that if any one should call she was particularly engaged. She was not afraid of her father's coming in, for at that hour he was always driving about town. When Morris stood there before her, the first thing that she was conscious of was that he was even more beautiful to look at than fond recollection had painted him; the next was that he had pressed her in his arms. When she was free again it appeared to her that she had now indeed thrown herself into the gulf of defiance, and even, for an instant, that she had been married to him.

He told her that she had been very cruel, and had made him very unhappy; and Catherine felt acutely the difficulty of her destiny, which forced her to give pain in such opposite quarters. But she wished that, instead of reproaches, however tender, he would give her help; he was certainly wise enough, and clever enough, to invent some issue from their troubles. She expressed this belief, and Morris received the assurance as if he thought it natural; but he interrogated, at first—as was natural too—rather than committed himself to marking out a course.

"You should not have made me wait so long," he said. "I don't know how I have been living; every hour seemed like years. You should have decided sooner."

"Decided?" Catherine asked.

"Decided whether you would keep me or give me up."

"Oh, Morris," she cried, with a long tender murmur, "I never thought of giving you up!"

"What, then, were you waiting for?" The young man was ardently logical.

"I thought my father might—might——" and she hesitated.

"Might see how unhappy you were?"

"Oh, no! But that he might look at it differently."

"And now you have sent for me to tell me that at last he does so. Is that it?"

This hypothetical optimism gave the poor girl a pang. "No, Morris," she said solemnly, "he looks at it still in the same way."

"Then why have you sent for me?"

"Because I wanted to see you!" cried Catherine, piteously.

"That's an excellent reason, surely. But did you want to look at me only? Have you nothing to tell me?"

His beautiful persuasive eyes were fixed upon her face, and she wondered what answer would be noble enough to make to such a gaze as that. For a moment her own eyes took it in, and then—"I *did* want to look at you!" she said, gently. But after this speech, most inconsistently, she hid her face.

Morris watched her for a moment, attentively. "Will you marry me to-morrow?" he asked suddenly.

"To-morrow?"

"Next week, then. Any time within a month."

"Isn't it better to wait?" said Catherine.

"To wait for what?"

She hardly knew for what; but this tremendous leap alarmed her. "Till we have thought about it a little more."

He shook his head, sadly and reproachfully. "I thought you had been thinking about it these three weeks. Do you want to turn it over in your mind for five years? You have given me more than time enough. My poor girl," he added in a moment, "you are not sincere!"

Catherine coloured from brow to chin, and her eyes filled with tears. "Oh, how can you say that?" she murmured.

"Why, you must take me or leave me," said Morris, very reasonably. "You can't please your father and me both; you must choose between us."

"I have chosen you!" she said, passionately.

"Then marry me next week."

She stood gazing at him. "Isn't there any other way?"

"None that I know of for arriving at the same result. If there is, I should be happy to hear of it."

Catherine could think of nothing of the kind, and Morris's luminosity seemed almost pitiless. The only thing she could think of was that her father might after all come round, and she articulated, with an awkward sense of her helplessness in doing so, a wish that this miracle might happen.

"Do you think it is in the least degree likely?" Morris asked.

"It would be, if he could only know you?"

"He can know me if he will. What is to prevent it?"

"His ideas, his reasons," said Catherine. "They are so—so terribly strong." She trembled with the recollection of them yet.

"Strong?" cried Morris. "I would rather you should think them weak."

"Oh, nothing about my father is weak!" said the girl.

Morris turned away, walking to the window, where he stood looking out. "You are terribly afraid of him!" he remarked at last.

She felt no impulse to deny it, because she had no shame in it; for if it was no honour to herself, at least it was an honour to him. "I suppose I must be," she said, simply.

"Then you don't love me—not as I love you. If you fear your father more than you love me, then your love is not what I hoped it was."

"Ah, my friend!" she said, going to him.

"Do *I* fear anything?" he demanded, turning round on her. "For your sake what am I not ready to face?"

"You are noble—you are brave!" she answered, stopping short at a distance that was almost respectful.

"Small good it does me, if you are so timid."

"I don't think that I am—*really*," said Catherine.

"I don't know what you mean by 'really.' It is really enough to make us miserable."

"I should be strong enough to wait—to wait a long time."

"And suppose after a long time your father should hate me worse than ever?"

"He wouldn't—he couldn't!"

"He would be touched by my fidelity? Is that what you mean? If he is so easily touched, then why should you be afraid of him?"

This was much to the point, and Catherine was struck by it. "I will try not to be," she said. And she stood there, submissively, the image, in advance, of a dutiful and responsible wife. This image could not fail to recommend itself to Morris Townsend, and he continued to give proof of the high estimation in which he held her. It could only have been at the prompting of such a sentiment that he presently mentioned to her that the course recommended by Mrs. Penniman was an immediate union, regardless of consequences.

"Yes, Aunt Penniman would like that," Catherine said, simply—and yet with a certain shrewdness. It must, however, have been in pure simplicity, and from motives quite untouched by sarcasm, that, a few moments after, she went on to say to Morris that her father had given her a message for him. It was quite on her conscience to deliver this message, and had the mission been ten times more painful she would have as scrupulously performed it. "He told me to tell you—to tell you very distinctly, and directly from himself, that if I marry without his consent, I shall not inherit a penny of his fortune. He made a great point of this. He seemed to think—he seemed to think ——"

Morris flushed, as any young man of spirit might have flushed at an imputation of baseness.

"What did he seem to think?"

"That it would make a difference."

"It *will* make a difference—in many things. We shall be by many thousands of dollars the poorer; and that is a great difference. But it will make none in my affection."

"We shall not want the money," said Catherine; "for you know I have a good deal myself."

"Yes, my dear girl, I know you have something. And he can't touch that!"

"He would never," said Catherine. "My mother left it to me."

Morris was silent awhile. "He was very positive about this, was he?" he asked at last. "He thought such a message would annoy me terribly, and make me throw off the mask, eh?"

"I don't know what he thought," said Catherine, wearily.

"Please tell him that I care for his message as much as for that!" And Morris snapped his fingers sonorously.

"I don't think I could tell him that."

"Do you know you sometimes disappoint me?" said Morris.

"I should think I might. I disappoint every one—father and Aunt Penniman."

"Well, it doesn't matter with me, because I am fonder of you than they are."

"Yes, Morris," said the girl, with her imagination—what there was of it—swimming in this happy truth, which seemed, after all, invidious to no one.

"Is it your belief that he will stick to it—stick to it for ever, to this idea of disinheriting you?—that your goodness and patience will never wear out his cruelty?"

"The trouble is that if I marry you, he will think I am not good. He will think that a proof."

"Ah, then, he will never forgive you!"

This idea, sharply expressed by Morris's handsome lips, renewed for a moment, to the poor girl's temporarily pacified conscience, all its dreadful vividness. "Oh, you must love me very much!" she cried.

"There is no doubt of that, my dear!" her lover rejoined. "You don't like that word 'disinherited,'" he added in a moment.

"It isn't the money; it is that he should—that he should feel so."

"I suppose it seems to you a kind of curse," said Morris. "It must be very dismal. But don't you think," he went on presently, "that if you were to try to be very clever, and to set rightly about it, you might in the end conjure it away? Don't you think," he continued further, in a tone of sympathetic speculation, "that a really clever woman, in your place, might bring him round at last? Don't you think——"

Here, suddenly, Morris was interrupted; these

ingenious inquiries had not reached Catherine's ears. The terrible word "disinheritance," with all its impressive moral reprobation, was still ringing there; seemed indeed to gather force as it lingered. The mortal chill of her situation struck more deeply into her child-like heart, and she was overwhelmed by a feeling of loneliness and danger. But her refuge was there, close to her, and she put out her hands to grasp it. "Ah, Morris," she said, with a shudder, "I will marry you as soon as you please!" And she surrendered herself, leaning her head on his shoulder.

"My dear good girl!" he exclaimed, looking down at his prize. And then he looked up again, rather vaguely, with parted lips and lifted eyebrows.

XXI.

Dr. Sloper very soon imparted his conviction to Mrs. Almond, in the same terms in which he had announced it to himself. "She's going to stick, by Jove! she's going to stick."

"Do you mean that she is going to marry him?" Mrs. Almond inquired.

"I don't know that; but she is not going to break down. She is going to drag out the engagement, in the hope of making me relent."

"And shall you not relent?"

"Shall a geometrical proposition relent? I am not so superficial."

"Doesn't geometry treat of surfaces?" asked Mrs. Almond, who, as we know, was clever, smiling,

"Yes; but it treats of them profoundly. Catherine and her young man are my surfaces; I have taken their measure."

"You speak as if it surprised you."

"It is immense; there will be a great deal to observe."

"You are shockingly cold-blooded!" said Mrs. Almond.

"I need to be, with all this hot blood about me. Young Townsend indeed is cool; I must allow him that merit."

"I can't judge him," Mrs. Almond answered; "but I am not at all surprised at Catherine."

"I confess I am a little; she must have been so deucedly divided and bothered."

"Say it amuses you outright! I don't see why it should be such a joke that your daughter adores you."

"It is the point where the adoration stops that I find it interesting to fix."

"It stops where the other sentiment begins."

"Not at all—that would be simple enough. The two things are extremely mixed up, and the mixture is extremely odd. It will produce some third element, and that's what I am waiting to see. I wait with suspense—with positive excitement; and that is a sort of emotion that I didn't suppose Catherine would ever provide for me. I am really very much obliged to her."

"She will cling," said Mrs. Almond; "she will certainly cling."

"Yes; as I say, she will stick."

"Cling is prettier. That's what those very simple natures always do, and nothing could be simpler than Catherine. She doesn't take many impressions; but when she takes one she keeps it. She is like a copper kettle that receives a dent; you may polish up the kettle, but you can't efface the mark."

"We must try and polish up Catherine," said the Doctor. "I will take her to Europe."

"She won't forget him in Europe."

"He will forget her, then."

Mrs. Almond looked grave. "Should you really like that?"

"Extremely!" said the Doctor.

Mrs. Penniman, meanwhile, lost little time in putting herself again in communication with Morris Townsend. She requested him to favour her with another interview, but she did not on this occasion select an oyster-saloon as the scene of their meeting. She proposed that he should join her at the door of a certain church, after service on Sunday afternoon, and she was careful not to appoint the place of worship which she usually visited, and where, as she said, the congregation would have spied upon her. She picked out a less elegant resort, and on issuing from its portal at the hour she had fixed she saw the young man standing apart. She offered him no recognition till she had crossed the street and he had followed her to some distance. Here, with a smile—"Excuse my apparent want of cordiality," she said. "You know what to believe about that. Prudence before everything." And on his asking her in what direction they should walk, "Where we shall be least observed," she murmured.

Morris was not in high good-humour, and his response to this speech was not particularly gallant. "I don't flatter myself we shall be much observed anywhere." Then he turned recklessly toward the centre of the town. "I hope you have come to tell me that he has knocked under," he went on.

"I am afraid I am not altogether a harbinger of good; and yet, too, I am to a certain extent a messenger of peace. I have been thinking a great deal, Mr. Townsend," said Mrs. Penniman.

"You think too much."

"I suppose I do; but I can't help it, my mind is

so terribly active. When I give myself, I give myself. I pay the penalty in my headaches, my famous headaches—a perfect circlet of pain! But I carry it as a queen carries her crown. Would you believe that I have one now? I wouldn't, however, have missed our rendezvous for anything. I have something very important to tell you."

"Well let's have it," said Morris.

"I was perhaps a little headlong the other day in advising you to marry immediately. I have been thinking it over, and now I see it just a little differently."

"You seem to have a great many different ways of seeing the same object."

"Their number is infinite!" said Mrs. Penniman, in a tone which seemed to suggest that this convenient faculty was one of her brightest attributes.

"I recommend you to take one way and stick to it," Morris replied.

"Ah! but it isn't easy to choose. My imagination is never quiet, never satisfied. It makes me a bad adviser, perhaps; but it makes me a capital friend!"

"A capital friend who gives bad advice!" said Morris.

"Not intentionally—and who hurries off, at every risk, to make the most humble excuses!"

"Well, what do you advise me now?"

"To be very patient; to watch and wait."

"And is that bad advice or good?"

"That is not for me to say," Mrs. Penniman rejoined, with some dignity. "I only pretend it's sincere."

"And will you come to me next week and recommend something different and equally sincere?"

"I may come to you next week and tell you that I am in the streets!"

"In the streets?"

"I have had a terrible scene with my brother, and he threatens, if anything happens, to turn me out of the house. You know I am a poor woman."

Morris had a speculative idea that she had a little property; but he naturally did not press this.

"I should be very sorry to see you suffer martyrdom for me," he said. "But you make your brother out a regular Turk."

Mrs. Penniman hesitated a little.

"I certainly do not regard Austin as a satisfactory Christian."

"And am I to wait till he is converted?"

"Wait at any rate till he is less violent. Bide your time, Mr. Townsend; remember the prize is great!"

Morris walked along some time in silence, tapping the railings and gateposts very sharply with his stick.

"You certainly are devilish inconsistent!" he broke out at last. "I have already got Catherine to consent to a private marriage."

Mrs. Penniman was indeed inconsistent, for at this news she gave a little jump of gratification.

"Oh! when and where?" she cried. And then she stopped short.

Morris was a little vague about this.

"That isn't fixed; but she consents. It's deuced awkward, now, to back out."

Mrs. Penniman, as I say, had stopped short; and she stood there with her eyes fixed, brilliantly, on her companion.

"Mr. Townsend," she proceeded, "shall I tell you something? Catherine loves you so much that you may do anything."

This declaration was slightly ambiguous, and Morris opened his eyes.

"I am happy to hear it! But what do you mean by 'anything'?"

"You may postpone—you may change about; she won't think the worse of you."

Morris stood there still, with his raised eyebrows; then he said simply and rather dryly—"Ah!" After this he remarked to Mrs. Penniman that if she walked so slowly she would attract notice, and he succeeded, after a fashion, in hurrying her back to the domicile of which her tenure had become so insecure.

XXII.

HE had slightly misrepresented the matter in saying that Catherine had consented to take the great step. We left her just now declaring that she would burn her ships behind her; but Morris, after having elicited this declaration, had become conscious of good reasons for not taking it up. He avoided, gracefully enough, fixing a day, though he left her under the impression that he had his eye on one. Catherine may have had her difficulties; but those of her circumspect suitor are also worthy of consideration. The prize was certainly great; but it was only to be won by striking the happy mean between precipitancy and caution. It would be all very well to take one's jump and trust to Providence; Providence was more especially on the side of clever people, and clever people were known by an indisposition to risk their bones. The ultimate reward of a union with a young woman who was both unattractive and impoverished ought to be connected with immediate disadvantages by some very palpable chain. Between the fear of losing Catherine and her possible fortune altogether, and the fear of taking her too soon and finding this possible fortune as void of actuality as a collection of emptied bottles, it was not comfortable for Morris Townsend to choose; a fact that should be remembered by readers disposed to judge harshly of a young man who may have struck them as making but an indifferently successful use of fine natural parts. He had not forgotten that in any event Catherine had her own ten thousand a year; he had devoted an abundance of meditation to this circumstance. But with his fine parts he rated himself high, and he had a perfectly definite appreciation of his value, which seemed to him inadequately represented by the sum I have mentioned. At the same time he reminded himself that this sum was considerable, that everything is relative, and that if a modest income is less desirable than a large one, the complete absence of revenue is nowhere accounted an advantage. These reflections gave him plenty of occupation, and made it necessary that he should trim his sail. Dr. Sloper's opposition was the unknown quantity in the problem he had to work out. The natural way to work it out was by marrying Catherine; but in mathematics there are many short cuts, and Morris was not without a hope that he should yet discover one. When Catherine took him at his word and consented to renounce the attempt to mollify her father, he drew back skilfully enough, as I have said, and kept the wedding-day still an open question. Her faith in his sincerity was so complete that she was incapable of suspecting that he was playing with her; her trouble just now was of another kind. The poor girl had an admirable sense of honour; and from the moment she had brought herself to the point of violating her father's wish, it seemed to her that she had no right to enjoy his protection. It was on her conscience that she ought not to live under his roof only so long as she conformed to his wisdom. There was a great deal of glory in such a position, but poor Catherine felt that she had forfeited her claim to it. She had cast her lot with a young man against whom he had solemnly warned her, and broken the contract under which he provided her with a happy home. She could not give up the young man, so she must leave the home; and the sooner the object of her preference offered her another, the sooner her situation would lose its awkward twist. This was close reasoning; but it was commingled with an infinite amount of merely instinctive penitence. Catherine's days, at this time, were dismal, and the weight of some of her hours was almost more than she could bear. Her father never looked at her, never spoke to her. He knew perfectly what he was about, and this was part of a plan. She looked at him as much as she dared (for she was afraid of seeming to offer herself to his observation), and she pitied him for the sorrow she had brought upon him. She held up her head and busied her hands, and went about her daily occupations; and when the state of things in Washington Square seemed intolerable, she closed her eyes and indulged herself with an intellectual vision of the man for whose sake she had broken a sacred law. Mrs. Penniman, of the three persons in Washington Square, had much the most of the manner that belongs to a great crisis. If Catherine was quiet, she was quietly quiet, as I may say, and her pathetic effects, which there was no one to notice, were entirely unstudied and unintended. If the Doctor was stiff and dry and absolutely indifferent to the presence of his companions, it was so lightly, neatly, easily done, that you would have had to know him well to discover that on the whole he rather enjoyed having to be so disagreeable. But Mrs. Penniman was elaborately reserved and significantly silent; there was a richer rustle in the very deliberate movements to which she confined herself, and when she occasionally spoke, in connection with some very trivial event, she had the air of meaning something deeper than what she said. Between Catherine and her father nothing had passed since the evening she went to speak to him in his study. She had something to say to him—it seemed to her she ought to say it; but she kept it back, for fear of irritating him. He also had something to say to her; but he was determined not to speak first. He was interested, as we know, in seeing how, if she were left to herself, she would "stick." At last she told him she had seen Morris Townsend again, and that their relations remained quite the same.

"I think we shall marry — before very long. And probably, meanwhile, I shall see him rather often; about once a week, not more."

The Doctor looked at her coldly from head to foot, as if she had been a stranger. It was the first time his eyes had rested on her for a week, which was fortunate, if that was to be their expression. "Why not three times a day?" he asked. "What prevents your meeting as often as you choose?"

She turned away a moment; there were tears in her eyes. Then she said, "It is better once a week."

"I don't see how it is better. It is as bad as it can be. If you flatter yourself that I care for little modifications of that sort, you are very much mistaken. It is as wrong of you to see him once a week as it would be to see him all day long. Not that it matters to me, however."

Catherine tried to follow these words, but they seemed to lead towards a vague horror from which she recoiled. "I think we shall marry pretty soon," she repeated at last.

Her father gave her his dreadful look again, as if she were some one else. "Why do you tell me that? It's no concern of mine."

"Oh, father!" she broke out, "don't you care, even if you do feel so?"

"Not a button. Once you marry, it's quite the same to me when or where or why you do it; and if you think to compound for your folly by hoisting your flag in this way, you may spare yourself the trouble."

With this he turned away. But the next day he spoke to her of his own accord, and his manner was somewhat changed. "Shall you be married within the next four or five months?" he asked.

"I don't know, father," said Catherine. "It is not very easy for us to make up our minds."

"Put it off, then, for six months, and in the meantime I will take you to Europe. I should like you very much to go."

It gave her such delight, after his words of the day before, to hear that he should "like" her to do something, and that he still had in his heart any of the tenderness of preference, that she gave a little exclamation of joy. But then she became conscious that Morris was not included in this proposal, and that—as regards really going—she would greatly prefer to remain at home with him. But she blushed, none the less, more comfortably than she had done of late. "It would be delightful to go to Europe," she remarked, with a sense that the idea was not original, and that her tone was not all it might be.

"Very well, then, we will go. Pack up your clothes."

"I had better tell Mr. Townsend," said Catherine.

Her father fixed his cold eyes upon her. "If you mean that you had better ask his leave, all that remains to me is to hope he will give it."

The girl was sharply touched by the pathetic ring of the words; it was the most calculated, the most dramatic little speech the Doctor had ever uttered. She felt that it was a great thing for her, under the circumstances, to have this fine opportunity of showing him her respect; and yet there was something else that she felt as well, and that she presently expressed. "I sometimes think that if I do what you dislike so much, I ought not to stay with you."

"To stay with me?"

"If I live with you, I ought to obey you."

"If that's your theory, it's certainly mine," said the Doctor, with a dry laugh.

"But if I don't obey you, I ought not to live with you—to enjoy your kindness and protection."

This striking argument gave the Doctor a sudden sense of having underestimated his daughter; it seemed even more than worthy of a young woman who had revealed the quality of unaggressive obstinacy. But it displeased him — displeased him deeply, and he signified as much. "That idea is in very bad taste," he said. "Did you get it from Mr. Townsend?"

"Oh no; it's my own!" said Catherine eagerly.

"Keep it to yourself, then," her father answered, more than ever determined she should go to Europe.

XXIII.

If Morris Townsend was not to be included in this journey, no more was Mrs. Penniman, who would have been thankful for an invitation, but who (to do her justice) bore her disappointment in a perfectly lady-like manner. "I should enjoy seeing the works of Raphael and the ruins—the ruins of the Pantheon," she said to Mrs. Almond; "but on the other hand, I shall not be sorry to be alone and at peace for the next few months in Washington Square. I want rest; I have been through so much in the last four months." Mrs. Almond thought it rather cruel that her brother should not take poor Lavinia abroad; but she easily understood that, if the purpose of his expedition was to make Catherine forget her lover, it was not in his interest to give his daughter this young man's best friend as a companion. "If Lavinia had not been so foolish, she might visit the ruins of the Pantheon," she said to herself; and she continued to regret her sister's folly, even though the latter assured her that she had often heard the relics in question most satisfactorily described by Mr. Penniman. Mrs. Penniman was perfectly aware that her brother's motive in undertaking a foreign tour was to lay a trap for

Catherine's constancy; and she imparted this conviction very frankly to her niece.

"He thinks it will make you forget Morris," she said (she always called the young man "Morris" now); "out of sight, out of mind, you know. He thinks that all the things you will see over there will drive him out of your thoughts."

Catherine looked greatly alarmed. "If he thinks that, I ought to tell him beforehand."

Mrs. Penniman shook her head. "Tell him afterwards my dear! After he has had all the trouble and the expense! That's the way to serve him." And she added, in a softer key, that it must be delightful to think of those who love us among the ruins of the Pantheon.

Her father's displeasure had cost the girl, as we know, a great deal of deep-welling sorrow—sorrow of the purest and most generous kind, without a touch of resentment or rancour; but for the first time, after he had dismissed with such contemptuous brevity her apology for being a charge upon him, there was a spark of anger in her grief. She had felt his contempt; it had scorched her; that speech about her bad taste made her ears burn for three days. During this period she was less considerate; she had an idea—a rather vague one, but it was agreeable to her sense of injury—that now she was absolved from penance, and might do what she chose. She chose to write to Morris Townsend to meet her in the Square and take her to walk about the town. If she were going to Europe out of respect to her father, she might at least give herself this satisfaction. She felt in every way at present more free and more resolute; there was a force that urged her. Now at last, completely and unreservedly, her passion possessed her.

Morris met her at last, and they took a long walk. She told him immediately what had happened—that her father wished to take her away. It would be for six months, to Europe; she would do absolutely what Morris should think best. She hoped inexpressibly that he would think it best she should stay at home. It was some time before he said what he thought: he asked, as they walked along, a great many questions. There was one that especially struck her; it seemed so incongruous.

"Should you like to see all those celebrated things over there?"

"Oh, no, Morris!" said Catherine quite deprecatingly.

"Gracious Heaven, what a dull woman!" Morris exclaimed to himself.

"He thinks I will forget you," said Catherine; "that all these things will drive you out of my mind."

"Well, my dear, perhaps they will!"

"Please don't say that," Catherine answered gently, as they walked along. "Poor father will be disappointed."

Morris gave a little laugh. "Yes, I verily believe that your poor father will be disappointed! But you will have seen Europe," he added humorously. "What a take-in!"

"I don't care for seeing Europe," Catherine said.

"You ought to care, my dear. And it may mollify your father."

Catherine, conscious of her obstinacy, expected little of this, and could not rid herself of the idea that in going abroad and yet remaining firm, she should play her father a trick. "Don't you think it would be a kind of deception?" she asked.

"Doesn't he want to deceive you?" cried Morris. "It will serve him right! I really think you had better go."

"And not be married for so long?"

"Be married when you come back. You can buy your wedding-clothes in Paris." And then Morris, with great kindness of tone, explained his view of the matter. It would be a good thing that she should go; it would put them completely in the right. It would show they were reasonable and willing to wait. Once they were so sure of each other, they could afford to wait—what had they to fear? If there was a particle of chance that her father would be favourably affected by her going, that ought to settle it; for, after all, Morris was very unwilling to be the cause of her being disinherited. It was not for himself, it was for her and for her children. He was willing to wait for her; it would be hard, but he could do it. And over there, among beautiful scenes and noble monuments, perhaps the old gentleman would be softened; such things were supposed to exert a humanising influence. He might be touched by her gentleness, her patience, her willingness to make any sacrifice but *that* one; and if she should appeal to him some day, in some celebrated spot—in Italy, say, in the evening; in Venice, in a gondola, by moonlight—if she should be a little clever about it and touch the right chord, perhaps he would fold her in his arms and tell her that he forgave her. Catherine was immensely struck with this conception of the affair, which seemed eminently worthy of her lover's brilliant intellect; though she viewed it askance in so far as it depended upon her own powers of execution. The idea of being "clever" in a gondola by moonlight appeared to her to involve elements of which her grasp was not active. But it was settled between them that she should tell her father that she was ready to follow him obediently anywhere, making the mental reservation that she loved Morris Townsend more than ever.

She informed the Doctor she was ready to embark, and he made rapid arrangements for this event. Catherine had many farewells to make, but with only two of them are we actively concerned. Mrs. Penniman took a discriminating view of her niece's journey; it seemed to her very proper that Mr. Townsend's destined bride should wish to embellish her mind by a foreign tour.

"You leave him in good hands," she said, pressing her lips to Catherine's forehead. (She was very fond of kissing people's foreheads; it was an involuntary expression of sympathy with the intellectual part.) "I shall see him often; I shall feel like one of the vestals of old, tending the sacred flame."

"You behave beautifully about not going with us," Catherine answered, not presuming to examine this analogy.

"It is my pride that keeps me up," said Mrs. Penniman, tapping the body of her dress, which always gave forth a sort of metallic ring.

Catherine's parting with her lover was short, and few words were exchanged.

"Shall I find you just the same when I come back?" she asked; though the question was not the fruit of scepticism.

"The same—only more so!" said Morris, smiling.

It does not enter into our scheme to narrate in detail Dr. Sloper's proceedings in the Eastern hemisphere. He made the grand tour of Europe, travelled in considerable splendour, and (as was to have been expected in a man of his high cultivation) found so much in art and antiquity to interest him, that he remained abroad, not for six months, but for twelve. Mrs. Penniman, in Washington Square, accommodated herself to his absence. She enjoyed her uncontested dominion in the empty house, and flattered herself that she made it more attractive to their friends than when her brother was at home. To Morris Townsend, at least, it would have appeared that she made it singularly attractive. He was altogether her most frequent visitor, and Mrs. Penniman was very fond of asking him to tea. He had his chair—a very easy one—at the fireside in the back-parlour (when the great mahogany sliding-doors, with silver knobs and hinges, which divided this apartment from its more formal neighbour, were closed), and he used to smoke cigars in the Doctor's study, where he often spent an hour in turning over the curious collections of its absent proprietor. He thought Mrs. Penniman a goose, as we know; but he was no goose himself, and, as a young man of luxurious tastes and scanty resources, he found the house a perfect castle of indolence. It became for him a club with a single member. Mrs. Penniman saw much less of her sister than while the Doctor was at home; for Mrs. Almond had felt moved to tell her that she disapproved of her relations with Mr. Townsend. She had no business to be so friendly to a young man of whom their brother thought so meanly, and Mrs. Almond was surprised at her levity in foisting a most deplorable engagement upon Catherine.

"Deplorable?" cried Lavinia. "He will make her a lovely husband!"

"I don't believe in lovely husbands," said Mrs. Almond; "I only believe in good ones. If he marries her, and she comes into Austin's money, they may get on. He will be an idle, amiable, selfish, and doubtless tolerably good-natured fellow. But if she doesn't get the money and he finds himself tied to her, Heaven have mercy on her! He will have none. He will hate her for his disappointment, and take his revenge; he will be pitiless and cruel. Woe betide poor Catherine! I recommend you to talk a little with his sister; it's a pity Catherine can't marry *her!*"

Mrs. Penniman had no appetite whatever for conversation with Mrs. Montgomery, whose acquaintance she made no trouble to cultivate; and the effect of this alarming forecast of her niece's destiny was to make her think it indeed a thousand pities that Mr. Townsend's generous nature should be embittered. Bright enjoyment was his natural element, and how could he be comfortable if there should prove to be nothing to enjoy? It became a fixed idea with Mrs. Penniman that he should yet enjoy her brother's fortune, on which she had acuteness enough to perceive that her own claim was small.

"If he doesn't leave it to Catherine, it certainly won't be to leave it to me," she said.

XXIV.

The Doctor, during the first six months he was abroad, never spoke to his daughter of their little difference; partly on system, and partly because he had a great many other things to think about. It was idle to attempt to ascertain the state of her affections without direct inquiry, because, if she had not had an expressive manner among the familiar influences of home, she failed to gather animation from the mountains of Switzerland or the monuments of Italy. She was always her father's docile and reasonable associate—going through their sight-seeing in deferential silence, never complaining of fatigue, always ready to start at the hour he had appointed over-night, making no foolish criticisms and indulging in no refinements of appreciation. "She is about as intelligent as the bundle of shawls," the Doctor said; her main superiority being that while the bundle of shawls sometimes got lost, or tumbled out of the carriage, Catherine was always at her post, and had a firm and ample seat. But her father had expected this, and he was not constrained to set down her intellectual limitations as a tourist to sentimental depression; she had completely divested herself of the characteristics of a victim, and during the whole time that they were abroad she never uttered an audible sigh. He supposed she was in correspondence with Morris Townsend; but he held his peace about it, for he never saw the young man's letters, and Catherine's own missives were always given to the courier to post. She heard from her lover with considerable regularity, but his letters came enclosed in Mrs. Penniman's; so that whenever the Doctor handed her a packet addressed in his sister's hand, he was an involuntary instrument of the passion he condemned. Catherine made this reflection, and six months earlier she would have felt bound to give him warning; but now she deemed herself absolved. There was a sore spot in her heart that his own words had made when once she spoke to him as she thought honour prompted; she would try and please him as far as she could, but she would never speak that way again. She read her lover's letters in secret.

One day, at the end of the summer, the two travellers found themselves in a lonely valley of the Alps. They were crossing one of the passes, and on the long ascent they had got out of the carriage and had wandered much in advance. After a while the Doctor descried a footpath which, leading through a transverse valley, would bring them out, as he justly supposed, at a much higher point of the ascent. They followed this devious way and finally lost the path; the valley proved very wild and rough, and their walk became rather a scramble. They were good walkers, however, and they took their adventure easily; from time to time they stopped, that Catherine might rest; and then she sat upon a stone and looked about her at the hard-featured rocks and the glowing sky. It was late in the afternoon, in the last of August; night was coming on, and, as they had reached a great elevation, the air was cold and sharp. In the west there was a great suffusion of cold, red light, which made the sides of the little valley look only the more rugged and dusky. During one of their pauses, her father left her and wandered away to some high place, at a distance, to get a view. He was out of sight; she sat there alone, in the stillness, which was just touched by the vague murmur, somewhere, of a mountain brook. She thought of Morris Townsend, and the place was so desolate and lonely that he seemed very far away. Her father remained absent a long time; she began to wonder what had become of him. But at last he reappeared, coming towards her in the clear twilight, and she got up, to go on. He made no motion to proceed, however, but came close to her, as if he had something to say. He stopped in front of her and stood looking at her, with eyes that had kept the light of the flushing snow-summits on which they had just been fixed. Then, abruptly, in a low tone, he asked her an unexpected question—

"Have you given him up?"

The question was unexpected, but Catherine was only superficially unprepared.

"No, father!" she answered.

He looked at her again, for some moments, without speaking.

"Does he write to you?" he asked.

"Yes—about twice a month."

The Doctor looked up and down the valley, swinging his stick; then he said to her, in the same low tone—

"I am very angry."

She wondered what he meant—whether he wished to frighten her. If he did, the place was well chosen; this hard, melancholy dell, abandoned by the summer light, made her feel her loneliness. She looked around her, and her heart grew cold; for a moment her fear was great. But she could think of nothing to say, save to murmur gently, "I am sorry."

"You try my patience," her father went on, "and you ought to know what I am, I am not a very good man. Though I am very smooth externally, at bottom I am very passionate; and I assure you I can be very hard."

She could not think why he told her these things. Had he brought her there on purpose, and was it part of a plan? What was the plan? Catherine asked herself. Was it to startle her suddenly into a retractation—to take an advantage of her by dread? Dread of what? The place was ugly and lonely, but the place could do her no harm. There was a kind of still intensity about her father which made him dangerous, but Catherine hardly went so far as to say to herself that it might be part of his plan to fasten his hand—the neat, fine, supple hand of a distinguished physician—in her throat. Nevertheless, she receded a step. "I am sure you can be anything you please," she said. And it was her simple belief.

"I am very angry," he replied, more sharply.

"Why has it taken you so suddenly?"

"It has not taken me suddenly. I have been raging inwardly for the last six months. But just now this seemed a good place to flare out. It's so quiet, and we are alone."

"Yes, it's very quiet," said Catherine vaguely, looking about her. "Won't you come back to the carriage?"

"In a moment. Do you mean that in all this time you have not yielded an inch?"

"I would if I could, father; but I can't."

The Doctor looked round him too. "Should you like to be left in such a place as this, to starve?"

"What do you mean?" cried the girl.

"That will be your fate—that's how he will leave you."

He would not touch her, but he had touched Morris. The warmth came back to her heart. "That is not true, father," she broke out, "and you ought not to say it! It is not right, and it's not true!"

He shook his head slowly. "No, it's not right, because you won't believe it. But it *is* true. Come back to the carriage."

He turned away, and she followed him; he went faster, and was presently much in advance. But from time to time he stopped, without turning round, to let her keep up with him, and she made her way forward with difficulty, her heart beating with the excitement of having for the first time spoken to him in violence. By this time it had grown almost dark, and she ended by losing sight of him. But she kept her course, and after a little, the valley making a sudden turn, she gained the road, where the carriage stood waiting. In it sat her father, rigid and silent; in silence, too, she took her place beside him.

It seemed to her, later, in looking back upon all this, that for days afterwards not a word had been exchanged between them. The scene had been a strange one, but it had not permanently affected her feeling towards her father, for it was natural, after all, that he should occasionally make a scene of some kind, and he had let her alone for six months. The strangest part of it was that he had said he was not a good man; Catherine wondered a great deal what he had meant by that. The statement failed to appeal to her credence, and it was not grateful to any resentment that she entertained. Even in the utmost bitterness that she might feel, it would give her no satisfaction to think him less complete. Such a saying as that was a part of his great subtlety—men so clever as he might say anything and mean anything. And as to his being hard, that surely, in a man, was a virtue.

He let her alone for six months more—six months during which she accommodated herself without a protest to the extension of their tour. But he spoke again at the end of this time; it was at the very last, the night before they embarked for New York, in the hotel at Liverpool. They had been dining together in a great dim, musty sitting-room; and then the cloth had been removed, and the Doctor walked slowly up and down. Catherine at last took her candle to go to bed, but her father motioned her to stay.

"What do you mean to do when you get home?" he asked, while she stood there with her candle in her hand.

"Do you mean about Mr. Townsend?"

"About Mr. Townsend."

"We shall probably marry."

The Doctor took several turns again while she waited. "Do you hear from him as much as ever?"

"Yes; twice a month," said Catherine, promptly.

"And does he always talk about marriage?"

"Oh, yes! That is, he talks about other things too, but he always says something about that."

"I am glad to hear he varies his subjects; his letters might otherwise be monotonous."

"He writes beautifully," said Catherine, who was very glad of a chance to say it.

"They always write beautifully. However, in a given case that doesn't diminish the merit. So, as soon as you arrive, you are going off with him?"

This seemed a rather gross way of putting it, and something that there was of dignity in Catherine resented it. "I cannot tell you till we arrive," she said.

"That's reasonable enough," her father answered. "That's all I ask of you—that you *do* tell me, that you give me definite notice. When a poor man is to lose his only child, he likes to have an inkling of it beforehand."

"Oh, father, you will not lose me!" Catherine said, spilling her candle-wax.

"Three days before will do," he went on, "if you are in a position to be positive then. He ought to be very thankful to me, do you know. I have done a mighty good thing for him in taking you abroad; your value is twice as great, with all the knowledge and taste that you have acquired. A year ago, you were perhaps a little limited—a little rustic; but now you have seen everything, and appreciated everything, and you will be a most entertaining companion. We have fattened the sheep for him before he kills it!" Catherine turned away, and stood staring at the blank door. "Go to bed," said her father; "and, as we don't go aboard till noon, you may sleep late. We shall probably have a most uncomfortable voyage."

XXV.

THE voyage was indeed uncomfortable, and Catherine, on arriving in New York, had not the compensation of "going off," in her father's phrase, with Morris Townsend. She saw him, however, the day after she landed; and, in the meantime, he formed a natural subject of conversation between our heroine and her Aunt Lavinia, with whom, the night she disembarked, the girl was closeted for a long time before either lady retired to rest.

"I have seen a great deal of him," said Mrs. Penniman. "He is not very easy to know. I suppose you think you know him; but you don't, my dear. You will some day; but it will only be after you have lived with him. I may almost say *I* have lived with him," Mrs. Penniman proceeded, while Catherine stared. "I think I know him now; I have had such remarkable opportunities. You will have the same—or rather, you will have better!" and Aunt Lavinia smiled. "Then you will see what I mean. It's a wonderful character, full of passion and energy, and just as true!"

Catherine listened with a mixture of interest and apprehension. Aunt Lavinia was intensely sympathetic, and Catherine, for the past year, while she wandered through foreign galleries and churches, and rolled over the smoothness of posting roads, nursing the thoughts that never passed her lips, had often longed for the company of some intelligent person of her own sex. To tell her story to some kind woman—at moments it seemed to her that this would give her comfort, and she had more than once been on the point of taking the landlady, or the nice young person from the dressmaker's into her confidence. If a woman had been near her she would on certain occasions have treated such a companion to a fit of weeping; and she had an apprehension that, on her return, this would form her response to Aunt Lavinia's first embrace. In fact, however, the two ladies had met, in Washington Square, without tears, and when they found themselves alone together a certain dryness fell upon the girl's emotion. It came over her with a greater force that Mrs. Penniman had enjoyed a whole year of her lover's society, and it was not a pleasure to her to hear her aunt explain and interpret the young man, speaking of him as if her own knowledge of him were supreme. It was not that Catherine was jealous; but her sense of Mrs. Penniman's innocent falsity, which had lain dormant, began to haunt her again, and she was glad that she was safely at home. With this, however, it was a blessing to be able to talk of Morris, to sound his name, to be with a person who was not unjust to him.

"You have been very kind to him," said Catherine. "He has written me that, often. I shall never forget that, Aunt Lavinia."

"I have done what I could; it has been very

little. To let him come and talk to me, and give him his cup of tea—that was all. Your Aunt Almond thought it was too much, and used to scold me terribly; but she promised me, at least, not to betray me."

"To betray you?"

"Not to tell your father. He used to sit in your father's study!" said Mrs. Penniman, with a little laugh.

Catherine was silent a moment. This idea was disagreeable to her, and she was reminded again, with pain, of her aunt's secretive habits. Morris, the reader may be informed, had had the tact not to tell her that he sat in her father's study. He had known her but for a few months, and her aunt had known her for fifteen years; and yet he would not have made the mistake of thinking that Catherine would see the joke of the thing. "I am sorry you made him go into father's room," she said, after a while.

"I didn't make him go; he went himself. He liked to look at the books, and at all those things in the glass cases. He knows all about them; he knows all about everything."

Catherine was silent again; then, "I wish he had found some employment," she said.

"He has found some employment! It's beautiful news, and he told me to tell you as soon as you arrived. He has gone into partnership with a commission-merchant. It was all settled, quite suddenly, a week ago."

This seemed to Catherine indeed beautiful news; it had a fine prosperous air. "Oh, I'm so glad!"

she said; and now, for a moment, she was disposed to throw herself on Aunt Lavinia's neck.

"It's much better than being under some one; and he has never been used to that," Mrs. Penniman went on. "He is just as good as his partner—they are perfectly equal! You see how right he was to wait. I should like to know what your father can say now! They have got an office in Duane Street, and little printed cards; he brought me one to show me. I have got it in my room, and you shall see it to-morrow. That's what he said to me the last time he was here—'You see how right I was to wait!' He has got other people under him, instead of being a subordinate. He could never be a subordinate; I have often told him I could never think of him in that way."

Catherine assented to this proposition, and was very happy to know that Morris was his own master; but she was deprived of the satisfaction of thinking that she might communicate this news in triumph to her father. Her father would care equally little whether Morris were established in business or transported for life. Her trunks had been brought into her room, and further reference to her lover was for a short time suspended, while she opened them and displayed to her aunt some of the spoils of foreign travel. These were rich and abundant; and Catherine had brought home a present to every one—to every one save Morris, to whom she had brought simply her undiverted heart. To Mrs. Penniman she had been lavishly generous, and Aunt Lavinia spent half-an-hour in unfolding and folding again, with little ejaculations of gratitude and taste. She marched about for some time in a splendid cashmere shawl, which Catherine had begged her to accept, settling it on her shoulders, and twisting down her head to see how low the point descended behind.

"I shall regard it only as a loan," she said. "I will leave it to you again when I die; or rather," she added, kissing her niece again, "I will leave it to your first-born little girl!" And draped in her shawl, she stood there smiling.

"You had better wait till she comes," said Catherine.

"I don't like the way you say that," Mrs. Penniman rejoined, in a moment. "Catherine, are you changed?"

"No; I am the same."

"You have not swerved a line?"

"I am exactly the same," Catherine repeated, wishing her aunt were a little less sympathetic.

"Well, I am glad!" and Mrs. Penniman surveyed her cashmere in the glass. Then, "How is your father?" she asked in a moment, with her eyes on her niece. "Your letters were so meagre—I could never tell!"

"Father is very well."

"Ah, you know what I mean," said Mrs. Penniman, with a dignity to which the cashmere gave a richer effect. "Is he still implacable!"

"Oh, yes!"

"Quite unchanged?"

"He is, if possible, more firm."

Mrs. Penniman took off her great shawl, and slowly folded it up. "That is very bad. You had no success with your little project?"

"What little project?"

"Morris told me all about it. The idea of turning the tables on him, in Europe; of watching him, when he was agreeably impressed by some celebrated sight—he pretends to be so artistic, you know—and then just pleading with him and bringing him round."

"I never tried it. It was Morris's idea; but if he had been with us, in Europe, he would have seen that father was never impressed in that way. He *is* artistic—tremendously artistic; but the more celebrated places we visited, and the more he admired them, the less use it would have been to plead with him. They seemed only to make him more determined—more terrible," said poor Catherine. "I shall never bring him round, and I expect nothing now."

"Well, I must say," Mrs. Penniman answered, "I never supposed you were going to give it up."

"I have given it up. I don't care now."

"You have grown very brave," said Mrs. Penniman, with a short laugh. "I didn't advise you to sacrifice your property."

"Yes, I am braver than I was. You asked me if I had changed; I have changed in that way. Oh," the girl went on, "I have changed very much. And it isn't my property. If *he* doesn't care for it, why should I?"

Mrs. Penniman hesitated. "Perhaps he does care for it."

"He cares for it for my sake, because he doesn't want to injure me. But he will know—he knows already—how little he need be afraid about that.

Besides," said Catherine, "I have got plenty of money of my own. We shall be very well off; and now hasn't he got his business? I am delighted about that business." She went on talking, showing a good deal of excitement as she proceeded. Her aunt had never seen her with just this manner, and Mrs. Penniman, observing her, set it down to foreign travel, which had made her more positive, more mature. She thought also that Catherine had improved in appearance; she looked rather handsome. Mrs. Penniman wondered whether Morris Townsend would be struck with that. While she was engaged in this speculation, Catherine broke out, with a certain sharpness, "Why are you so contradictory, Aunt Penniman? You seem to think one thing at one time, and another at another. A year ago, before I went away, you wished me not to mind about displeasing father; and now you seem to recommend me to take another line. You change about so."

This attack was unexpected, for Mrs. Penniman was not used, in any discussion, to seeing the war carried into her own country—possibly because the enemy generally had doubts of finding subsistence there. To her own consciousness, the flowery fields of her reason had rarely been ravaged by a hostile force. It was perhaps on this account that in defending them she was majestic rather than agile.

"I don't know what you accuse me of, save of being too deeply interested in your happiness. It is the first time I have been told I am capricious. That fault is not what I am usually reproached with."

"You were angry last year that I wouldn't marry immediately, and now you talk about my winning my father over. You told me it would serve him right if he should take me to Europe for nothing. Well, he has taken me for nothing, and you ought to be satisfied. Nothing is changed—nothing but my feeling about father. I don't mind nearly so much now. I have been as good as I could, but he doesn't care. Now I don't care either. I don't know whether I have grown bad; perhaps I have. But I don't care for that. I have come home to be married—that's all I know. That ought to please you, unless you have taken up some new idea; you are so strange. You may do as you please; but you must never speak to me again about pleading with father. I shall never plead with him for anything; that is all over. He has put me off. I am come home to be married."

This was a more authoritative speech than she had ever heard on her niece's lips, and Mrs. Penniman was proportionately startled. She was indeed a little awe-struck, and the force of the girl's emotion and resolution left her nothing to reply. She was easily frightened, and she always carried off her discomfiture by a concession; a concession which was often accompanied, as in the present case, by a little nervous laugh.

XXVI.

If she had disturbed her niece's temper—she began from this moment forward to talk a good deal about Catherine's temper, an article which up to that time had never been mentioned in connection with our heroine—Catherine had opportunity, on the morrow, to recover her serenity. Mrs. Penniman had given her a message from Morris Townsend, to the effect that he would come and welcome her home on the day after her arrival. He came in the afternoon; but, as may be imagined, he was not on this occasion made free of Dr. Sloper's study. He had been coming and going, for the past year, so comfortably and irresponsibly, that he had a certain sense of being wronged by finding himself reminded that he must now limit his horizon to the front-parlour, which was Catherine's particular province.

"I am very glad you have come back," he said; "it makes me very happy to see you again." And he looked at her, smiling, from head to foot; though it did not appear, afterwards, that he agreed with Mrs. Penniman (who, womanlike, went more into details) in thinking her embellished.

To Catherine he appeared resplendent; it was some time before she could believe again that this beautiful young man was her own exclusive property. They had a great deal of characteristic lovers' talk—a soft exchange of inquiries and assurances. In these matters Morris had an excellent grace, which flung a picturesque interest even over the account of his début in the commission-business—a subject as to which his companion earnestly questioned him. From time to time he got up from the sofa where they sat together, and walked about the room; after which he came back, smiling and passing his hand through his hair. He was unquiet, as was natural in a young man who has just been re-united to a long-absent mistress, and Catherine made the reflection that she had never seen him so excited. It gave her pleasure, somehow, to note this fact. He asked her questions about her travels, to some of which she was unable to reply, for she had forgotten the names of places and the order of her father's journey. But for the moment she was so happy, so lifted up by the belief that her troubles at last were over, that she forgot to be ashamed of her meagre answers. It seemed to her now that she could marry him without the remnant of a scruple or a single tremor save those that belonged to joy. Without waiting for him to ask, she told him that her father had come back in exactly the same state of mind—that he had not yielded an inch.

"We must not expect it now," she said, "and we must do without it."

Morris sat looking and smiling. "My poor dear girl!" he exclaimed.

"You mustn't pity me," said Catherine; "I don't mind it now—I am used to it."

Morris continued to smile, and then he got up and walked about again. "You had better let me try him!"

"Try to bring him over? You would only make him worse," Catherine answered, resolutely.

"You say that because I managed it so badly before. But I should manage it differently now. I am much wiser; I have had a year to think of it. I have more tact."

"Is that what you have been thinking of for a year?"

"Much of the time. You see, the idea sticks in my crop. I don't like to be beaten."

"How are you beaten if we marry?"

"Of course, I am not beaten on the main issue; but I am, don't you see, on all the rest of it—on the question of my reputation, of my relations with your father, of my relations with my own children, if we should have any."

"We shall have enough for our children—we shall have enough for everything. Don't you expect to succeed in business?"

"Brilliantly, and we shall certainly be very comfortable. But it isn't of the mere material comfort I speak; it is of the moral comfort," said Morris—"of the intellectual satisfaction!"

"I have great moral comfort now," Catherine declared, very simply.

"Of course you have. But with me it is different. I have staked my pride on proving to your father that he is wrong; and now that I am at the head of a flourishing business, I can deal with him as an equal. I have a capital plan—do let me go at him!"

He stood before her with his bright face, his jaunty air, his hands in his pockets; and she got up, with her eyes resting on his own. "Please don't, Morris; please don't," she said; and there was a certain mild, sad firmness in her tone which he heard for the first time. "We must ask no favours of him—we must ask nothing more. He won't relent, and nothing good will come of it. I know it now—I have a very good reason."

"And pray what is your reason?"

She hesitated to bring it out, but at last it came. "He is not very fond of me!"

"Oh, bother!" cried Morris, angrily.

"I wouldn't say such a thing without being sure. I saw it, I felt it, in England, just before he came away. He talked to me one night—the last night; and then it came over me. You can tell when a person feels that way. I wouldn't accuse him if he hadn't made me feel that way. I don't accuse him; I just tell you that that's how it is. He can't help it; we can't govern our affections. Do I govern mine? mightn't he say that to me? It's because he is so fond of my mother, whom we lost so long ago. She was beautiful, and very, very brilliant; he is always thinking of her. I am not at all like her; Aunt Penniman has told me that. Of course it isn't my fault; but neither is it his fault. All I mean is, it's true; and it's a stronger reason for his never being reconciled than simply his dislike for you."

"'Simply?'" cried Morris, with a laugh, "I am much obliged for that!"

"I don't mind about his disliking you now; I

mind everything less. I feel differently; I feel separated from my father."

"Upon my word," said Morris, "you are a queer family!"

"Don't say that—don't say anything unkind," the girl entreated. "You must be very kind to me now, because, Morris—because," and she hesitated a moment—"because I have done a great deal for you."

"Oh, I know that, my dear!"

She had spoken up to this moment without vehemence or outward sign of emotion, gently, reasoningly, only trying to explain. But her emotion had been ineffectually smothered, and it betrayed itself at last in the trembling of her voice. "It is a great thing to be separated like that from your father, when you have worshipped him before. It has made me very unhappy; or it would have made me so if I didn't love you. You can tell when a person speaks to you as if—as if——"

"As if what?"

"As if they despised you!" said Catherine, passionately. "He spoke that way the night before we sailed. It wasn't much, but it was enough, and I thought of it on the voyage, all the time. Then I made up my mind. I will never ask him for anything again, or expect anything from him. It would not be natural now. We must be very happy together, and we must not seem to depend upon his forgiveness. And Morris, Morris, you must never despise me!"

This was an easy promise to make, and Morris made it with fine effect. But for the moment he undertook nothing more onerous.

XXVII.

THE Doctor, of course, on his return, had a good deal of talk with his sisters. He was at no great pains to narrate his travels or to communicate his impressions of distant lands to Mrs. Penniman, upon whom he contented himself with bestowing a memento of his enviable experience, in the shape of a velvet gown. But he conversed with her at some length about matters nearer home, and lost no time in assuring her that he was still an inflexible father.

"I have no doubt you have seen a great deal of Mr. Townsend, and done your best to console him for Catherine's absence," he said. "I don't ask you, and you needn't deny it. I wouldn't put the question to you for the world, and expose you to the inconvenience of having to—a—excogitate an answer. No one has betrayed you, and there has been no spy upon your proceedings. Elizabeth has told no tales, and has never mentioned you except to praise your good looks and good spirits. The thing is simply an inference of my own—an induction, as the philosophers say. It seems to me likely that you would have offered an asylum to an interesting sufferer. Mr. Townsend has been a good deal in the house; there is something in the house that tells me so. We doctors, you know, end by acquiring fine perceptions, and it is impressed upon my sensorium that he has sat in these chairs, in a very easy attitude, and warmed himself at that fire. I don't grudge him the comfort of it; it is the only one he will ever enjoy at my expense. It seems likely, indeed, that I shall be able to economise at his own. I don't know what you may have said to him, or what you may say hereafter; but I should like you to know that if you have encouraged him to believe that he will gain anything by hanging on, or that I have budged a hair's breadth from the position I took up a year ago, you have played him a trick for which he may exact reparation. I'm not sure that he may not bring a suit against you. Of course you have done it conscientiously; you have made yourself believe that I can be tired out. This is the most baseless hallucination that ever visited the brain of a genial optimist. I am not in the least tired; I am as fresh as when I started; I am good for fifty years yet. Catherine appears not to have budged an inch either; she is equally fresh; so we are about where we were before. This, however, you know as well as I. What I wish is simply to give you notice of my own state of mind! Take it to heart, dear Lavinia. Beware of the just resentment of a deluded fortune-hunter!"

"I can't say I expected it," said Mrs. Penniman. "And I had a sort of foolish hope that you would come home without that odious ironical tone with which you treat the most sacred subjects."

"Don't undervalue irony, it is often of great use. It is not, however, always necessary, and I will show you how gracefully I can lay it aside. I should like to know whether you think Morris Townsend will hang on."

"I will answer you with your own weapons," said Mrs. Penniman. "You had better wait and see!"

"Do you call such a speech as that one of my own weapons? I never said anything so rough."

"He will hang on long enough to make you very uncomfortable, then."

"My dear Lavinia," exclaimed the Doctor, "do you call that irony? I call it pugilism."

Mrs. Penniman, however, in spite of her pugilism, was a good deal frightened, and she took counsel of her fears. Her brother meanwhile took counsel, with many reservations, of Mrs. Almond, to whom he was no less generous than to Lavinia, and a good deal more communicative.

"I suppose she has had him there all the while," he said. "I must look into the state of my wine! You needn't mind telling me now; I have already said all I mean to say to her on the subject."

"I believe he was in the house a good deal," Mrs. Almond answered. "But you must admit that your leaving Lavinia quite alone was a great change for her, and that it was natural she should want some society."

"I do admit that, and that is why I shall make no row about the wine; I shall set it down as compensation to Lavinia. She is capable of telling me that she drank it all herself. Think of the inconceivable bad taste, in the circumstances, of that fellow making free with the house—or coming there at all! If that doesn't describe him, he is indescribable."

"His plan is to get what he can. Lavinia will have supported him for a year," said Mrs. Almond. "It's so much gained."

"She will have to support him for the rest of his life, then!" cried the Doctor. "But without wine, as they say at the *tables d'hôte*."

"Catherine tells me he has set up a business, and is making a great deal of money."

The Doctor stared. "She has not told me that—and Lavinia didn't deign. Ah!" he cried, "Catherine has given me up. Not that it matters, for all that the business amounts to."

"She has not given up Mr. Townsend," said Mrs. Almond. "I saw that in the first half-minute. She has come home exactly the same."

"Exactly the same; not a grain more intelligent. She didn't notice a stick or a stone all the while we were away—not a picture nor a view, not a statue nor a cathedral."

"How could she notice? She had other things to think of; they are never for an instant out of her mind. She touches me very much."

"She would touch me if she didn't irritate me. That's the effect she has upon me now. I have tried everything upon her; I really have been quite merciless. But it is of no use whatever; she is absolutely *glued*. I have passed, in consequence, into the exasperated stage. At first I had a good deal of a certain genial curiosity about it; I wanted to see if she really would stick. But, good Lord, one's curiosity is satisfied! I see she is capable of it, and now she can let go."

"She will never let go," said Mrs. Almond.

"Take care, or you will exasperate me too. If she doesn't let go, she will be shaken off—sent tumbling into the dust! That's a nice position for my daughter. She can't see that if you are going to be pushed you had better jump. And then she will complain of her bruises."

"She will never complain," said Mrs. Almond.

"That I shall object to even more. But the deuce will be that I can't prevent anything."

"If she is to have a fall," said Mrs. Almond, with a gentle laugh, "we must spread as many carpets as we can." And she carried out this idea by showing a great deal of motherly kindness to the girl.

Mrs. Penniman immediately wrote to Morris Townsend. The intimacy between these two was by this time consummate, but I must content myself with noting but a few of its features. Mrs. Penniman's own share in it was a singular sentiment, which might have been misinterpreted, but which in itself was not discreditable to the poor lady. It was a romantic interest in this attractive and unfortunate young man, and yet it was not such an interest as Catherine might have been jealous of. Mrs. Penniman had not a particle of jealousy of her niece. For herself, she felt as if she were Morris's mother or sister—a mother or sister of an emotional temperament—and she had an absorbing desire to make him comfortable and happy. She had striven to do so during the year that her brother left her an open field, and her efforts had been attended with the success that has been pointed out. She had never had a child of her own, and Catherine, whom she had done her best to invest with the importance that would naturally belong to a youthful Penniman, had only partly rewarded her zeal. Catherine, as an object of affection and solicitude, had never had that picturesque charm which (as it seemed to her) would have been a natural attribute of her own progeny. Even the maternal passion in Mrs. Penniman would have been romantic and factitious, and Catherine was not constituted to inspire a romantic passion. Mrs. Penniman was as fond of her as ever but she had grown to feel that with Catherine she lacked opportunity. Sentimentally speaking, therefore, she had (though she had not disinherited her niece) adopted Morris Townsend, who gave her opportunity in abundance. She would have been very happy to have a handsome and tyrannical son, and would have taken an extreme interest in his love affairs. This was the light in which she had come to regard Morris, who had conciliated her at first, and made his impression by his delicate and calculated deference—a sort of exhibition to which Mrs. Penniman was particularly sensitive. He had largely abated his deference afterwards, for he economised his resources, but the impression was made, and the young man's very brutality came to have a sort of filial value. If Mrs. Penniman had had a son, she would probably have been afraid of him, and at this stage of our narrative she was certainly afraid of Morris Townsend. This was one of the results of his domestication in Washington Square. He took his ease with her—as, for that matter, he would certainly have done with his own mother.

XXVIII.

THE letter was a word of warning; it informed him that the Doctor had come home more impracticable than ever. She might have reflected that Catherine would supply him with all the information he needed on this point; but we know that Mrs. Penniman's reflections were rarely just; and, moreover, she felt that it was not for her to depend on what Catherine might do. She was to do her duty, quite irrespective of Catherine. I have said that her young friend took his ease with her, and it is an illustration of the fact that he made no answer to her letter. He took note of it, amply; but he lighted his cigar with it, and he waited, in tranquil confidence that he should receive another. "His state of mind really freezes my blood," Mrs. Penniman had written, alluding to her brother; and it would have seemed that upon this statement she could hardly improve. Nevertheless, she wrote again, expressing herself with the aid of a different figure. "His hatred of you burns with a lurid flame—the flame that never dies," she wrote. "But it doesn't light up the darkness of your future. If my affection could do so, all the years of your life would be an eternal sunshine. I can extract nothing from C.;

she is so terribly secretive, like her father. She seems to expect to be married very soon, and has evidently made preparations in Europe—quantities of clothing, ten pairs of shoes, etc. My dear friend, you cannot set up in married life simply with a few pairs of shoes, can you? Tell me what you think of this. I am intensely anxious to see you; I have so much to say. I miss you dreadfully; the house seems so empty without you. What is the news down town? Is the business extending? That dear little business—I think it's so brave of you! Couldn't I come to your office?—just for three minutes? I might pass for a customer—is that what you call them. I might come in to buy something—some shares or some railroad things. *Tell me what you think of this plan.* I would carry a little reticule, like a woman of the people."

In spite of the suggestion about the reticule, Morris appeared to think poorly of the plan, for he gave Mrs. Penniman no encouragement whatever to visit his office, which he had already represented to her as a place peculiarly and unnaturally difficult to find. But as she persisted in desiring an interview—up to the last, after months of intimate colloquy, she called these meetings "interviews"—he agreed that they should take a walk together, and was even kind enough to leave his office for this purpose, during the hours at which business might have been supposed to be liveliest. It was no surprise to him, when they met at a street-corner, in a region of empty lots and undeveloped pavements (Mrs. Penniman being attired as much as possible like a "woman of the people"), to find that, in spite of her urgency, what she chiefly had to convey to him was the assurance of her sympathy. Of such assurances, however, he had already a voluminous collection, and it would not have been worth his while to forsake a fruitful avocation merely to hear Mrs. Penniman say, for the thousandth time, that she had made his cause her own. Morris had something of his own to say. It was an easy thing to bring out, and while he turned it over the difficulty made him acrimonious.

"Oh yes, I know perfectly that he combines the properties of a lump of ice and a red-hot coal," he observed. "Catherine has made it thoroughly clear, and you have told me so till I am sick of it. You needn't tell me again; I am perfectly satisfied. He will never give us a penny; I regard that as mathematically proved."

Mrs. Penniman at this point had an inspiration.

"Couldn't you bring a lawsuit against him?" She wondered that this simple expedient had never occurred to her before.

"I will bring a lawsuit against *you,*" said Morris, "if you ask me any more such aggravating questions. A man should know when he is beaten," he added, in a moment. "I must give her up!"

Mrs. Penniman received this declaration in silence, though it made her heart beat a little. It found her by no means unprepared, for she had accustomed herself to the thought that, if Morris should decidedly not be able to get her brother's money, it would not do for him to marry Catherine without it. "It would not do" was a vague way of putting the thing; but Mrs. Penniman's natural affection completed the idea, which, though it had not as yet been so crudely expressed between them as in the form that Morris had just given it, had nevertheless been implied so often, in certain easy intervals of talk, as he sat stretching his legs in the Doctor's well-stuffed arm-chairs, that she had grown first to regard it with an emotion which she flattered herself was philosophic, and then to have a secret tenderness for it. The fact that she kept her tenderness secret proves, of course, that she was ashamed of it; but she managed to blink her shame by reminding herself that she was, after all, the official protector of her niece's marriage. Her logic would scarcely have passed muster with the Doctor. In the first place, Morris *must* get the money, and she would help him to it. In the second, it was plain it would never come to him, and it would be a grievous pity he should marry without it—a young man who might so easily find something better. After her brother had delivered himself, on his return from Europe, of that incisive little address that has been quoted, Morris's cause seemed so hopeless that Mrs. Penniman fixed her attention exclusively upon the latter branch of her argument. If Morris had been her son, she would certainly have sacrificed Catherine to a superior conception of his future; and to be ready to do so as the case stood was therefore even a finer degree of devotion. Nevertheless, it checked her breath a little to have the sacrificial knife, as it were, suddenly thrust into her hand.

Morris walked along a moment, and then he repeated, harshly—

"I must give her up!"

"I think I understand you," said Mrs. Penniman, gently.

"I certainly say it distinctly enough—brutally and vulgarly enough."

He was ashamed of himself, and his shame was uncomfortable; and as he was extremely intolerant of discomfort, he felt vicious and cruel. He wanted to abuse somebody, and he began, cautiously—for he was always cautious—with himself.

"Couldn't you take her down a little?" he asked.

"Take her down?"

"Prepare her—try and ease me off."

Mrs. Penniman stopped, looking at him very solemnly.

'My poor Morris, do you know how much she loves you."

"No, I don't. I don't want to know. I have always tried to keep from knowing. It would be too painful."

"She will suffer much," said Mrs. Penniman.

"You must console her. If you are as good a friend to me as you pretend to be, you will manage it."

Mrs. Penniman shook her head, sadly.

"You talk of my 'pretending' to like you; but I can't pretend to hate you. I can only tell her I think very highly of you; and how will that console her for losing you?"

"The Doctor will help you. He will be delighted at the thing being broken off, and, as he is a knowing fellow, he will invent something to comfort her."

"He will invent a new torture!" cried Mrs. Penniman. "Heaven deliver her from her father's comfort. It will consist of his crowing over her and saying, 'I always told you so!'"

Morris coloured a most uncomfortable red.

"If you don't console her any better than you console me, you certainly won't be of much use! It's a damned disagreeable necessity; I feel it extremely, and you ought to make it easy for me."

"I will be your friend for life!" Mrs. Penniman declared.

"Be my friend *now!*" And Morris walked on.

She went with him; she was almost trembling.

"Should you like me to tell her?" she asked.

"You mustn't tell her, but you can—you can ——." And he hesitated, trying to think what Mrs. Penniman could do. "You can explain to her why it is. It's because I can't bring myself to step in between her and her father—to give him the pretext he grasps at so eagerly (it's a hideous sight) for depriving her of her rights."

Mrs. Penniman felt with remarkable promptitude the charm of this formula.

"That's so like you," she said; "it's so finely felt."

Morris gave his stick an angry swing.

"Oh botheration!" he exclaimed perversely.

Mrs. Penniman, however, was not discouraged.

"It may turn out better than you think. Catherine is, after all, so very peculiar." And she thought she might take it upon herself to assure him that, whatever happened, the girl would be very quiet—she wouldn't make a noise. They extended their walk, and, while they proceeded, Mrs. Penniman took upon herself other things besides, and ended by having assumed a considerable burden; Morris being ready enough, as may be imagined, to put everything off upon her. But he was not for a single instant the dupe of her blundering alacrity; he knew that of what she promised she was competent to perform but an insignificant fraction, and the more she professed her willingness to serve him, the greater fool he thought her.

"What will you do if you don't marry her?" she ventured to inquire in the course of this conversation.

"Something brilliant," said Morris. "Shouldn't you like me to do something brilliant?"

The idea gave Mrs. Penniman exceeding pleasure. "I shall feel sadly taken in if you don't."

"I shall have to, to make up for this. This isn't at all brilliant, you know."

Mrs. Penniman mused a little, as if there might be some way of making out that it was; but she had to give up the attempt, and, to carry off the awkwardness of failure, she risked a new inquiry.

"Do you mean—do you mean another marriage?"

Morris greeted this question with a reflection which was hardly the less impudent from being inaudible. "Surely, women are more crude than men!" And then he answered audibly—

"Never in the world!"

Mrs. Penniman felt disappointed and snubbed, and she relieved herself in a little vaguely sarcastic cry. He was certainly perverse.

"I give her up not for another woman, but for a wider career!" Morris announced.

This was very grand; but still Mrs. Penniman,

who felt that she had exposed herself, was faintly rancorous.

"Do you mean never to come to see her again?" she asked, with some sharpness.

"Oh no, I shall come again; but what is the use of dragging it out? I have been four times since she came back, and it's terribly awkward work. I can't keep it up indefinitely; she oughtn't to expect that, you know. A woman should never keep a man dangling!" he added, finely.

"Ah, but you must have your last parting!" urged his companion, in whose imagination the idea of last partings occupied a place inferior in dignity only to that of first meetings.

XXIX.

He came again, without managing the last parting; and again and again, without finding that Mrs. Penniman had as yet done much to pave the path of retreat with flowers. It was devilish awkward, as he said, and he felt a lively animosity for Catherine's aunt, who, as he had now quite formed the habit of saying to himself, had dragged him into the mess and was bound in common charity to get him out of it. Mrs. Penniman, to tell the truth, had, in the seclusion of her own apartment—and, I may add, amid the suggestiveness of Catherine's, which wore in those days the appearance of that of a young lady laying out her *trousseau*—Mrs. Penniman had measured her responsibilities, and taken fright at their magnitude. The task of preparing Catherine and easing off Morris presented difficulties which increased in the execution, and even led the impulsive Lavinia to ask herself whether the modification of the young man's original project had been conceived in a happy spirit. A brilliant future, a wider career, a conscience exempt from the reproach of interference between a young lady and her natural rights—these excellent things might be too troublesomely purchased. From Catherine herself Mrs. Penniman received no assistance whatever; the poor girl was apparently without suspicion of her danger. She looked at her lover with eyes of undiminished trust, and though she had less confidence in her aunt than in a young man with whom she had exchanged so many tender vows, she gave her no handle for explaining or confessing. Mrs. Penniman, faltering and wavering, declared Catherine was very stupid, put off the great scene, as she would have called it, from day to day, and wandered about very uncomfortably, primed, to repletion, with her apology, but unable to bring it to the light. Morris's own scenes were very small ones just now; but even these were beyond his strength. He made his visits as brief as possible, and, while he sat with his mistress, found terribly little to talk about. She was waiting for him, in vulgar parlance, to name the day; and so long as he was unprepared to be explicit on this point, it seemed a mockery to pretend to talk about matters more abstract. She had no airs and no arts; she never attempted to disguise her expectancy. She was waiting on his good pleasure, and would wait modestly and patiently; his hanging back at this supreme time might appear strange, but of course he must have a good reason for it. Catherine would have made a wife of the gentle old-fashioned pattern—regarding reasons as favours and windfalls, but no more expecting one every day than she would have expected a bouquet of camellias. During the period of her engagement, however, a young lady even of the most slender pretensions counts upon more bouquets than at other times; and there was a want of perfume in the air at this moment which at last excited the girl's alarm.

"Are you sick?" she asked of Morris. "You seem so restless, and you look pale."

"I am not at all well," said Morris; and it occurred to him that, if he could only make her pity him enough, he might get off.

"I am afraid you are overworked; you oughtn't to work so much."

"I must do that." And then he added, with a sort of calculated brutality, "I don't want to owe you everything!"

"Ah, how can you say that?"

"I am too proud," said Morris.

"Yes—you are too proud!"

"Well, you must take me as I am," he went on. "you can never change me."

"I don't want to change you," she said, gently. "I will take you as you are!" And she stood looking at him.

"You know people talk tremendously about a man's marrying a rich girl," Morris remarked. "It's excessively disagreeable."

"But I am not rich?" said Catherine.

"You are rich enough to make me talked about!"

"Of course you are talked about. It's an honour!"

"It's an honour I could easily dispense with."

She was on the point of asking him whether it were not a compensation for this annoyance that the poor girl who had the misfortune to bring it upon him, loved him so dearly and believed in him so truly; but she hesitated, thinking that this would perhaps seem an exacting speech, and while she hesitated, he suddenly left her.

The next time he came, however, she brought it

out, and she told him again that he was too proud. He repeated that he couldn't change, and this time she felt the impulse to say that with a little effort he might change.

Sometimes he thought that if he could only make a quarrel with her it might help him; but the question was how to quarrel with a young woman who had such treasures of concession. "I suppose you think the effort is all on your side!" he was reduced to exclaiming. "Don't you believe that I have my own effort to make?"

"It's all yours now," she said, "My effort is finished and done with!"

"Well, mine is not."

"We must bear things together," said Catherine. "That's what we ought to do."

Morris attempted a natural smile. "There are some things which we can't very well bear together—for instance, separation."

"Why do you speak of separation?"

"Ah! you don't like it; I knew you wouldn't!"

"Where are you going, Morris?" she suddenly asked.

He fixed his eye on her a moment, and for a part of that moment she was afraid of it. "Will you promise not to make a scene?"

"A scene!—do I make scenes?"

"All women do!" said Morris, with the tone of large experience.

"I don't. Where are you going?"

"If I should say I was going away on business, should you think it very strange?"

She wondered a moment, gazing at him. "Yes—no. Not if you will take me with you."

"Take you with me—on business?"

"What is your business? Your business is to be with me."

"I don't earn my living with you," said Morris, "Or rather," he cried with a sudden inspiration, "that's just what I do—or what the world says I do?"

This ought perhaps to have been a great stroke, but it miscarried. "Where are you going?" Catherine simply repeated.

"To New Orleans. About buying some cotton."

"I am perfectly willing to go to New Orleans," Catherine said.

"Do you suppose I would take you to a nest of yellow fever?" cried Morris. "Do you suppose I would expose you at such a time as this?"

"If there is yellow fever, why should you go? Morris, you must not go?"

"It is to make six thousand dollars," said Morris. "Do you grudge me that satisfaction?"

"We have no need of six thousand dollars. You think too much about money!"

"You can afford to say that? This is a great chance; we heard of it last night." And he explained to her in what the chance consisted; and told her a long story, going over more than once several of the details, about the remarkable stroke of business which he and his partner had planned between them.

But Catherine's imagination, for reasons best known to herself, absolutely refused to be fired. "If you can go to New Orleans, I can go," she said. "Why shouldn't you catch yellow fever quite as easily as I? I am every bit as strong as you, and not in the least afraid of any fever. When we were in Europe, we were in very unhealthy places; my father used to make me take some pills. I never caught anything, and I never was nervous. What will be the use of six thousand dollars if you die of a fever? When persons are going to be married, they oughtn't to think so much about business. You shouldn't think about cotton, you should think about me. You can go to New Orleans some other time—there will always be plenty of cotton. It isn't the moment to choose—we have waited too long already." She spoke more forcibly and volubly than he had ever heard her, and she held his arm in her two hands.

"You said you wouldn't make a scene!" cried Morris. "I call this a scene."

"It's you that are making it! I have never asked you anything before. We have waited too long already." And it was a comfort to her to think that she had hitherto asked so little; it seemed to make her right to insist the greater now.

Morris bethought himself a little. "Very well, then; we won't talk about it any more. I will transact my business by letter." And he began to smooth his hat, as if to take leave.

"You won't go?" And she stood looking up at him.

He could not give up his idea of provoking a quarrel; it was so much the simplest way! He bent his eyes on her upturned face, with the darkest frown he could achieve. "You are not discreet. You mustn't bully me!"

But, as usual, she conceded everything. "No, I

am not discreet; I know I am too pressing. But isn't it natural? It is only for a moment."

"In a moment you may do a great deal of harm. Try and be calmer the next time I come."

"When will you come?"

"Do you want to make conditions?" Morris asked. "I will come next Saturday."

"Come to-morrow," Catherine begged; "I want you to come to-morrow. I will be very quiet," she added; and her agitation had by this time become so great that the assurance was not unbecoming. A sudden fear had come over her; it was like the solid conjunction of a dozen disembodied doubts, and her imagination, at a single bound, had traversed an enormous distance. All her being, for the moment, centred in the wish to keep him in the room.

Morris bent his head and kissed her forehead. "When you are quiet, you are perfection," he said; "but when you are violent, you are not in character."

It was Catherine's wish that there should be no violence about her save the beating of her heart, which she could not help; and she went on, as gently as possible, "Will you promise to come to-morrow?"

"I said Saturday!" Morris answered smiling. He tried a frown at one moment, a smile at another; he was at his wit's end.

"Yes, Saturday too," she answered, trying to smile. "But to-morrow first." He was going to the door, and she went with him, quickly. She leaned her shoulder against it; it seemed to her that she would do anything to keep him.

"If I am prevented from coming to-morrow, you will say I have deceived you!" he said.

"How can you be prevented? You can come if you will."

"I am a busy man—I am not a dangler!" cried Morris, sternly.

His voice was so hard and unnatural that, with a helpless look at him, she turned away; and then he quickly laid his hand on the door-knob. He felt as if he were absolutely running away from her. But in an instant she was close to him again, and murmuring in a tone none the less penetrating for being low, "Morris, you are going to leave me."

"Yes, for a little while."

"For how long?"

"Till you are reasonable again."

"I shall never be reasonable in that way!" And she tried to keep him longer; it was almost a struggle. "Think of what I have done!" she broke out. "Morris, I have given up everything!"

"You shall have everything back!"

"You wouldn't say that if you didn't mean something. What is it?—what has happened?—what have I done?—what has changed you?"

"I will write to you—that is better," Morris stammered.

"Ah, you won't come back!" she cried, bursting into tears.

"Dear Catherine," he said, "don't believe that! I promise you that you shall see me again!" And he managed to get away and to close the door behind him.

XXX.

It was almost her last outbreak of passive grief; at least, she never indulged in another that the world knew anything about. But this one was long and terrible; she flung herself on the sofa and gave herself up to her misery. She hardly knew what had happened; ostensibly she had only had a difference with her lover, as other girls had had before, and the thing was not only not a rupture, but she was under no obligation to regard it even as a menace. Nevertheless, she felt a wound, even if he had not dealt it; it seemed to her that a mask had suddenly fallen from his face. He had wished to get away from her; he had been angry and cruel, and said strange things, with strange looks. She was smothered and stunned; she buried her head in the cushions, sobbing and talking to herself. But at last she raised herself, with the fear that either her father or Mrs. Penniman would come in; and then she sat there, staring before her, while the room grew darker. She said to herself that perhaps he would come back to tell her he had not meant what he said; and she listened for his ring at the door, trying to believe that this was probable. A long time passed, but Morris remained absent; the shadows gathered; the evening settled down on the meagre elegance of the light, clear-coloured room; the fire went out. When it had grown dark, Catherine went to the window and looked out; she stood there for half an hour, on the mere chance that he would come up the steps. At last she turned away, for she saw her father come in. He had seen her at the window looking out, and he stopped a moment at the bottom of the white steps, and gravely, with an air of exaggerated courtesy, lifted his hat to her. The gesture was so incongruous to the condition she was in, this stately tribute of respect to a poor girl despised and forsaken was so out of place, that the thing gave her a kind of horror, and she hurried away to her room. It seemed to her that she had given Morris up.

She had to show herself half an hour later, and she was sustained at table by the immensity of her desire that her father should not perceive that anything had happened. This was a great help to her afterwards, and it served her (though never as much as she supposed) from the first. On this occasion Dr. Sloper was rather talkative. He told a great many stories about a wonderful poodle that he had seen at the house of an old lady whom he visited professionally. Catherine not only tried to appear to listen to the anecdotes of the poodle, but she endeavoured to interest herself in them, so as not to think of her scene with Morris. That perhaps was an hallucination; he was mistaken, she was jealous; people didn't change like that from one day to another. Then she knew that she had had doubts before—strange suspicions, that were at once vague and acute—and that he had been different ever since her return from Europe: whereupon she tried again to listen to her father, who told a story so remarkably well. Afterwards she went straight to her own room; it was beyond her strength to undertake to spend the evening with her aunt. All the evening, alone, she questioned herself. Her trouble was terrible; but was it a thing of her imagination, engendered by an extravagant sensibility, or did it represent a clear-cut reality, and had the worst that was possible actually come to pass? Mrs. Penniman, with a degree of tact that was as unusual as it was commendable, took the line of leaving her alone. The truth is, that her suspicions having been aroused, she indulged a desire, natural to a timid person, that the explosion should be localised. So long as the air still vibrated she kept out of the way.

She passed and repassed Catherine's door several times in the course of the evening, as if she expected to hear a plaintive moan behind it. But the room remained perfectly still; and accordingly, the last thing before retiring to her own couch, she applied for admittance. Catherine was sitting up, and had a book that she pretended to be reading. She had no wish to go to bed, for she had no expectation of sleeping. After Mrs. Penniman had left her she sat up half the night, and she offered her visitor no inducement to remain. Her aunt came stealing in very gently, and approached her with great solemnity.

"I am afraid you are in trouble, my dear. Can I do anything to help you?"

"I am not in any trouble whatever, and do not need any help," said Catherine, fibbing roundly, and proving thereby that not only our faults, but our most involuntary misfortunes, tend to corrupt our morals.

"Has nothing happened to you?"

"Nothing whatever."

"Are you very sure, dear?"

"Perfectly sure."

"And can I really do nothing for you?"

"Nothing, aunt, but kindly leave me alone," said Catherine.

Mrs. Penniman, though she had been afraid of too warm a welcome before, was now disappointed at so cold a one; and in relating afterwards, as she did to many persons, and with considerable variations of detail, the history of the termination of her niece's engagement, she was usually careful to mention that the young lady, on a certain occasion, had "hustled" her out of the room. It was characteristic of Mrs. Penniman that she related this fact, not in the least out of malignity to Catherine, whom she very sufficiently pitied, but simply from a natural disposition to embellish any subject that she touched.

Catherine, as I have said, sat up half the night, as if she still expected to hear Morris Townsend ring at the door. On the morrow this expectation was less unreasonable; but it was not gratified by the reappearance of the young man. Neither had he written; there was not a word of explanation or reassurance. Fortunately for Catherine she could take refuge from her excitement, which had now become intense, in her determination that her father should see nothing of it. How well she deceived her father we shall have occasion to learn; but her innocent arts were of little avail before a person of the rare perspicacity of Mrs. Penniman. This lady easily saw that she was agitated, and if there was any agitation going forward, Mrs. Penniman was not a person to forfeit her natural share in it. She returned to the charge the next evening, and requested her niece to lean upon her—to unburden her heart. Perhaps she should be able to explain certain things that now seemed dark, and that she knew more about than Catherine supposed. If Catherine had been frigid the night before, to-day she was haughty.

"You are completely mistaken, and I have not the least idea what you mean. I don't know what you are trying to fasten on me, and I have never had less need of any one's explanations in my life."

In this way the girl delivered herself, and from hour to hour kept her aunt at bay. From hour to hour Mrs. Penniman's curiosity grew. She would have given her little finger to know what Morris had said and done, what tone he had taken, what pretext he had found. She wrote to him, naturally, to request an interview; but she received, as naturally, no answer to her petition. Morris was not in a writing mood; for Catherine had addressed him two short notes which met with no acknowledgment. These notes were so brief that I may give them entire. "Won't you give me some sign that you didn't mean to be so cruel as you seemed on Tuesday?"—that was the first; the other was a little longer. "If I was unreasonable or suspicious, on Tuesday—if I annoyed you or troubled you in any way—I beg your forgiveness, and I promise never again to be so foolish. I am punished enough, and I don't understand. Dear Morris, you are killing me!" These notes were despatched on the Friday and Saturday; but Saturday and Sunday passed without bringing the poor girl the satisfaction she desired. Her punishment accumulated; she continued to bear it, however, with a good deal of superficial fortitude. On Saturday morning, the Doctor, who had been watching in silence, spoke to his sister Lavinia.

"The thing has happened—the scoundrel has backed out!"

"Never!" cried Mrs. Penniman, who had bethought herself what she should say to Catherine, but was not provided with a line of defence against her brother, so that indignant negation was the only weapon in her hands.

"He has begged for a reprieve, then, if you like that better!"

"It seems to make you very happy that your daughter's affections have been trifled with."

"It does," said the Doctor; "for I had foretold it! It's a great pleasure to be in the right."

"Your pleasures make one shudder!" his sister exclaimed.

Catherine went rigidly through her usual occupations; that is, up to the point of going with her aunt to church on Sunday morning. She generally went to afternoon service as well; but on this occasion her courage faltered, and she begged of Mrs. Penniman to go without her.

"I am sure you have a secret," said Mrs. Penniman, with great significance, looking at her rather grimly.

"If I have, I shall keep it!" Catherine answered, turning away.

Mrs. Penniman started for church; but before she had arrived, she stopped and turned back, and before twenty minutes had elapsed she re-entered the house, looked into the empty parlours, and then went upstairs and knocked at Catherine's door. She got no answer; Catherine was not in her room, and Mrs. Penniman presently ascertained that she was not in the house. "She has gone to him, she has fled!" Lavinia cried, clasping her hands with admiration and envy. But she soon perceived that Catherine had taken nothing with her—all her personal property in her room was intact—and then she jumped at the hypothesis that the girl had gone forth, not in tenderness, but in resentment. "She has followed him to his own door—she has burst upon him in his own apartment!" It was in these terms that Mrs. Penniman depicted to herself her niece's errand, which, viewed in this light, gratified her sense of the picturesque only a shade less strongly than the idea of a clandestine marriage. To visit one's lover, with tears and reproaches, at his own residence, was an image so agreeable to Mrs. Penniman's mind that she felt a sort of æsthetic disappointment at its lacking, in this case, the harmonious accompaniments of darkness and storm. A quiet Sunday afternoon appeared an inadequate setting for it; and, indeed, Mrs. Penniman was quite out of humour with the conditions of the time, which passed very slowly as she sat in the front-parlour, in her bonnet and her cashmere shawl, awaiting Catherine's return.

This event at last took place. She saw her—at the window—mount the steps, and she went to await her in the hall, where she pounced upon her as soon as she had entered the house, and drew her into the parlour, closing the door with solemnity. Catherine was flushed, and her eye was bright. Mrs. Penniman hardly knew what to think.

"May I venture to ask where you have been?" she demanded.

"I have been to take a walk," said Catherine. "I thought you had gone to church."

"I did go to church; but the service was shorter than usual. And pray where did you walk?"

"I don't know!" said Catherine.

"Your ignorance is most extraordinary! Dear Catherine, you can trust me."

"What am I to trust you with?"

"With your secret—your sorrow."

"I have no sorrow!" said Catherine fiercely.

"My poor child," Mrs. Penniman insisted, "you can't deceive me. I know everything. I have been requested to—a—to converse with you."

"I don't want to converse!"

"It will relieve you. Don't you know Shakespeare's lines?—'the grief that does not speak!' My dear girl, it is better as it is."

"What is better?" Catherine asked.

She was really too perverse. A certain amount of perversity was to be allowed for in a young lady whose lover had thrown her over; but not such an amount as would prove inconvenient to his apologists. "That you should be reasonable," said Mrs. Penniman, with some sternness. "That you should take counsel of worldly prudence, and submit to practical considerations. That you should agree to —a—separate."

Catherine had been ice up to this moment, but at this word she flamed up. "Separate? What do you know about our separating?"

Mrs. Penniman shook her head with a sadness in which there was almost a sense of injury. "Your pride is my pride, and your susceptibilities are mine. I see your side perfectly, but I also"—and she smiled with melancholy suggestiveness—"I also see the situation as a whole!"

This suggestiveness was lost upon Catherine, who repeated her violent inquiry. "Why do you talk about separation; what do you know about it?"

"We must study resignation," said Mrs. Penniman, hesitating, but sententious at a venture.

"Resignation to what?"

"To a change of—of our plans."

"My plans have not changed!" said Catherine, with a little laugh.

"Ah, but Mr. Townsend's have," her aunt answered very gently.

"What do you mean?"

There was an imperious brevity in the tone of this inquiry, against which Mrs. Penniman felt bound to protest; the information with which she had undertaken to supply her niece was after all a favour. She had tried sharpness, and she had tried sternness; but neither would do; she was shocked at the girl's obstinacy. "Ah, well," she said, "if he hasn't told you! . . ." and she turned away.

Catherine watched her a moment in silence; then she hurried after her, stopping her before she reached the door. "Told me what? What do you mean? What are you hinting at and threatening me with?"

"Isn't it broken off?" asked Mrs. Penniman.

"My engagement? Not in the least!"

"I beg your pardon in that case. I have spoken too soon!"

"Too soon! Soon or late," Catherine broke out, "you speak foolishly and cruelly!"

"What has happened between you then?" asked her aunt struck by the sincerity of this cry. "For something certainly has happened."

"Nothing has happened but that I love him more and more!"

Mrs. Penniman was silent an instant. "I suppose that's the reason you went to see him this afternoon."

Catherine flushed as if she had been struck. "Yes, I did go to see him! But that's my own business."

"Very well, then; we won't talk about it." And Mrs. Penniman moved towards the door again. But she was stopped by a sudden imploring cry from the girl.

"Aunt Lavinia, *where* has he gone?"

"Ah, you admit then that he has gone away? Didn't they know at his house?"

"They said he had left town. I asked no more questions; I was ashamed," said Catherine simply enough.

"You needn't have taken so compromising a step if you had had a little more confidence in me," Mrs. Penniman observed, with a good deal of grandeur.

"Is it to New Orleans!" Catherine went on, irrelevantly.

It was the first time Mrs. Penniman had heard of New Orleans in this connection; but she was averse to letting Catherine know that she was in the dark. She attempted to strike an illumination from the instructions she had received from Morris. "My dear Catherine," she said, "when a separation has been agreed upon, the farther he goes away the better."

"Agreed upon? Has he agreed upon it with you?" A consummate sense of her aunt's meddlesome folly had come over her during the last five minutes, and she was sickened at the thought that Mrs. Penniman had been let loose, as it were, upon her happiness.

"He certainly has sometimes advised with me," said Mrs. Penniman.

"Is it you then that have changed him and made him so unnatural?" Catherine cried. "Is it you that have worked on him and taken him from me! He doesn't belong to you, and I don't see how you have anything to do with what is between us! Is it you that have made this plot and told him to leave me? How could you be so wicked, so cruel? What have I ever done to you; why can't you leave me alone? I was afraid you would spoil everything; for you *do* spoil everything you touch! I was afraid of you all the time we were abroad; I had no rest when I thought that you were always talking to him." Catherine went on with growing vehemence, pouring out in her bitterness and in the clairvoyance of her passion (which suddenly, jumping all processes, made her judge her aunt finally and without appeal), the uneasiness which had lain for so many months upon her heart.

Mrs. Penniman was scared and bewildered; she saw no prospect of introducing her little account of the purity of Morris's motives. "You are a most ungrateful girl!" she cried. "Do you scold me for talking with him! I am sure we never talked of anything but you!"

"Yes; and that was the way you worried him; you made him tired of my very name! I wish you had never spoken of me to him; I never asked your help!"

"I am sure if it hadn't been for me he would never have come to the house, and you would never have known what he thought of you," Mrs. Penniman rejoined with a good deal of justice.

"I wish he never had come to the house, and that I never had known it! That's better than this," said poor Catherine.

"You are a very ungrateful girl," Aunt Lavinia repeated.

Catherine's outbreak of anger and the sense of wrong gave her, while they lasted, the satisfaction that comes from all assertion of force; they hurried her along, and there is always a sort of pleasure in cleaving the air. But at the bottom she hated to be violent, and she was conscious of no aptitude for organised resentment. She calmed herself with a great effort, but with great rapidity, and walked about the room a few moments, trying to say to herself that her aunt had meant everything for the best. She did not succeed in saying it with much conviction, but after a little she was able to speak quietly enough.

"I am not ungrateful, but I am very unhappy. It's hard to be grateful for that," she said. "Will you please tell me where he is?"

"I haven't the least idea; I am not in secret correspondence with him!" And Mrs. Penniman wished indeed that she were, so that she might let him know how Catherine abused her, after all she had done.

"Was it a plan of his, then, to break off——?" By this time Catherine had become completely quiet.

Mrs. Penniman began again to have a glimpse of her chance for explaining. "He shrank—he shrank," she said. "He lacked courage, but it was the courage to injure you! He couldn't bear to bring down on you your father's curse."

Catherine listened to this with her eyes fixed upon her aunt, and continued to gaze at her for some time afterwards "Did he tell you to say that?"

"He told me to say many things—all so delicate, so discriminating. And he told me to tell you he hoped you wouldn't despise him."

"I don't," said Catherine. And then she added: "And will he stay away for ever?"

"Oh, for ever is a long time. Your father, perhaps, won't live for ever."

"Perhaps not."

"I am sure you appreciate—you understand—even though your heart bleeds," said Mrs. Penniman. "You doubtless think him too scrupulous. So do I, but I respect his scruples. What he asks of you is that you should do the same."

Catherine was still gazing at her aunt, but she spoke, at last, as if she had not heard or not understood her. "It has been a regular plan, then. He has broken it off deliberately; he has given me up."

"For the present, dear Catherine. He has put it off, only."

"He has left me alone," Catherine went on.

"Haven't you *me?*" asked Mrs. Penniman, with much expression.

Catherine shook her head slowly. "I don't believe it!" and she left the room.

XXXI.

THOUGH she had forced herself to be calm, she preferred practising this virtue in private, and she forbore to show herself at tea—a repast which, on Sundays, at six o'clock, took the place of dinner. Dr. Sloper and his sister sat face to face, but Mrs. Penniman never met her brother's eye. Late in the evening she went with him, but without Catherine, to their sister Almond's, where, between the two ladies, Catherine's unhappy situation was discussed with a frankness that was conditioned by a good deal of mysterious reticence on Mrs. Penniman's part.

"I am delighted he is not to marry her," said Mrs. Almond, "but he ought to be horsewhipped all the same."

Mrs. Penniman, who was shocked at her sister's coarseness, replied that he had been actuated by the noblest of motives—the desire not to impoverish Catherine.

"I am very happy that Catherine is not to be impoverished—but I hope he may never have a penny too much! And what does the poor girl say to *you?*" Mrs. Almond asked.

"She says I have a genius for consolation," said Mrs. Penniman.

This was the account of the matter that she gave to her sister, and it was perhaps with the consciousness of genius that, on her return that evening to Washington Square, she again presented herself for admittance at Catherine's door. Catherine came and opened it; she was apparently very quiet.

"I only want to give you a little word of advice," she said. "If your father asks you, say that everything is going on."

Catherine stood there, with her hand on the knob, looking at her aunt, but not asking her to come in. "Do you think he will ask me?"

"I am sure he will. He asked me just now, on our way home from your Aunt Elizabeth's. I explained the whole thing to your Aunt Elizabeth. I said to your father I know nothing about it."

"Do you think he will ask me, when he sees—when he sees——?" But here Catherine stopped.

"The more he sees, the more disagreeable he will be," said her aunt.

"He shall see as little as possible!" Catherine declared.

"Tell him you are to be married."

"So I am," said Catherine, softly; and she closed the door upon her aunt.

She could not have said this two days later—for instance, on Tuesday, when she at last received a letter from Morris Townsend. It was an epistle of considerable length, measuring five large square pages, and written at Philadelphia. It was an explanatory document, and it explained a great many things, chief among which were the considerations that had led the writer to take advantage of an urgent "professional" absence to try and banish from his mind the image of one whose path he had crossed only to scatter it with ruins. He ventured to expect but partial success in this attempt, but he could promise her that, whatever his failure, he would never again interpose between her generous heart and her brilliant prospects and filial duties. He closed with an intimation that his professional pursuits might compel him to travel for some months, and with the hope that when they should each have accommodated themselves to what was sternly involved in their respective positions—even should this result not be reached for years—they should meet as friends, as fellow-sufferers, as innocent but philosophic victims of a great social law. That her life should be peaceful and happy was the dearest wish of him who ventured still to subscribe himself her most obedient servant. The letter was beautifully written, and Catherine, who kept it for many years after this, was able, when her sense of the bitterness of its meaning and the hollowness of its tone had grown less acute, to admire its grace of expression. At present, for a long time after she received it, all she had to help her was the determination, daily more rigid, to make no appeal to the compassion of her father.

He suffered a week to elapse, and then one day, in the morning, at an hour at which she rarely saw him, he strolled into the back-parlour. He had watched his time, and he found her alone. She was sitting with some work, and he came and stood in front of her. He was going out, he had on his hat and was drawing on his gloves.

"It doesn't seem to me that you are treating me just now with all the consideration I deserve," he said in a moment.

"I don't know what I have done," Catherine answered, with her eyes on her work.

"You have apparently quite banished from your mind the request I made you at Liverpool, before we sailed; the request that you would notify me in advance before leaving my house."

"I have not left your house!" said Catherine.

"But you intend to leave it, and by what you gave me to understand, your departure must be impending. In fact, though you are still here in body, you are already absent in spirit. Your mind has taken up its residence with your prospective husband, and you might quite as well be lodged under the conjugal roof, for all the benefit we get from your society."

"I will try and be more cheerful!" said Catherine.

"You certainly ought to be cheerful, you ask a great deal if you are not. To the pleasure of marrying a brilliant young man, you add that of having your own way; you strike me as a very lucky young lady!"

Catherine got up; she was suffocating. But she folded her work, deliberately and correctly, bending her burning face upon it. Her father stood where he had planted himself; she hoped he would go, but he smoothed and buttoned his gloves, and then he rested his hands upon his hips.

"It would be a convenience to me to know when I may expect to have an empty house," he went on. "When you go, your aunt marches."

She looked at him at last, with a long silent gaze, which, in spite of her pride and her resolution, uttered part of the appeal she had tried not to make. Her father's cold gray eye sounded her own, and he insisted on his point.

"Is it to-morrow? Is it next week, or the week after?"

"I shall not go away!" said Catherine.

The Doctor raised his eyebrows. "Has he backed out?"

"I have broken off my engagement."

"Broken it off?"

"I have asked him to leave New York, and he has gone away for a long time."

The Doctor was both puzzled and disappointed, but he solved his perplexity by saying to himself that his daughter simply misrepresented—justifiably, if one would, but nevertheless, misrepresented—the facts; and he eased off his disappointment, which was that of a man losing a chance for a little triumph that he had rather counted on, by a few words that he uttered aloud.

"How does he take his dismissal?"

"I don't know!" said Catherine, less ingeniously than she had hitherto spoken.

"You mean you don't care? You are rather cruel, after encouraging him and playing with him for so long!"

The Doctor had his revenge after all.

XXXII.

OUR story has hitherto moved with very short steps, but as it approaches its termination it must take a long stride. As time went on, it might have appeared to the Doctor that his daughter's account of her rupture with Morris Townsend, mere bravado as he had deemed it, was in some degree justified by the sequel. Morris remained as rigidly and unremittingly absent as if he had died of a broken heart, and Catherine had apparently buried the memory of this fruitless episode as deep as if it had terminated by her own choice. We know that she had been deeply and incurably wounded, but the Doctor had no means of knowing it. He was certainly curious about it, and would have given a good deal to discover the exact truth; but it was his punishment that he never knew—his punishment, I mean, for the abuse of sarcasm in his relations with his daughter. There was a good deal of effective sarcasm in her keeping him in the dark, and the rest of the world conspired with her, in this sense, to be sarcastic. Mrs. Penniman told him nothing, partly because he never questioned her—he made too light of Mrs. Penniman for that—and partly because she flattered herself that a tormenting reserve, and a serene profession of ignorance, would avenge her for his theory that she had meddled in the matter. He went two or three times to see Mrs. Montgomery, but Mrs. Montgomery had nothing to impart. She simply knew that her brother's engagement was broken off, and now that Miss Sloper was out of danger, she preferred not to bear witness in any way against Morris. She had done so before—however unwillingly—because she was sorry for Miss Sloper; but she was not sorry for Miss Sloper now—not at all sorry. Morris had told her nothing about his relations with Miss Sloper at the time, and he had told her nothing since. He was always away, and he very seldom wrote to her; she believed he had gone to California. Mrs. Almond had, in her sister's phrase, "taken up" Catherine violently since the recent catastrophe; but though the girl was very grateful to her for her kindness, she revealed no secrets, and the good lady could give the Doctor no satisfaction. Even, however, had she been able to narrate to him the private history of his daughter's unhappy love-affair, it would have given her a certain comfort to leave him in ignorance; for Mrs. Almond was at this time not altogether in sympathy with her brother. She had guessed for herself that Catherine had been cruelly jilted — she knew nothing from Mrs. Penniman, for Mrs. Penniman had not ventured to lay the famous explanation of Morris's motives before Mrs. Almond, though she had thought it good enough for Catherine—and she pronounced her brother too consistently indifferent to what the poor creature must have suffered and must still be suffering. Dr. Sloper had his theory, and he rarely altered his theories. The marriage would have been an abominable one, and the girl had had a blessed escape. She was not to be pitied for that, and to pretend to condole with her would have been to make concessions to the idea that she had ever had a right to think of Morris.

"I put my foot on this idea from the first, and I keep it there now," said the Doctor. "I don't see anything cruel in that; one can't keep it there too long." To this Mrs. Almond more than once replied that if Catherine had got rid of her incongruous lover, she deserved the credit of it, and that to bring herself to her father's enlightened view of the matter must have cost her an effort that he was bound to appreciate.

"I am by no means sure she has got rid of him," the Doctor said. "There is not the smallest probability that, after having been as obstinate as a mule for two years, she suddenly became amenable to reason. It is infinitely more probable that he got rid of her."

"All the more reason you should be gentle with her."

"I *am* gentle with her. But I can't do the pathetic; I can't pump up tears, to look graceful, over the most fortunate thing that ever happened to her."

"You have no sympathy," said Mrs. Almond; "that was never your strong point. You have only to look at her to see that, right or wrong, and whether the rupture came from herself or from him, her poor little heart is grievously bruised."

"Handling bruises—and even dropping tears on them—doesn't make them any better! My business is to see she gets no more knocks, and that I shall carefully attend to. But I don't at all recognise your description of Catherine. She doesn't strike me in the least as a young woman going about in search of a moral poultice. In fact, she seems to me much better than while the fellow was hanging about. She is perfectly comfortable and blooming; she eats and sleeps, takes her usual exercise, and overloads herself, as usual, with finery. She is always knitting some purse or embroidering some handkerchief, and it seems to me she turns these articles out about as fast as ever. She hasn't much to say; but when had she anything to say? She had her little dance, and now she is sitting down to rest. I suspect that, on the whole, she enjoys it."

"She enjoys it as people enjoy getting rid of a leg that has been crushed. The state of mind after amputation is doubtless one of comparative repose."

"If your leg is a metaphor for young Townsend, I can assure you he has never been crushed. Crushed? Not he! He is alive and perfectly intact, and that's why I am not satisfied."

"Should you have liked to kill him?" asked Mrs. Almond.

"Yes, very much. I think it is quite possible that it is all a blind."

"A blind?"

"An arrangement between them. *Il fait le mort*, as they say in France; but he is looking out of the corner of his eye. You can depend upon it he has not burned his ships; he has kept one to come back in. When I am dead, he will set sail again, and then she will marry him."

"It is interesting to know that you accuse your only daughter of being the vilest of hypocrites," said Mrs. Almond.

"I don't see what difference her being my only daughter makes. It is better to accuse one than a dozen. But I don't accuse any one. There is not the smallest hypocrisy about Catherine, and I deny that she even pretends to be miserable."

The Doctor's idea that the thing was a "blind" had its intermissions and revivals; but it may be said on the whole to have increased as he grew older; together with his impression of Catherine's blooming and comfortable condition. Naturally, if he had not found grounds for viewing her as a lovelorn maiden during the year or two that followed her great trouble, he found none at a time when she had completely recovered her self-possession. He was obliged to recognise the fact that if the two young people were waiting for him to get out of the way, they were at least waiting very patiently. He had heard from time to time that Morris was in New York; but he never remained there long, and, to the best of the Doctor's belief, had no communication with Catherine. He was sure they never met, and he had reason to suspect that Morris never wrote to her. After the letter that has been mentioned, she heard from him twice again, at considerable intervals; but on none of these occasions did she write herself. On the other hand, as the Doctor observed, she averted herself rigidly from the idea of marrying other people. Her opportunities for doing so were not numerous, but they occurred often enough to test her disposition. She refused a widower, a man with a genial temperament, a handsome fortune, and three little girls (he had heard that she was very fond of children, and he pointed to his own with some confidence); and she turned a deaf ear to the solicitations of a clever young lawyer, who, with the prospect of a great practice, and the reputation of a most agreeable man, had had the shrewdness, when he came to look about him for a wife, to believe that she would suit him better than several younger and prettier girls. Mr. Macalister, the widower, had desired to make a marriage of reason, and had chosen Catherine for what he supposed to be her latent matronly qualities; but John Ludlow, who was a year the girl's junior, and spoken of always as a young man who might have his "pick," was seriously in love with her. Catherine, however, would never look at him; she made it plain to him that she thought he came to see her too often. He afterwards consoled himself, and married a very different person, little Miss Sturtevant, whose attractions were obvious to the dullest comprehension. Catherine, at the time of these events, had left her thirtieth year well behind her, and had quite taken her place as an old maid. Her father would have preferred she should marry, and he once told her that he hoped she would not be too fastidious. "I should like to see you an honest man's wife before I die," he said. This was after John Ludlow had been compelled to give it up, though the Doctor had advised him to persevere. The Doctor exercised no further pressure, and had the credit of not "worrying" at all over his daughter's singleness. In fact he worried rather more than appeared, and there were considerable periods during which he felt sure that Morris Townsend was hidden behind some door. "If he is not, why doesn't she marry?" he asked himself. "Limited as her intelligence may be, she must understand perfectly well that she is made to do the usual thing." Catherine, however, became an admirable old maid. She formed habits, regulated her days upon a system of her own, interested herself in charitable institutions, asylums, hospitals, and aid-societies; and went generally, with an even and noiseless step, about the rigid business of her life. This life had, however, a secret history as well as a public one—if I may talk of the public history of a mature and diffident spinster for whom publicity had always a combination of terrors. From her own point of view the great facts of her career were that Morris Townsend had trifled with her affection, and that her father had broken its spring. Nothing could ever alter these facts; they were always there, like her name, her age, her plain face. Nothing could ever undo the wrong or cure the pain that Morris had inflicted on her, and nothing could ever make her feel towards her father as she felt in her younger years. There was something dead in her life, and her duty was to try and fill the void. Catherine recognised this duty to the utmost; she had a great disapproval of brooding and moping. She had of course no faculty for quenching memory in dissipation; but she mingled freely in the usual gaieties of the town, and she became at last an inevitable figure at all respectable entertainments. She was greatly liked, and as time went on she grew to be a sort of kindly maiden-aunt to the younger portion of society. Young girls were apt to confide to her their love-affairs (which they never did to Mrs. Penniman), and young men to be fond of her without knowing why. She developed a few harmless eccentricities; her habits, once formed, were rather stiffly maintained; her opinions, on all moral and social matters, were extremely conservative; and before she was forty she was regarded as an old-fashioned person, and an authority on customs that had passed away. Mrs. Penniman, in comparison, was quite a girlish figure; she grew younger as she advanced in life. She lost none of her relish for beauty and mystery, but she had little opportunity to exercise it. With Catherine's later wooers she failed to establish relations as intimate as those which had given her so many interesting hours in the society of Morris Townsend. These gentlemen had an indefinable mistrust of her good offices, and they never talked to her about Catherine's charms. Her ringlets, her buckles and bangles glistened more brightly with each succeeding year, and she remained quite the same officious and imaginative Mrs. Penniman, and the odd mixture of impetuosity and circumspection, that we have hitherto known. As regards one point, however, her circumspection prevailed, and she must be given due credit for it. For upwards of seventeen years she never mentioned Morris Townsend's name to her niece. Catherine was grateful to her, but this consistent silence so little in accord with her aunt's character, gave her a certain alarm, and she could never wholly rid herself of a suspicion that Mrs. Penniman sometimes had news of him.

XXXIII.

LITTLE by little Dr. Sloper had retired from his profession; he visited only those patients in whose symptoms he recognised a certain originality. He went again to Europe, and remained two years; Catherine went with him, and on this occasion Mrs. Penniman was of the party. Europe apparently had few surprises for Mrs. Penniman, who frequently remarked, in the most romantic sites—"You know I am very familiar with all this." It should be added that such remarks were usually not addressed to her brother, or yet to her niece, but to fellow-tourists who happened to be at hand, or even to the cicerone or the goat-herd in the foreground.

One day, after his return from Europe, the Doctor said something to his daughter that made her start—it seemed to come from so far out of the past.

"I should like you to promise me something before I die."

"Why do you talk about your dying?" she asked.

"Because I am sixty-eight years old."

"I hope you will live a long time," said Catherine.

"I hope I shall! But some day I shall take a

bad cold, and then it will not matter much what any one hopes. That will be the manner of my exit, and when it takes place, remember I told you so. Promise me not to marry Morris Townsend after I am gone."

This was what made Catherine start, as I have said; but her start was a silent one, and for some moments she said nothing. "Why do you speak of him?" she asked at last.

"You challenge everything I say. I speak of him because he's a topic, like any other. He's to be seen, like any one else, and he is still looking for a wife—having had one and got rid of her, I don't know by what means. He has lately been in New York, and at your cousin Marian's house; your Aunt Elizabeth saw him there."

"They neither of them told me," said Catherine.

"That's their merit; it's not yours. He has grown fat and bald, and he has not made his fortune. But I can't trust those facts alone to steel your heart against him, and that's why I ask you to promise."

"Fat and bald:" these words presented a strange image to Catherine's mind, out of which the memory of the most beautiful young man in the world had never faded. "I don't think you understand," she said. "I very seldom think of Mr. Townsend."

"It will be very easy for you to go on, then. Promise me, after my death, to do the same."

Again, for some moments, Catherine was silent; her father's request deeply amazed her; it opened an old wound and made it ache afresh. "I don't think I can promise that," she answered.

"It would be a great satisfaction," said her father.

"You don't understand. I can't promise that."

The Doctor was silent a minute. "I ask you for a particular reason. I am altering my will."

This reason failed to strike Catherine; and indeed she scarcely understood it. All her feelings were merged in the sense that he was trying to treat her as he had treated her years before. She had suffered from it then; and now all her experience, all her acquired tranquillity and rigidity, protested. She had been so humble in her youth that she could now afford to have a little pride, and there was something in this request, and in her father's thinking himself so free to make it, that seemed an injury to her dignity. Poor Catherine's dignity was not aggressive; it never sat in state; but if you pushed far enough you could find it. Her father had pushed very far.

"I can't promise," she simply repeated.

"You are very obstinate," said the Doctor.

"I don't think you understand."

"Please explain, then."

"I can't explain," said Catherine. "And I can't promise."

"Upon my word," her father exclaimed, "I had no idea how obstinate you are!"

She knew herself that she was obstinate, and it gave her a certain joy. She was now a middle-aged woman.

About a year after this, the accident that the Doctor had spoken of occurred; he took a violent cold. Driving out to Bloomingdale one April day to see a patient of unsound mind, who was confined in a private asylum for the insane, and whose family greatly desired a medical opinion from an eminent source, he was caught in a spring shower, and being in a buggy, without a hood, he found himself soaked to the skin. He came home with an ominous chill, and on the morrow he was seriously ill. "It is congestion of the lungs," he said to Catherine; "I shall need very good nursing. It will make no difference, for I shall not recover; but I wish everything to be done, to the smallest detail, as if I should. I hate an ill-conducted sick-room; and you will be so good as to nurse me on the hypothesis that I shall get well." He told her which of his fellow-physicians to send for, and gave her a multitude of minute directions; it was quite on the optimistic hypothesis that she nursed him. But he had never been wrong in his life, and he was not wrong now. He was touching his seventieth year, and though he had a very well-tempered constitution, his hold upon life had lost its firmness. He died after three weeks' illness, during which Mrs. Penniman, as well as his daughter, had been assiduous at his bedside.

On his will being opened after a decent interval, it was found to consist of two portions. The first of these dated from ten years back, and consisted of a series of dispositions by which he left the great mass of property to his daughter, with becoming legacies to his two sisters. The second was a codicil, of recent origin, maintaining the annuities to Mrs. Penniman and Mrs. Almond, but reducing Catherine's share to a fifth of what he had first bequeathed her. "She is amply provided for from her mother's side," the document ran, "never having spent more than a fraction of her income from this source; so that her fortune is already more than sufficient to attract those unscrupulous adventurers whom she has given me reason to believe that she persists in regarding as an interesting class." The large remainder of his property, therefore, Dr. Sloper had divided into seven unequal parts, which he left, as endowments, to as many different hospitals and shools of medicine, in various cities of the Union.

To Mrs. Penniman it seemed monstrous that a man should play such tricks with other people's money; for after his death, of course, as she said, it was other people's. "Of course you will dispute the will," she remarked, fatuously, to Catherine.

"Oh no," Catherine answered, "I like it very much. Only I wish it had been expressed a little differently!"

XXXIV.

It was her habit to remain in town very late in the summer; she preferred the house in Washington Square to any other habitation whatever, and it was under protest that she used to go to the seaside for the month of August. At the sea she spent her month at an hotel. The year that her father died she intermitted this custom altogether, not thinking it consistent with deep mourning; and the year after that she put off her departure till so late that the middle of August found her still in the heated solitude of Washington Square. Mrs. Penniman, who was fond of a change, was usually eager for a visit to the country; but this year she appeared quite content with such rural impressions as she could gather, at the parlour window, from the ailantus-trees behind the wooden paling. The peculiar fragrance of this vegetation used to diffuse itself in the evening air, and Mrs. Penniman, on the warm nights of July, often sat at the open window and inhaled it. This was a happy moment for Mrs. Penniman; after the death of her brother she felt more free to obey her impulses. A vague oppression had disappeared from her life, and she enjoyed a sense of freedom of which she had not been conscious since the memorable time, so long ago, when the Doctor went abroad with Catherine and left her at home to entertain Morris Townsend. The year that had elapsed since her brother's death reminded her of that happy time, because, although Catherine, in growing older, had become a person to be reckoned with, yet her society was a very different thing, as Mrs. Penniman said, from that of a tank of cold water. The elder lady hardly knew what use to make of this larger margin of her life; she sat and looked at it very much as she had often sat, with her poised needle in her hand, before her tapestry-frame. She had a confident hope, however, that her rich impulses, her talent for embroidery, would still find their application, and this confidence was justified before many months had elapsed.

Catherine continued to live in her father's house in spite of its being represented to her that a maiden-lady of quiet habits might find a more convenient abode in one of the smaller dwellings, with brown stone fronts, which had at this time begun to adorn the transverse thoroughfares in the upper part of the town. She liked the earlier structure—it had begun by this time to be called an "old" house—and proposed to herself to end her days in it. If it was too large for a pair of unpretending gentlewomen, this was better than the opposite fault; for Catherine had no desire to find herself in closer quarters with her aunt. She expected to spend the rest of her life in Washington Square, and to enjoy Mrs. Penniman's society for the whole of this period; as she had a conviction that, long as she might live, her aunt would live at least as long, and always retain her brilliancy and activity. Mrs. Penniman suggested to her the idea of a rich vitality.

On one of those warm evenings in July of which mention has been made, the two ladies sat together at an open window, looking out on the quiet Square. It was too hot for lighted lamps, for reading, or for work; it might have appeared too hot even for conversation, Mrs. Penniman having long been speechless. She sat forward in the window, half on the balcony, humming a little song. Catherine was within the room, in a low rocking-chair, dressed in white, and slowly using a large palmetto fan. It was in this way, at this season, that the aunt and niece, after they had had tea, habitually spent their evenings.

"Catherine," said Mrs. Penniman at last, "I am going to say something that will surprise you."

"Pray do," Catherine answered; "I like surprises. And it is so quiet now."

"Well, then, I have seen Morris Townsend."

If Catherine was surprised, she checked the expression of it; she gave neither a start nor an exclamation. She remained, indeed, for some moments intensely still, and this may very well have been a symptom of emotion. "I hope he was well," she said at last.

"I don't know; he is a great deal changed. He would like very much to see you."

"I would rather not see him," said Catherine, quickly.

"I was afraid you would say that. But you don't seem surprised!"

"I am—very much."

"I met him at Marian's," said Mrs. Penniman. "He goes to Marian's, and they are so afraid you will meet him there. It's my belief that that's why he goes. He wants so much to see you." Catherine made no response to this, and Mrs. Penniman went on. "I didn't know him at first; he is so remarkably changed. But he knew me in a minute. He says I am not in the least changed. You know how polite he always was. He was coming away when I came, and we walked a little distance together. He is still very handsome, only, of course, he looks older, and he is not so—so animated as he used to be. There was a touch of sadness about him; but there was a touch of sadness about him before—especially when he went away. I am afraid he has not been very successful—that he has never got thoroughly established. I don't suppose he is sufficiently plodding, and that, after all, is what succeeds in this world." Mrs. Penniman had not mentioned Morris Townsend's name to her niece for upwards of the fifth of a century; but now that she had broken the spell, she seemed to wish to make up for lost time, as if there had been a sort of exhilaration in hearing herself talk of him. She proceeded, however, with considerable caution, pausing occasionally to let Catherine give some sign. Catherine gave no other sign than to stop the rocking of her chair and the swaying of her fan; she sat motionless and silent. "It was on Tuesday last," said Mrs. Penniman, "and I have been hesitating ever since about telling you. I didn't know how you might like it. At last I thought that it was so long ago that you would probably not have any particular feeling. I saw him again, after meeting him at Marian's. I met him in the street, and he went a few steps with me. The first thing he said was about you; he asked ever so many questions. Marian didn't want me to speak to you; she didn't want you to know that they receive him. I told him I was sure that after all these years you couldn't have any feeling about that; you couldn't grudge him the hospitality of his own cousin's house. I said you would be bitter indeed if you did that. Marian has the most extraordinary ideas about what happened between you; she seems to think he behaved in some very unusual manner. I took the liberty of reminding her of the real facts, and placing the story in its true light. *He* has no bitterness, Catherine, I can assure you; and he might be excused for it, for things have not gone well with him. He has been all over the world, and tried to establish himself everywhere; but his evil star was against him. It is most interesting to hear him talk of his evil star. Everything failed; everything but his—you know, you remember—his proud, high spirit. I believe he married some lady somewhere in Europe. You know they marry in such a peculiar matter-of-course way in Europe; a marriage of reason they call it. She died soon afterwards; as he said to me, she only flitted across his life. He has not been in New York for ten years; he came back a few days ago. The first thing he did was to ask me about you. He had heard you had never married; he seemed very much interested about that. He said you had been the real romance of his life."

Catherine had suffered her companion to proceed from point to point, and pause to pause, without interrupting her; she fixed her eyes on the ground and listened. But the last phrase I have quoted was followed by a pause of peculiar significance, and then, at last, Catherine spoke. It will be observed that before doing so she had received a good deal of information about Morris Townsend. "Please say no more; please don't follow up that subject."

"Doesn't it interest you?" asked Mrs. Penniman, with a certain timorous archness.

"It pains me," said Catherine.

"I was afraid you would say that. But don't you think you could get used to it? He wants so much to see you."

"Please don't, Aunt Lavinia," said Catherine, getting up from her seat. She moved quickly away, and went to the other window, which stood open to the balcony; and here, in the embrasure, concealed from her aunt by the white curtains, she remained a long time, looking out into the warm darkness. She had had a great shock; it was as if the gulf of the past had suddenly opened, and a spectral figure had risen out of it. There were some things she believed she had got over, some feelings that she had thought of as dead; but apparently there was a certain vitality in them still. Mrs. Penniman had made them stir themselves. It was but a momentary agitation, Catherine said to herself; it would presently pass away. She was trembling, and her heart was beating so that she could feel it; but this also would subside.

Then, suddenly, while she waited for a return of her calmness, she burst into tears. But her tears flowed very silently, so that Mrs. Penniman had no observation of them. It was perhaps, however, because Mrs. Penniman suspected them that she said no more that evening about Morris Townsend.

XXXV.

HER refreshed attention to this gentleman had not those limits of which Catherine desired, for herself, to be conscious; it lasted long enough to enable her to wait another week before speaking of him again. It was under the same circumstances that she once more attacked the subject. She had been sitting with her niece in the evening; only on this occasion, as the night was not so warm, the lamp had been lighted, and Catherine had placed herself near it with a morsel of fancy-work. Mrs. Penniman went and sat alone for half an hour on the balcony; then she came in, moving vaguely about the room. At last she sank into a seat near Catherine, with clasped hands, and a little look of excitement.

"Shall you be angry if I speak to you again about *him?*" she asked.

Catherine looked up at her quietly. "Who is *he?*"

"He whom you once loved."

"I shall not be angry, but I shall not like it."

"He sent you a message," said Mrs. Penniman. "I promised him to deliver it, and I must keep my promise."

In all these years Catherine had had time to forget how little she had to thank her aunt for in the season of her misery; she had long ago forgiven Mrs. Penniman for taking too much upon herself. But for a moment this attitude of interposition and disinterestedness, this carrying of messages and redeeming of promises, brought back the sense that her companion was a dangerous woman. She had said she would not be angry; but for an instant she felt sore. "I don't care what you do with your promise!" she answered.

Mrs. Penniman, however, with her high conception of the sanctity of pledges, carried her point. "I have gone too far to retreat," she said, though precisely what this meant she was not at pains to explain. "Mr. Townsend wishes most particularly to see you, Catherine; he believes that if you knew how much, and why, he wishes it, you would consent to do so."

"There can be no reason," said Catherine; "no good reason."

"His happiness depends upon it. Is not that a good reason?" asked Mrs. Penniman, impressively.

"Not for me. My happiness does not."

"I think you will be happier after you have seen him. He is going away again—going to resume his wanderings. It is a very lonely, restless, joyless life. Before he goes, he wishes to speak to you; it is a fixed idea with him—he is always thinking of it. He has something very important to say to you. He believes that you never understood him—that you never judged him rightly, and the belief has always weighed upon him terribly. He wishes to justify himself; he believes that in a very few words he could do so. He wishes to meet you as a friend."

Catherine listened to this wonderful speech, without pausing in her work; she had now had several days to accustom herself to think of Morris Townsend again as an actuality. When it was over she said simply, "Please say to Mr. Townsend that I wish he would leave me alone."

She had hardly spoken when a sharp, firm ring at the door vibrated through the summer night. Catherine looked up at the clock; it marked a quarter-past nine—a very late hour for visitors, especially in the empty condition of the town. Mrs. Penniman at the same moment gave a little start, and then Catherine's eyes turned quickly to her aunt. They met Mrs. Penniman's and sounded them for a moment, sharply. Mrs. Penniman was blushing; her look was a conscious one; it seemed to confess something. Catherine guessed its meaning, and rose quickly from her chair.

"Aunt Penniman," she said, in a tone that scared her companion, "have you taken *the liberty* . . . ?"

"My dearest Catherine," stammered Mrs. Penniman, "just wait till you see him!"

Catherine had frightened her aunt, but she was also frightened herself; she was on the point of rushing to give orders to the servant, who was passing to the door, to admit no one; but the fear of meeting her visitor checked her.

"Mr. Morris Townsend."

This was what she heard, vaguely but recognisably articulated by the domestic, while she hesitated. She had her back turned to the door of the parlour, and for some moments she kept it turned, feeling that he had come in. He had not spoken, however, and at last she faced about. Then she saw a gentleman standing in the middle of the room, from which her aunt had discreetly retired.

She would never have known him. He was forty-five years old, and his figure was not that of the straight, slim young man she remembered. But it was a very fine person, and a fair and lustrous beard, spreading itself upon a well-presented chest, contributed to its effect. After a moment Catherine recognised the upper half of the face, which, though her visitor's clustering locks had grown thin, was still remarkably handsome. He stood in a deeply deferential attitude, with his eyes on her face. "I have ventured—I have ventured," he said; and then he paused, looking about him, as if he expected her to ask him to sit down. It was the old voice; but it had not the old charm. Catherine, for a minute, was conscious of a distinct determination not to invite him to take a seat. Why had he come? It was wrong for him to come. Morris was embarrassed, but Catherine gave him no help. It was not that she was glad of his embarrassment; on the contrary, it excited all her own liabilities of this kind, and gave her great pain. But how could she welcome him when she felt so vividly that he ought not to have come? "I wanted so much—I was determined," Morris went on. But he stopped again; it was not easy. Catherine still said nothing, and he may well have recalled with apprehension her ancient faculty of silence. She continued to look at him, however, and as she did so she made the strangest observation. It seemed to be he, and yet not he; it was the man who had been everything, and yet this person was nothing. How long ago it was—how old she had grown—how much she had lived! She had lived on something that was connected with *him*, and she had consumed it in doing so. This person did not look unhappy. He was fair and well-preserved, perfectly dressed, mature and complete. As Catherine looked at him, the story of his life defined itself in his eyes: he had made himself comfortable, and he had never been caught. But even while her perception opened itself to this, she had no desire to catch him; his presence was painful to her, and she only wished he would go.

"Will you not sit down?" he asked.

"I think we had better not," said Catherine.

"I offend you by coming?" He was very grave; he spoke in a tone of the richest respect.

"I don't think you ought to have come."

"Did not Mrs. Penniman tell you—did she not give you my message?"

"She told me something, but I did not understand."

"I wish you would let *me* tell you—let me speak for myself."

"I don't think it is necessary," said Catherine.

"Not for you, perhaps, but for me. It would be a great satisfaction—and I have not many." He seemed to be coming nearer; Catherine turned away. "Can we not be friends again?" he asked.

"We are not enemies," said Catherine. "I have none but friendly feelings to you."

"Ah, I wonder whether you know the happiness it gives me to hear you say that!" Catherine uttered no intimation that she measured the influence of her words; and he presently went on, "You have not changed—the years have passed happily for you."

"They have passed very quietly," said Catherine.

"They have left no marks; you are admirably young." This time he succeeded in coming nearer—he was close to her; she saw his glossy perfumed beard, and his eyes above it looking strange and hard. It was very different from his old—from his young—face. If she had first seen him this way she would not have liked him. It seemed to her that he was smiling, or trying to smile. "Catherine," he said, lowering his voice, "I have never ceased to think of you."

"Please don't say those things," she answered.

"Do you hate me?"

"Oh no," said Catherine.

Something in her tone discouraged him, but in a moment he recovered himself. "Have you still some kindness for me, then?"

"I don't know why you have come here to ask me such things!" Catherine exclaimed.

"Because for many years it has been the desire of my life that we should be friends again."

"That is impossible."

"Why so? Not if you will allow it."

"I will not allow it!" said Catherine.

He looked at her again in silence. "I see; my

presence troubles you and pains you. I will go away; but you must give me leave to come again."

"Please don't come again," she said.

"Never?—never?"

She made a great effort; she wished to say something that would make it impossible he should ever again cross her threshold. "It is wrong of you. There is no propriety in it—no reason for it."

"Ah, dearest lady, you do me injustice!" cried Morris Townsend. "We have only waited, and now we are free."

"You treated me badly," said Catherine.

"Not if you think of it rightly. You had your quiet life with your father—which was just what I could not make up my mind to rob you of."

"Yes; I had that."

Morris felt it to be a considerable damage to his cause that he could not add that she had had something more besides; for it is needless to say that he had learnt the contents of Doctor Sloper's will. He was nevertheless not at a loss. "There are worse fates than that!" he exclaimed with expression; and he might have been supposed to refer to his own unprotected situation. Then he added, with a deeper tenderness, "Catherine, have you never forgiven me?"

"I forgave you years ago, but it is useless for us to attempt to be friends."

"Not if we forget the past. We have still a future, thank God!"

"I can't forget—I don't forget," said Catherine. "You treated me too badly. I felt it very much; I felt it for years." And then she went on, with her wish to show him that he must not come to her this way, "I can't begin again—I can't take it up. Everything is dead and buried. It was too serious; it made a great change in my life. I never expected to see you here."

"Ah, you are angry!" cried Morris, who wished immensely that he could extort some flash of passion from her mildness. In that case he might hope.

"No, I am not angry. Anger does not last, that way, for years. But there are other things. Impressions last, when they have been strong.—But I can't talk."

Morris stood stroking his beard, with a clouded eye. "Why have you never married?" he asked abruptly. "You have had opportunities."

"I didn't wish to marry."

"Yes, you are rich, you are free; you had nothing to gain."

"I had nothing to gain," said Catherine.

Morris looked vaguely round him, and gave a deep sigh. "Well, I was in hopes that we might still have been friends."

"I meant to tell you, by my aunt, in answer to your message—if you had waited for an answer—that it was unnecessary for you to come in that hope."

"Good-bye, then," said Morris. "Excuse my indiscretion."

He bowed, and she turned away—standing there, averted, with her eyes on the ground, for some moments after she had heard him close the door of the room.

In the hall he found Mrs. Penniman, fluttered

and eager; she appeared to have been hovering there under the irreconcilable promptings of her curiosity and her dignity.

"That was a precious plan of yours!" said Morris, clapping on his hat.

"Is she so hard!" asked Mrs. Penniman.

"She doesn't care a button for me—with her confounded little dry manner."

"Was it very dry?" pursued Mrs. Penniman, with solicitude.

Morris took no notice of her question; he stood musing an instant, with his hat on. "But why the deuce, then, would she never marry?"

"Yes—why indeed?" sighed Mrs. Penniman. And then, as if from a sense of the inadequacy of this explanation, "But you will not despair—you will come back?"

"Come back? Damnation!" And Morris Townsend strode out of the house, leaving Mrs. Penniman staring.

Catherine, meanwhile, in the parlour, picking up her morsel of fancy-work, had seated herself with it again—for life, as it were.

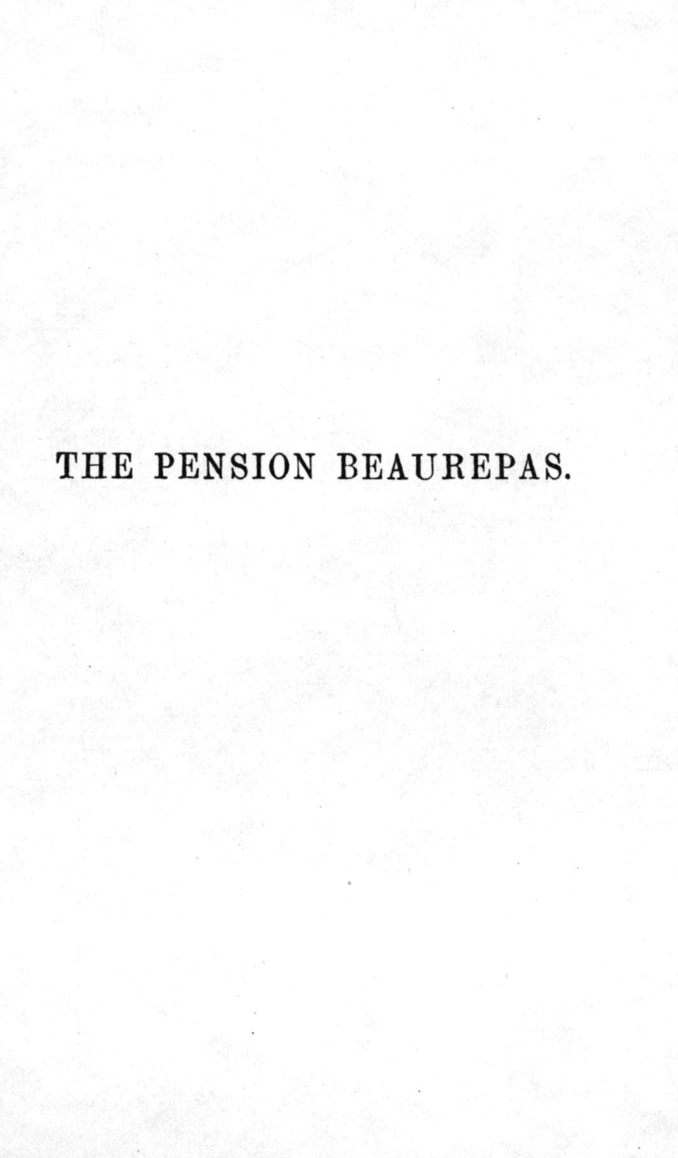

THE PENSION BEAUREPAS.

THE PENSION BEAUREPAS.

I.

I WAS not rich—on the contrary; and I had been told the Pension Beaurepas was cheap. I had, moreover, been told that a boarding-house is a capital place for the study of human nature. I had a fancy for a literary career, and a friend of mine had said to me, "If you mean to write you ought to go and live in a boarding-house; there is no other such place to pick up material." I had read something of this kind in a letter addressed by Stendhal to his sister: "I have a passionate desire to know human nature, and have a great mind to live in a boarding-house, where people cannot conceal their real characters." I was an admirer of *La Chartreuse de Parme,* and it appeared to me that one could not do better than follow in the footsteps of its author. I remembered, too, the magnificent boarding-house in Balzac's Père Goriot,—the "*pension bourgeoise des deux sexes et autres,*" kept by Madame Vauquer, *née* De Conflans. Magnificent, I mean, as a piece of portraiture; the establishment, as an establishment, was certainly sordid enough, and I hoped for better things from the Pension Beaurepas. This institution was one of the most esteemed in Geneva, and, standing in a little garden of its own, not far from the lake, had a very homely, comfortable, sociable aspect. The regular entrance was, as one might say, at the back, which looked upon the street, or rather upon a little *place*, adorned like every place in Geneva, great or small, with a fountain. This fact was not prepossessing, for on crossing the threshold you found yourself more or less in the kitchen, encompassed with culinary odours. This, however, was no great matter, for at the Pension Beaurepas there was no attempt at gentility or at concealment of the domestic machinery. The latter was of a very simple sort. Madame Beaurepas was an excellent little old woman—she was very far advanced in life, and had been keeping a pension for forty years—whose only faults were that she was slightly deaf, that she was fond of a surreptitious pinch of snuff, and that, at the age of seventy-three, she wore flowers in her cap. There was a tradition in the house that she was not so deaf as she pretended; that she feigned this infirmity in order to possess herself of the secrets of her lodgers. But I never subscribed to this theory; I am convinced that Madame Beaurepas had outlived the period of indiscreet curiosity. She was a philosopher, on a matter-of-fact basis; she had been having lodgers for forty years, and all that she asked of them was that they should pay their bills, make use of the door-mat, and fold their napkins. She cared very little for their secrets. "J'en ai vus de toutes les couleurs," she said to me. She had quite ceased to care for individuals; she cared only for types, for categories. Her large observation had made her acquainted with a great number, and her mind was a complete collection of "heads." She flattered herself that she knew at a glance where to pigeon-hole a new-comer, and if she made any mistakes her deportment never betrayed them. I think that, as regards individuals, she had neither likes nor dislikes; but she was capable of expressing esteem or contempt for a species. She had her own ways, I suppose, of manifesting her approval, but her manner of indicating the reverse was simple and unvarying. "Je trouve que c'est déplacé!"—this exhausted her view of the matter. If one of her inmates had put arsenic into the *pot-au-feu,* I believe Madame Beaurepas would have contented herself with remarking that the proceeding was out of place. The line of misconduct to which she most objected was an undue assumption of gentility; she had no patience with boarders who gave themselves airs. "When people come *chez moi,* it is not to cut a figure in the world; I have never had that illusion," I remember hearing her say; "and when you pay seven francs a day, *tout compris,* it comprises everything but the right to look down upon the others. But there are people who, the less they pay, the more they take themselves *au sérieux.* My most difficult boarders have always been those who have had the little rooms."

Madame Beaurepas had a niece, a young woman of some forty odd years; and the two ladies, with the assistance of a couple of thick-waisted, red-armed peasant women, kept the house going. If on your exits and entrances you peeped into the kitchen, it made very little difference; for Célestine, the cook, had no pretension to be an invisible functionary or to deal in occult methods. She was always at your service, with a grateful grin: she blacked your boots; she trudged off to fetch a cab; she would have carried your baggage, if you had allowed her, on her broad little back. She was always tramping in and out, between her kitchen and the fountain in the place, where it often seemed to me that a large part of the preparation for our dinner went forward—the wringing out of towels and table-cloths, the washing of potatoes and cabbages, the scouring of saucepans and cleansing of water-bottles. You enjoyed, from the door-step, a perpetual back view of Célestine and of her large, loose, woollen ankles, as she craned, from the waist, over into the fountain and dabbled in her various utensils. This sounds as if life went on in a very make-shift fashion at the Pension Beaurepas—as if the tone of the establishment were sordid. But such was not at all the case. We were simply very *bourgeois;* we practised the good old Genevese principle of not sacrificing to appearances. This is an excellent principle—when you have the reality. We had the reality at the Pension Beaurepas: we had it in the shape of soft, short beds, equipped with fluffy *duvets;* of admirable coffee, served to us in the morning by Célestine in person, as we lay recumbent on these downy couches; of copious, wholesome, succulent dinners, conformable to the best provincial traditions. For myself, I thought the Pension Beaurepas picturesque, and this, with me, at that time was a great word. I was young and ingenuous; I had just come from America. I wished to perfect myself in the French tongue, and I innocently believed that it flourished by Lake Leman. I used to go to lectures at the Academy, and come home with a violent appetite. I always enjoyed my morning walk across the long bridge (there was only one, just there, in those days) which spans the deep blue out-gush of the lake, and up the dark, steep streets of the old Calvinistic city. The garden faced this way, toward the lake and the old town; and this was the pleasantest approach to the house. There was a high wall, with a double gate in the middle, flanked by a couple of ancient massive posts; the big rusty *grille* contained some old-fashioned iron-work. The garden was rather mouldy and weedy, tangled and untended; but it contained a little thin-flowing fountain, several green benches, a rickety little table of the same complexion, and three orange-trees, in tubs, which were deposited as effectively as possible in front of the windows of the *salon*.

II.

As commonly happens in boarding-houses, the rustle of petticoats was, at the Pension Beaurepas, the most familiar form of the human tread. There was the usual allotment of economical widows and old maids, and to maintain the balance of the sexes there were only an old Frenchman and a young American. It hardly made the matter easier that the old Frenchman came from Lausanne. He was a native of that estimable town, but he had once spent six months in Paris, he had tasted of the tree of knowledge; he had got beyond Lausanne, whose resources he pronounced inadequate. Lausanne, as he said "*manquait d'agréments.*" When obliged, for reasons which he never specified, to bring his residence in Paris to a close, he had fallen back on Geneva; he had broken his fall at the Pension Beaurepas. Geneva was, after all, more like Paris, and at a Genevese boarding-house there was sure to be plenty of Americans with whom one could talk about the French metropolis. M. Pigeonneau was a little lean man, with a large, narrow nose, who sat a great deal in the garden, reading with the aid of a large magnifying glass a volume from the *cabinet de lecture.*

One day, a fortnight after my arrival at the

Pension Beaurepas, I came back rather earlier than usual from my academic session; it wanted half an hour of the midday breakfast. I went into the salon with the design of possessing myself of the day's *Galignani* before one of the little English old maids should have removed it to her virginal bower—a privilege to which Madame Beaurepas frequently alluded as one of the attractions of the establishment. In the salon I found a new-comer, a tall gentleman in a high black hat, whom I immediately recognised as a compatriot. I had often seen him, or his equivalent, in the hotel-parlours of my native land. He apparently supposed himself to be at the present moment in a hotel-parlour; his hat was on his head, or, rather, half off it—pushed back from his forehead, and rather suspended than poised. He stood before a table on which old newspapers were scattered, one of which he had taken up and, with his eye-glass on his nose, was holding out at arm's-length. It was that honourable but extremely diminutive sheet, the *Journal de Genève*, a newspaper of about the size of a pocket-handkerchief. As I drew near, looking for my *Galignani*, the tall gentleman gave me, over the top of his eye-glass, a somewhat solemn stare. Presently however, before I had time to lay my hand on the object of my search, he silently offered me the *Journal de Genève*.

"It appears," he said, "to be the paper of the country."

"Yes," I answered, "I believe it's the best,"

He gazed at it again, still holding it at arm's-length, as if it had been a looking-glass. "Well," he said, "I suppose it's natural a small country should have small papers. You could wrap it up, mountains and all, in one of our dailies!"

I found my *Galignani* and went off with it into the garden, where I seated myself on a bench in the shade. Presently I saw the tall gentleman in the hat appear in one of the open windows of the salon, and stand there with his hands in his pockets and his legs a little apart. He looked very much bored, and—I don't know why—I immediately began to feel sorry for him. He was not at all a picturesque personage; he looked like a jaded, faded man of business. But after a little he came into the garden and began to stroll about; and then his restless, unoccupied carriage, and the vague, unacquainted manner in which his eyes wandered over the place seemed to make it proper that, as an older resident, I should exercise a certain hospitality. I said something to him, and he came and sat down beside me on my bench, clasping one of his long knees in his hands.

"When is it this big breakfast of theirs comes off?" he inquired. "That's what I call it—the little breakfast and the big breakfast. I never thought I should live to see the time when I should care to eat two breakfasts. But a man's glad to do anything, over here."

"For myself," I observed, "I find plenty to do."

He turned his head and glanced at me with a dry, deliberate, kind-looking eye. "You're getting used to the life, are you?"

"I like the life very much," I answered, laughing.

"How long have you tried it?"

"Do you mean in this place?"

"Well, I mean anywhere. It seems to me pretty much the same all over."

"I have been in this house only a fortnight," I said.

"Well, what should you say, from what you have seen?" my companion asked.

"Oh," said I, "you can see all there is immediately. It's very simple."

"Sweet simplicity, eh? I'm afraid my two ladies will find it too simple."

"Everything is very good," I went on. "And Madame Beaurepas is a charming old woman. And then it's very cheap."

"Cheap, is it?" my friend repeated meditatively.

"Doesn't it strike you so?" I asked. I thought it very possible he had not inquired the terms. But he appeared not to have heard me; he sat there, clasping his knee and blinking, in a contemplative manner, at the sunshine.

"Are you from the United States, sir?" he presently demanded, turning his head again.

"Yes, sir," I replied; and I mentioned the place of my nativity.

"I presumed," he said, "that you were American or English. I'm from the United States myself; from New York city. Many of our people here?"

"Not so many as, I believe, there have sometimes been. There are two or three ladies."

"Well," my interlocutor declared, "I am very fond of ladies' society. I think when its superior there's nothing comes up to it. I've got two ladies here myself; I must make you acquainted with them."

I rejoined that I should be delighted, and I inquired of my friend whether he had been long in Europe.

"Well, it seems precious long," he said, "but my time's not up yet. We have been here fourteen weeks and a half."

"Are you travelling for pleasure?" I asked.

My companion turned his head again and looked at me—looked at me so long in silence that I at last also turned and met his eyes.

"No, sir," he said presently. "No, sir," he repeated, after a considerable interval.

"Excuse me," said I, for there was something so solemn in his tone that I feared I had been indiscreet.

He took no notice of my ejaculation; he simply continued to look at me. "I'm travelling," he said, at last, "to please the doctors. They seemed to think they would like it."

"Ah, they sent you abroad for your health?"

"They sent me abroad because they were so confoundedly muddled they didn't know what else to do."

"That's often the best thing," I ventured to remark.

"It was a confession of weakness; they wanted me to stop plaguing them. They didn't know enough to cure me, and that's the way they thought they would get round it. I wanted to be cured—I didn't want to be transported. I hadn't done any harm."

I assented to the general proposition of the inefficiency of doctors, and asked my companion if he had been seriously ill.

"I didn't sleep," he said, after some delay.

"Ah, that's very annoying. I suppose you were overworked."

"I didn't eat; I took no interest in my food."

"Well, I hope you both eat and sleep now," I said.

"I couldn't hold a pen," my neighbour went on. "I couldn't sit still. I couldn't walk from my house to the cars—and it's only a little way. I lost my interest in business."

"You needed a holiday," I observed.

"That's what the doctors said. It wasn't so very smart of them. I had been paying strict attention to business for twenty-three years."

"In all that time you have never had a holiday?" I exclaimed, with horror.

My companion waited a little. "Sundays," he said at last.

"No wonder, then, you were out of sorts."

"Well, sir," said my friend, "I shouldn't have been where I was three years ago if I had spent my time travelling round Europe. I was in a very advantageous position. I did a very large business. I was considerably interested in lumber." He paused, turned his head, and looked at me a moment. "Have you any business interests yourself?" I answered that I had none, and he went on again, slowly, softly, deliberately. "Well, sir, perhaps you are not aware that business in the United States is not what it was a short time since. Business interests are very insecure. There seems to be a general falling-off. Different parties offer different explanations of the fact, but so far as I am aware none of their observations have set things going again." I ingeniously intimated that if business was dull, the time was good for coming away; whereupon my neighbour threw back his head and stretched his legs a while. "Well, sir, that's one view of the matter certainly. There's something to be said for that. These things should be looked at all round. That's the ground my wife took. That's the ground," he added in a moment "that a lady would naturally take;" and he gave a little dry laugh.

"You think it's slightly illogical," I remarked.

"Well, sir, the ground I took was that the worse a man's business is, the more it requires looking after. I shouldn't want to go out to take a walk—not even to go to church—if my house was on fire. My firm is not doing the business it was; it's like a sick child, it requires nursing. What I wanted the doctors to do was to fix me up, so that I could go on at home. I'd have taken anything they'd have given me, and as many times a day. I wanted to be right there; I had my reasons; I have them still. But I came off, all the same," said my friend, with a melancholy smile.

I was a great deal younger than he, but there was something so simple and communicative in his tone, so expressive of a desire to fraternise, and so exempt from any theory of human differences, that I quite forgot his seniority, and found myself offering him paternal advice. "Don't think about all that," said I. "Simply enjoy yourself, amuse yourself, get well. Travel about and see Europe. At the end of a year, by the time you are ready to go home, things will have improved over there, and you will be quite well and happy."

My friend laid his hand on my knee; he looked at me for some moments, and I thought he was going to say, "You are very young!" But he said presently, "*You* have got used to Europe any way!"

III.

At breakfast I encountered his ladies—his wife and daughter. They were placed, however, at a distance from me, and it was not until the *pensionnaires* had dispersed, and some of them, according to custom, had come out into the garden, that he had an opportunity of making me acquainted with them.

"Will you allow me to introduce you to my daughter?" he said, moved apparently by a paternal inclination to provide this young lady with social diversion. She was standing with her mother, in one of the paths, looking about with no great complacency, as I imagined, at the homely characteristics of the place, and old M. Pigeonneau was hovering near, hesitating apparently between the desire to be urbane and the absence of a pretext. "Mrs. Ruck—Miss Sophy Ruck," said my friend, leading me up.

Mrs. Ruck was a large, plump, light coloured person, with a smooth fair face, a somnolent eye, and an elaborate coiffure. Miss Sophy was a girl of one and twenty, very small and very pretty—what I suppose would have been called a lively brunette. Both of these ladies were attired in black silk dresses, very much trimmed; they had an air of the highest elegance.

"Do you think highly of this pension?" inquired Mrs. Ruck, after a few preliminaries.

"It's a little rough, but it seems to me comfortable," I answered.

"Does it take a high rank in Geneva?" Mrs. Ruck pursued.

"I imagine it enjoys a very fair fame," I said, smiling.

"I should never dream of comparing it to a New York boarding-house," said Mrs. Ruck.

"It's quite a different style," her daughter observed. Miss Ruck had folded her arms; she was holding her elbows with a pair of white little hands, and she was tapping the ground with a pretty little foot.

"We hardly expected to come to a pension," said Mrs. Ruck. "But we thought we would try; we had heard so much about Swiss pensions. I was saying to Mr. Ruck that I wondered whether this was a favourable specimen. I was afraid we might have made a mistake."

"We knew some people who had been here; they thought everything of Madame Beaurepas," said Miss Sophy. "They said she was a real friend."

"Mr. and Mrs. Parker—perhaps you have heard her speak of them," Mrs. Ruck pursued.

"Madame Beaurepas has had a great many Americans; she is very fond of Americans," I replied.

"Well, I must say I should think she would be, if she compares them with some others."

"Mother is always comparing," observed Miss Ruck.

"Of course I am always comparing," rejoined the elder lady. "I never had a chance till now; I never knew my privileges. Give me an American!" And Mrs. Ruck indulged in a little laugh.

"Well, I must say there are some things I like over here," said Miss Sophy, with courage. And indeed I could see that she was a young woman of great decision.

"You like the shops—that's what you like," her father affirmed.

The young lady addressed herself to me, without heeding this remark. "I suppose you feel quite at home here."

"Oh, he likes it; he has got used to the life!" exclaimed Mr. Ruck.

"I wish you'd teach Mr. Ruck," said his wife. "It seems as if he couldn't get used to anything."

"I'm used to you, my dear," the husband retorted, giving me a humorous look.

"He's intensely restless," continued Mrs. Ruck. "That's what made me want to come to a pension. I thought he would settle down more."

"I don't think I *am* used to you, after all," said her husband.

In view of a possible exchange of conjugal repartee I took refuge in conversation with Miss Ruck, who seemed perfectly able to play her part in any colloquy. I learned from this young lady that, with her parents, after visiting the British islands, she had been spending a month in Paris, and that she thought she should have died when she left that city. "I hung out of the carriage, when we left the hotel," said Miss Ruck, "I assure you I did. And mother did, too."

"Out of the other window, I hope," said I.

"Yes, one out of each window," she replied, promptly. "Father had hard work, I can tell you. We hadn't half finished; there were ever so many places we wanted to go to."

"Your father insisted on coming away?"

"Yes; after we had been there about a month he said he had enough. He's fearfully restless; he's very much out of health. Mother and I said to him that if he was restless in Paris he needn't hope for peace anywhere. We don't mean to leave him alone till he takes us back." There was an air of keen resolution in Miss Ruck's pretty face, of lucid apprehension of desirable ends, which made me, as she pronounced these words, direct a glance of covert compassion toward her poor recalcitrant father. He had walked away a little with his wife, and I saw only his back and his stooping, patient-looking shoulders, whose air of acute resignation was thrown into relief by the voluminous tranquillity of Mrs. Ruck. "He will have to take us back in September, any way," the young girl pursued; "he will have to take us back to get some things we have ordered."

"Have you ordered a great many things?" I asked, jocosely.

"Well, I guess we have ordered *some*. Of course we wanted to take advantage of being in Paris—ladies always do. We have left the principal things till we go back. Of course that is the principal interest, for ladies. Mother said she should feel so shabby, if she just passed through. We have promised all the people to be back in September, and I never broke a promise yet. So Mr. Ruck has got to make his plans accordingly."

"And what are his plans?"

"I don't know; he doesn't seem able to make any. His great idea was to get to Geneva; but now that he has got here he doesn't seem to care. It's the effect of ill health. He used to be so bright; but now he is quite subdued. It's about time he should improve, any way. We went out last night to look at the jewellers' windows—in that street behind the hotel. I had always heard of those jewellers' windows. We saw some lovely things, but it didn't seem to rouse father. He'll get tired of Geneva sooner than he did of Paris."

"Ah," said I, "there are finer things here than the jewellers' windows. We are very near some of the most beautiful scenery in Europe."

"I suppose you mean the mountains. Well, we have seen plenty of mountains at home. We used to go to the mountains every summer. We are familiar enough with the mountains. Aren't we, mother?" the young lady demanded, appealing to Mrs. Ruck, who, with her husband, had drawn near again.

"Aren't we what?" inquired the elder lady.

"Aren't we familiar with the mountains?"

"Well, I hope so," said Mrs. Ruck.

Mr. Ruck, with his hands in his pockets, gave me a sociable wink. "There's nothing much you can tell them!" he said.

The two ladies stood face to face a few moments,

surveying each other's garments. "Don't you want to go out?" the young girl at last inquired of her mother.

"Well, I think we had better; we have got to go up to that place."

"To what place?" asked Mr. Ruck.

"To that jeweller's—to that big one."

"They all seemed big enough; they were too big!" And Mr. Ruck gave me another wink.

"That one where we saw the blue cross," said his daughter.

"Oh, come, what do you want of that blue cross?" poor Mr. Ruck demanded.

"She wants to hang it on a black velvet ribbon and tie it round her neck," said his wife.

"A black velvet ribbon? No, I thank you!" cried the young lady. "Do you suppose I would wear that cross on a black velvet ribbon? On a nice little gold chain, if you please—a little narrow gold chain, like an old-fashioned watch-chain. That's the proper thing for that blue cross. I know the sort of chain I mean; I'm going to look for one. When I want a thing," said Miss Ruck, with decision, "I can generally find it."

"Look here, Sophy," her father urged, "you don't want that blue cross."

"I do want it—I happen to want it." And Sophy glanced at me with a little laugh.

Her laugh, which in itself was pretty, suggested that there were various relations in which one might stand to Miss Ruck; but I think I was conscious of a certain satisfaction in not occupying the paternal one. "Don't worry the poor child," said her mother.

"Come on, mother," said Miss Ruck.

"We are going to look about a little," explained the elder lady to me, by way of taking leave.

"I know what that means," remarked Mr. Ruck, as his companions moved away. He stood looking at them a moment, while he raised his hand to his head, behind, and stood rubbing it a little, with a movement that displaced his hat. (I may remark in parenthesis that I never saw a hat more easily displaced than Mr. Ruck's.) I supposed he was going to say something querulous, but I was mistaken. Mr. Ruck was unhappy, but he was very good-natured. "Well, they want to pick up something," he said. "That's the principal interest, for ladies."

IV.

MR. RUCK distinguished me, as the French say. He honoured me with his esteem, and, as the days elapsed, with a large portion of his confidence. Sometimes he bored me a little, for the tone of his conversation was not cheerful, tending as it did almost exclusively to a melancholy dirge over the financial prostration of our common country. "No, sir, business in the United States is not what it once was," he found occasion to remark several times a day. "There's not the same spring—there's not the same hopeful feeling. You can see it in all departments." He used to sit by the hour in the little garden of the pension, with a roll of American newspapers in his lap and his high hat pushed back, swinging one of his long legs and reading the *New York Herald*. He paid a daily visit to the American banker's, on the other side of the Rhône, and remained there a long time, turning over the old papers on the green velvet table in the middle of the Salon des Étrangers and fraternising with chance compatriots. But in spite of these diversions his time hung heavily upon his hands. I used sometimes to propose to him to take a walk; but he had a mortal horror of pedestrianism, and regarded my own taste for it as a morbid form of activity. "You'll kill yourself, if you don't look out," he said, "walking all over the country. I don't want to walk round that way; I ain't a postman!" Briefly speaking, Mr. Ruck had few resources. His wife and daughter, on the other hand, it was to be supposed, were possessed of a good many that could not be apparent to an unobtrusive young man. They also sat a great deal in the garden or in the salon, side by side, with folded hands, contemplating material objects, and were remarkably independent of most of the usual feminine aids to idleness—light literature, tapestry, the use of the piano. They were, however, much fonder of locomotion than their companion, and I often met them in the Rue du Rhône and on the quays, loitering in front of the jewellers' windows. They might have had a cavalier in the person of old M. Pigeonneau, who possessed a high appreciation of their charms, but who, owing to the absence of a common idiom, was deprived of the pleasures of intimacy. He knew no English, and Mrs. Ruck and her daughter had, as it seemed, an incurable mistrust of the beautiful tongue which, as the old man endeavoured to impress upon them, was pre-eminently the language of conversation.

"They have a *tournure de princesse*—a *distinction supreme*," he said to me. "One is surprised to find them in a little pension, at seven francs a day."

"Oh, they don't come for economy," I answered. "They must be rich."

"They don't come for my *beaux yeux*—for mine,"

said M. Pigeonneau, sadly. "Perhaps it's for yours, young man. Je vous recommande la mère."

I reflected a moment. "They came on account of Mr. Ruck—because at hotels he's so restless."

M. Pigeonneau gave me a knowing nod. "Of course he is, with such a wife as that!—a *femme superbe.* Madame Ruck is preserved in perfection —a miraculous *fraîcheur.* I like those large, fair, quiet women; they are often, *dans l'intimité*, the most agreeable. I'll warrant you that at heart Madame Ruck is a finished coquette."

"I rather doubt it," I said.

"You suppose her cold? Ne vous y fiez pas!"

"It is a matter in which I have nothing at stake."

"You young Americans are droll," said M. Pigeonneau; "you never have anything at stake! But the little one, for example; I'll warrant you she's not cold. She is admirably made."

"She is very pretty."

"'She is very pretty!' Vous dites cela d'un ton! When you pay compliments to Mademoiselle Ruck, I hope that's not the way you do it."

"I don't pay compliments to Mademoiselle Ruck."

"Ah, decidedly," said M. Pigeonneau, "you young Americans are droll!"

I should have suspected that these two ladies would not especially commend themselves to Madame Beaurepas; that as a *maîtresse de salon,* which she in some degree aspired to be, she would have found them wanting in a certain flexibility of deportment. But I should have gone quite wrong; Madame Beaurepas had no fault at all to find with her new pensionnaires. "I have no observation whatever to make about them," she said to me one evening. "I see nothing in those ladies which is at all *déplacé*. They don't complain of anything; they don't meddle; they take what's given them; they leave me tranquil. The Americans are often like that. Often, but not always," Madame Beaurepas pursued. "We are to have a specimen to-morrow of a very different sort."

"An American?" I inquired.

"Two *Américaines*—a mother and a daughter. There are Americans and Americans: when you are *difficiles*, you are more so than any one, and when you have pretensions—ah, *par exemple*, it's serious. I foresee that with this little lady everything will be serious, beginning with her *café au lait*. She has been staying at the Pension Chamousset—my *concurrent*, you know, farther up the street; but she is coming away because the coffee is bad. She holds to her coffee, it appears. I don't know what liquid Madame Chamousset may have invented, but we will do the best we can for her. Only, I know she will make me *des histoires* about something else. She will demand a new lamp for the salon; *vous allez voir cela*. She wishes to pay but eleven francs a day for herself and her daughter, *tout compris*; and for their eleven francs they expect to be lodged like princesses. But she is very 'ladylike'—isn't that what you call it in English? Oh, *pour cela*, she is ladylike!"

I caught a glimpse on the morrow of this ladylike person, who was arriving at her new residence as I came in from a walk. She had come in a cab, with her daughter and her luggage; and, with an air of perfect softness and serenity, she was disputing the fare as she stood among her boxes, on the steps. She addressed her cabman in a very English accent, but with extreme precision and correctness. "I wish to be perfectly reasonable, but I don't wish to encourage you in exorbitant demands. With a franc and a half you are sufficiently paid. It is not the custom at Geneva to give a *pour-boire* for so short a drive. I have made inquiries, and I find it is not the custom, even in the best families. I am a stranger, yes, but I always adopt the custom of the native families. I think it my duty toward the natives."

"But I am a native, too, *moi!*" said the cabman, with an angry laugh.

"You seem to me to speak with a German accent," continued the lady. "You are probably from Basel. A franc and a half is sufficient. I see you have left behind the little red bag which I asked you to hold between your knees; you will please to go back to the other house and get it. Very well, if you are impolite I will make a complaint of you to-morrow at the administration. Aurora, you will find a pencil in the outer pocket of my embroidered satchel; please to write down his number,—87; do you see it distinctly?—in case we should forget it."

The young lady addressed as "Aurora"—a slight, fair girl, holding a large parcel of umbrellas—stood at hand while this allocution went forward, but she apparently gave no heed to it. She stood looking about her, in a listless manner, at the front of the house, at the corridor, at Célestine tucking up her apron in the door-way, at me as I passed in amid the disseminated luggage; her mother's parsimonious attitude seeming to produce in Miss Aurora neither sympathy nor embarrassment. At dinner the two ladies were placed on the same side of the table as myself, below Mrs. Ruck and her daughter, my own position being on the right of Mr. Ruck. I had therefore little observation of Mrs. Church—such I learned to be her name—but I occasionally heard her soft, distinct voice.

"White wine, if you please; we prefer white wine. There is none on the table? Then you will please to get some, and to remember to place a bottle of it always here, between my daughter and myself."

"That lady seems to know what she wants," said Mr. Ruck, "and she speaks so I can understand her. I can't understand every one, over here. I should like to make that lady's acquaintance. Perhaps she knows what *I* want, too; it seems hard to find out. But I don't want any of their sour white wine; that's one of the things I don't want. I expect she'll be an addition to the pension."

Mr. Ruck made the acquaintance of Mrs. Church that evening in the parlour, being presented to her by his wife, who presumed on the rights conferred upon herself by the mutual proximity, at table, of the two ladies. I suspected that in Mrs. Church's view Mrs. Ruck presumed too far. The fugitive from the Pension Chamousset, as M. Pigeonneau called her, was a little fresh, plump, comely woman, looking less than her age, with a round, bright, serious face. She was very simply and frugally dressed, not at all in the manner of Mr. Ruck's companions, and she had an air of quiet distinction which was an excellent defensive weapon. She exhibited a polite disposition to listen to what Mr. Ruck might have to say, but her manner was equivalent to an intimation that what she valued least in boarding-house life was its social opportunities. She had placed herself near a lamp, after carefully screwing it and turning it up, and she had opened in her lap, with the assistance of a large embroidered marker, an octavo volume, which I perceived to be in German. To Mrs. Ruck and her daughter she was evidently a puzzle, with her economical attire and her expensive culture. The two younger ladies, however, had begun to fraternise very freely, and Miss Ruck presently went wandering out of the room with her arm round the waist of Miss Church. It was a very warm evening; the long windows of the salon stood wide open into the garden, and, inspired by the balmy darkness, M. Pigeonneau and Mademoiselle Beaurepas, a most obliging little woman, who lisped and always wore a huge cravat, declared they would organise a *fête de nuit.* They engaged in this undertaking, and the fête developed itself, consisting of half a dozen red paper lanterns, hung about on the trees, and of several glasses of *sirop*, carried on a tray by the stout-armed Célestine. As the festival deepened to its climax I went out into the garden, where M. Pigeonneau was master of ceremonies.

"But where are those charming young ladies," he cried, "Miss Ruck and the new-comer, *l'aimable transfuge?* Their absence has been remarked, and they are wanting to the brilliancy of the occasion. *Voyez* I have selected a glass of syrup—a generous glass—for Mademoiselle Ruck, and I advise you, my young friend, if you wish to make a good impression, to put aside one which you may offer to the other young lady. What is her name? Miss Church. I see; it's a singular name. There is a church in which I would willingly worship!"

Mr. Ruck presently came out of the salon, having concluded his interview with Mrs. Church. Through the open window I saw the latter lady sitting under the lamp with her German octavo, while Mrs. Ruck, established, empty-handed, in an arm-chair near her, gazed at her with an air of fascination.

"Well, I told you she would know what I want," said Mr. Ruck. "She says I want to go up to Appenzell, wherever that is; that I want to drink whey and live in a high latitude—what did she call it?—a high altitude. She seemed to think we ought to leave for Appenzell to-morrow; she'd got it all fixed. She says this ain't a high enough lat—a high enough altitude. And she says I mustn't go too high, either; that would be just as bad; she seems to know just the right figure. She says she'll give me a list of the hotels where we must stop, on the way to Appenzell. I asked her if she didn't want to go with us, but she says she'd rather sit still and read. I expect she's a big reader."

The daughter of this accomplished woman now reappeared, in company with Miss Ruck, with whom she had been strolling through the outlying parts of the garden.

"Well," said Miss Ruck, glancing at the red paper lanterns, "are they trying to stick the flower-pots into the trees?"

"It's an illumination in honour of our arrival," the other young girl rejoined. "It's a triumph over Madame Chamousset."

"Meanwhile, at the Pension Chamousset," I ventured to suggest, "they have put out their lights; they are sitting in darkness, lamenting your departure."

She looked at me, smiling; she was standing in the light that came from the house. M. Pigeonneau, meanwhile, who had been awaiting his chance, advanced to Miss Ruck with his glass of syrup. "I have kept it for you, mademoiselle," he said; "I have jealously guarded it. It is very delicious!"

Miss Ruck looked at him and his syrup, without making any motion to take the glass. "Well, I guess it's sour," she said in a moment; and she gave a little shake of her head.

M. Pigeonneau stood staring, with his syrup in his hand; then he slowly turned away. He looked about at the rest of us, as if to appeal from Miss Ruck's insensibility, and went to deposit his rejected tribute on a bench.

"Won't you give it to me?" asked Miss Church, in faultless French. "J'adore le sirop, moi."

M. Pigeonneau came back with alacrity, and presented the glass with a very low bow. "I adore good manners," murmured the old man.

This incident caused me to look at Miss Church with quickened interest. She was not strikingly pretty, but in her charming, irregular face there was something brilliant and ardent. Like her mother, she was very simply dressed.

"She wants to go to America, and her mother

won't let her," said Miss Sophy to me, explaining her companion's situation.

"I am very sorry—for America," I answered, laughing.

"Well, I don't want to say anything against your mother, but I think it's shameful," Miss Ruck pursued.

"Mamma has very good reasons; she will tell you them all."

"Well, I'm sure I don't want to hear them," said Miss Ruck. "You have got a right to go to your own country; every one has a right to go to their own country."

"Mamma is not very patriotic," said Aurora Church, smiling.

"Well, I call that dreadful," her companion declared. "I have heard that there are some Americans like that, but I never believed it."

"There are all sorts of Americans," I said, laughing.

"Aurora's one of the right sort," rejoined Miss Ruck, who had apparently become very intimate with her new friend.

"Are you very patriotic?" I asked of the young girl.

"She's right down homesick," said Miss Sophy; "she's dying to go. If I were you my mother would have to take me."

"Mamma is going to take me to Dresden."

"Well, I declare I never heard of anything so dreadful!" cried Miss Ruck. "It's like something in a story."

"I never heard there was anything very dreadful in Dresden," I interposed.

Miss Ruck looked at me a moment. "Well, I don't believe *you* are a good American," she replied, "and I never supposed you were. You had better go in there and talk to Mrs. Church."

"Dresden is really very nice, isn't it?" I asked of her companion.

"It isn't nice if you happen to prefer New York," said Miss Sophy. "Miss Church prefers New York. Tell him you are dying to see New York; it will make him angry," she went on.

"I have no desire to make him angry," said Aurora, smiling.

"It is only Miss Ruck who can do that," I rejoined. "Have you been a long time in Europe?"

"Always."

"I call that wicked!" Miss Sophy declared.

"You might be in a worse place," I continued. "I find Europe very interesting."

Miss Ruck gave a little laugh. "I was saying that you wanted to pass for a European."

"Yes, I want to pass for a Dalmatian."

Miss Ruck looked at me a moment. "Well, you had better not come home," she said. "No one will speak to you."

"Were you born in these countries?" I asked of her companion.

"Oh, no; I came to Europe when I was a small child. But I remember America a little, and it seems delightful."

"Wait till you see it again. It's just too lovely," said Miss Sophy.

"It's the grandest country in the world," I added.

Miss Ruck began to toss her head. "Come away, my dear," she said. "If there's a creature I despise it's a man that tries to say funny things about his own country."

"Don't you think one can be tired of Europe?" Aurora asked, lingering.

"Possibly—after many years."

"Father was tired of it after three weeks," said Miss Ruck.

"I have been here sixteen years," her friend went on, looking at me with a charming intentness, as if she had a purpose in speaking. "It used to be for my education. I don't know what it's for now."

"She's beautifully educated," said Miss Ruck. "She knows four languages."

"I am not very sure that I know English."

"You should go to Boston!" cried Miss Sophy. "They speak splendidly in Boston."

"C'est mon rêve," said Aurora, still looking at me.

"Have you been all over Europe," I asked—"in all the different countries?"

She hesitated a moment. "Everywhere that there's a *pension*. Mamma is devoted to *pensions*. We have lived, at one time or another, in every *pension* in Europe."

"Well, I should think you had seen about enough," said Miss Ruck.

"It's a delightful way of seeing Europe," Aurora rejoined, with her brilliant smile. "You may imagine how it has attached me to the different countries. I have such charming souvenirs! There is a *pension* awaiting us now at Dresden,—eight francs a day, without wine. That's rather dear. Mamma means to make them give us wine. Mamma is a great authority on *pensions;* she is known, that way, all over Europe. Last winter we were in Italy, and she discovered one at Piacenza,—four francs a day. We made economies."

"Your mother doesn't seem to mingle much," observed Miss Ruck, glancing through the window at the scholastic attitude of Mrs. Church.

"No, she doesn't mingle, except in the native society. Though she lives in *pensions*, she detests them."

"Why does she live in them, then?" asked Miss Sophy, rather resentfully.

"Oh, because we are so poor; it's the cheapest way to live. We have tried having a cook, but the cook always steals. Mamma used to set me to watch her; that's the way I passed my *jeunesse*—my *belle jeunesse.* We are frightfully poor," the young girl went on, with the same strange frankness—a curious mixture of girlish grace and conscious cynicism. "Nous n'avons pas le sou. That's one of the reasons we don't go back to America; mamma says we can't afford to live there."

"Well, any one can see that you're an American girl," Miss Ruck remarked, in a consolatory manner. "I can tell an American girl a mile off. You've got the American style."

"I'm afraid I haven't the American *toilette,*" said Aurora, looking at the other's superior splendour.

"Well, your dress was cut in France; any one can see that."

"Yes," said Aurora, with a laugh, "my dress was cut in France—at Avranches."

"Well, you've got a lovely figure, any way," pursued her companion.

"Ah," said the young girl, "at Avranches, too, my figure was admired." And she looked at me askance, with a certain coquetry. But I was an innocent youth, and I only looked back at her, wondering. She was a great deal nicer than Miss Ruck, and yet Miss Ruck would not have said that. "I try to be like an American girl," she continued; "I do my best, though mamma doesn't at all encourage it. I am very patriotic. I try to copy them, though mamma has brought me up *à la française;* that is, as much as one can in *pensions.* For instance, I have never been out of the house without mamma; oh, never, never. But sometimes I despair; American girls are so wonderfully frank. I can't be frank, like that. I am always afraid. But I do what I can, as you see. Excusez du peu!"

I thought this young lady at least as outspoken as most of her unexpatriated sisters; there was something almost comical in her despondency. But she had by no means caught, as it seemed to me, the American tone. Whatever her tone was, however, it had a fascination; there was something dainty about it, and yet it was decidedly audacious.

The young ladies began to stroll about the garden again, and I enjoyed their society until M. Pigeonneau's festival came to an end.

V

Mr. Ruck did not take his departure for Appenzell on the morrow, in spite of the eagerness to witness such an event which he had attributed to Mrs. Church. He continued, on the contrary, for many days after, to hang about the garden, to wander up to the banker's and back again, to engage in desultory conversation with his fellow-boarders, and to endeavour to assuage his constitutional restlessness by perusal of the American journals. But on the morrow I had the honour of making Mrs. Church's acquaintance. She came into the salon, after the midday breakfast, with her German octavo under her arm, and she appealed to me for assistance in selecting a quiet corner.

"Would you very kindly," she said, "move that large fauteuil a little more this way? Not the largest; the one with the little cushion. The fauteuils here are very insufficient; I must ask Madame Beaurepas for another. Thank you; a little more to the left, please; that will do. Are you particularly engaged?" she inquired, after she had seated herself. "If not, I should like to have some conversation with you. It is some time since I have met a young American of your—what shall

I call it?—your affiliations. I have learned your name from Madame Beaurepas; I think I used to know some of your people. I don't know what has become of all my friends. I used to have a charming little circle at home, but now I meet no one I know. Don't you think there is a great difference between the people one meets and the people one would like to meet? Fortunately, sometimes," added my interlocutress graciously, "it's quite the same. I suppose you are a specimen, a favourable specimen," she went on, "of young America. Tell me, now, what is young America thinking of in these days of ours? What are its feelings, its opinions, its aspirations? What is its *ideal?*" I had seated myself near Mrs. Church, and she had pointed this interrogation with the gaze of her bright little eyes. I felt it embarrassing to be treated as a favourable specimen of young America, and to be expected to answer for the great republic. Observing my hesitation, Mrs. Church clasped her hands on the open page of her book and gave an intense, melancholy smile. "*Has* it an ideal?" she softly asked. "Well, we must talk of this," she went on, without insisting. "Speak, for the present, for yourself simply. Have you come to Europe with any special design?"

"Nothing to boast of," I said. "I am studying a little."

"Ah, I am glad to hear that. You are gathering up a little European culture; that's what we lack, you know, at home. No individual can do much, of course. But you must not be discouraged; every little counts."

"I see that you, at least, are doing your part," I

rejoined gallantly, dropping my eyes on my companion's learned volume.

"Yes, I frankly admit that I am fond of study. There is no one, after all, like the Germans. That is, for facts. For opinions I by no means always go with them. I form my opinions myself. I am sorry to say, however," Mrs. Church continued, "that I can hardly pretend to diffuse my acquisitions. I am afraid I am sadly selfish; I do little to irrigate the soil. I belong—I frankly confess it—to the class of absentees."

"I had the pleasure, last evening," I said, "of making the acquaintance of your daughter. She told me you had been a long time in Europe."

Mrs. Church smiled benignantly. "Can one ever be too long? We shall never leave it."

"Your daughter won't like that," I said, smiling too.

"Has she been taking you into her confidence? She is a more sensible young lady than she sometimes appears. I have taken great pains with her; she is really—I may be permitted to say it—superbly educated."

"She seemed to me a very charming girl," I rejoined. "And I learned that she speaks four languages."

"It is not only that," said Mrs. Church, in a tone which suggested that this might be a very superficial species of culture. "She has made what we call *de fortes études*—such as I suppose you are making now. She is familiar with the results of modern science; she keeps pace with the new historical school."

"Ah," said I, "she has gone much farther than I!"

"You doubtless think I exaggerate, and you force me, therefore, to mention the fact that I am able to speak of such matters with a certain intelligence."

'That is very evident," I said. "But your daughter thinks you ought to take her home." I began to fear, as soon as I had uttered these words, that they savoured of treachery to the young lady, but I was reassured by seeing that they produced on her mother's placid countenance no symptom whatever of irritation.

"My daughter has her little theories," Mrs. Church observed; "she has, I may say, her illusions. And what wonder! What would youth be without its illusions? Aurora has a theory that she would be happier in New York, in Boston, in Philadelphia, than in one of the charming old cities in which our lot is cast. But she is mistaken, that is all. We must allow our children their illusions, must we not? But we must watch over them."

Although she herself seemed proof against discomposure, I found something vaguely irritating in her soft, sweet positiveness.

"American cities," I said, "are the paradise of young girls."

"Do you mean," asked Mrs. Church, "that the young girls who come from those places are angels?"

"Yes," I said, resolutely.

"This young lady—what is her odd name?—with whom my daughter has formed a somewhat precipitate acquaintance: is Miss Ruck an angel? But I won't force you to say anything uncivil. It would be too cruel to make a single exception."

"Well," said I, "at any rate, in America young girls have an easier lot. They have much more liberty."

My companion laid her hand for an instant on my arm. "My dear young friend, I know America, I know the conditions of life there, so well. There is perhaps no subject on which I have reflected more than on our national idiosyncrasies."

"I am afraid you don't approve of them," said I, a little brutally.

Brutal indeed my proposition was, and Mrs. Church was not prepared to assent to it in this rough shape. She dropped her eyes on her book, with an air of acute meditation. Then, raising them, "We are very crude," she softly observed—"we are very crude." Lest even this delicately-uttered statement should seem to savour of the vice that she deprecated, she went on to explain. "There are two classes of minds, you know—those that hold back, and those that push forward. My daughter and I are not pushers; we move with little steps. We like the old, trodden paths; we like the old, old world."

"Ah," said I, "you know what you like; there is a great virtue in that."

"Yes, we like Europe; we prefer it. We like the opportunities of Europe; we like the *rest*. There is so much in that, you know. The world seems to me to be hurrying, pressing forward so fiercely, without knowing where it is going. 'Whither?' I often ask, in my little quiet way. But I have yet to learn that any one can tell me."

"You're a great conservative," I observed, while

I wondered whether I myself could answer this inquiry.

Mrs. Church gave me a smile which was equivalent to a confession. "I wish to retain a *little*—just a little. Surely, we have done so much, we might rest a while; we might pause. That is all my feeling—just to stop a little, to wait! I have seen so many changes. I wish to draw in, to draw in—to hold back, to hold back."

"You shouldn't hold your daughter back!" I answered, laughing and getting up. I got up, not by way of terminating our interview, for I perceived Mrs. Church's exposition of her views to be by no means complete, but in order to offer a chair to Miss Aurora, who at this moment drew near. She thanked me and remained standing, but without at first, as I noticed, meeting her mother's eye.

"You have been engaged with your new acquaintance, my dear?" this lady inquired.

"Yes, mamma dear," said the young girl, gently.

"Do you find her very edifying?"

Aurora was silent a moment; then she looked at her mother. "I don't know, mamma; she is very fresh."

I ventured to indulge in a respectful laugh. "Your mother has another word for that. But I must not," I added, "be crude."

"Ah, vous m'en voulez?" inquired Mrs. Church. "And yet I can't pretend I said it in jest. I feel it too much. We have been having a little social discussion," she said to her daughter. "There is still so much to be said. And I wish," she continued, turning to me, "that I could give you our point of view. Don't you wish, Aurora, that we could give him our point of view?"

"Yes, mamma," said Aurora.

"We consider ourselves very fortunate in our point of view, don't we dearest?" mamma demanded.

"Very fortunate, indeed, mamma."

"You see we have acquired an insight into European life," the elder lady pursued. "We have our place at many a European fireside. We find so much to esteem—so much to enjoy. Do we not, my daughter?"

"So very much, mamma," the young girl went on, with a sort of inscrutable submissiveness. I wondered at it; it offered so strange a contrast to the mocking freedom of her tone the night before; but while I wondered I was careful not to let my perplexity take precedence of my good manners.

"I don't know what you ladies may have found at European firesides," I said, "but there can be very little doubt what you have left there."

Mrs. Church got up, to acknowledge my compliment. "We have spent some charming hours. And that reminds me that we have just now such an occasion in prospect. We are to call upon some Genevese friends—the family of the Pasteur Galopin. They are to go with us to the old library at the Hôtel de Ville, where there are some very interesting documents of the period of the Reformation; we are promised a glimpse of some manuscripts of poor Servetus, the antagonist and victim, you know, of Calvin. Here, of course, one can only speak of Calvin under one's breath, but some day, when we are more private," and Mrs. Church looked round the room, "I will give you my view of him. I think it has a touch of originality. Aurora is familiar with, are you not, my daughter, familiar with my view of Calvin?"

"Yes, mamma," said Aurora, with docility, while the two ladies went to prepare for their visit to the Pasteur Galopin.

VI.

"SHE has demanded a new lamp; I told you she would!" This communication was made me by Madame Beaurepas a couple of days later. "And she has asked for a new *tapis de lit*, and she has requested me to provide Célestine with a pair of light shoes. I told her that, as a general thing, cooks are not shod with satin. That poor Célestine!"

"Mrs. Church may be exacting," I said, "but she is a clever little woman."

"A lady who pays but five francs and a half shouldn't be too clever. C'est déplacé. I don't like the type."

"What type do you call Mrs. Church's?'

"Mon Dieu," said Madame Beaurepas, "c'est une de ces mamans comme vous en avez, qui promènent leur fille."

"She is trying to marry her daughter? I don't think she's of that sort."

But Madame Beaurepas shrewdly held to her idea. "She is trying it in her own way; she does it very quietly. She doesn't want an American; she wants a foreigner. And she wants a *mari sérieux*. But she is travelling over Europe in search of one. She would like a magistrate."

"A magistrate?"

"A *gros bonnet* of some kind; a professor or a deputy."

"I am very sorry for the poor girl," I said, laughing.

"You needn't pity her too much; she's a sly thing."

"Ah, for that, no!" I exclaimed. "She's a charming girl."

Madame Beaurepas gave an elderly grin. "She has hooked you, eh? But the mother won't have you."

I developed my idea, without heeding this insinuation. "She's a charming girl, but she is a little odd. It's a necessity of her position. She is less submissive to her mother than she has to pretend to be. That's in self-defence; it's to make her life possible."

"She wishes to get away from her mother," continued Madame Beaurepas. "She wishes to *courir les champs*."

"She wishes to go to America, her native country."

"Precisely. And she will certainly go."

"I hope so!" I rejoined.

"Some fine morning—or evening—she will go off with a young man; probably with a young American."

"Allons donc!" said I, with disgust.

"That will be quite America enough," pursued my cynical hostess. "I have kept a boarding-house for forty years. I have seen that type."

"Have such things as that happened *chez vous?*" I asked.

"Everything has happened *chez moi*. But nothing has happened more than once. Therefore this won't happen here. It will be at the next place they go to, or the next. Besides, here there is no young American *pour la partie*—none except you, monsieur. You are susceptible, but you are too reasonable."

"It's lucky for you I am reasonable," I answered. "It's thanks to that fact that you escape a scolding!"

One morning, about this time, instead of coming back to breakfast at the *pension*, after my lectures at the Academy, I went to partake of this meal with a fellow-student, at an ancient eating-house in the collegiate quarter. On separating from my friend, I took my way along that charming public walk known in Geneva as the Treille, a shady terrace, of immense elevation, overhanging a portion of the lower town. There are spreading trees and well-worn benches, and over the tiles and chimneys of the *ville basse* there is a view of the snow-crested Alps. On the other side, as you turn your back to the view, the promenade is overlooked by a row of tall, sober-faced *hôtels*, the dwellings of the local aristocracy. I was very fond of the place, and often resorted to it to stimulate my sense of the picturesque. Presently, as I lingered there on this occasion, I became aware that a gentleman was seated not far from where I stood, with his back to the Alpine chain, which this morning was brilliant and distinct, and a newspaper, unfolded, in his lap. He was not reading, however; he was staring before him in gloomy contemplation. I don't know whether I recognised first the newspaper or its proprietor; one, in either case, would have helped me to identify the other. One was the *New York Herald*; the other, of course, was Mr. Ruck. As I drew nearer, he transferred his eyes from the stony, high-featured masks of the gray old houses on the other side of the terrace, and I knew by the expression of his face just how he had been feeling about these distinguished abodes. He had made up his mind that their proprietors were a dusky, narrow-minded, unsociable company; plunging their roots into a superfluous past. I endeavoured, therefore, as I sat down beside him, to suggest something more impersonal.

"That's a beautiful view of the Alps," I observed.

"Yes," said Mr. Ruck, without moving, "I've examined it. Fine thing, in its way—fine thing. Beauties of nature—that sort of thing. We came up on purpose to look at it."

"Your ladies, then, have been with you?"

"Yes; they are just walking round. They're awfully restless. They keep saying I'm restless, but I'm as quiet as a sleeping child to them. It takes," he added in a moment, drily, "the form of shopping."

"Are they shopping now?"

"Well, if they ain't, they're trying to. They told me to sit here a while, and they'd just walk round. I generally know what that means. But that's the principal interest for ladies," he added, retracting his irony. "We thought we'd come up here and see the cathedral; Mrs. Church seemed to think it a dead loss that we shouldn't see the cathedral, especially as we hadn't seen many yet. And I had to come up to the banker's any way. Well, we certainly saw the cathedral. I don't know as we are any the better for it, and I don't know as I should know it again. But we saw it, any way. I don't know as I should want to go there regularly; but I suppose it will give us, in conversation, a kind of hold on Mrs. Church, eh? I guess we want something of that kind. Well," Mr. Ruck continued, "I stepped in at the banker's to see if there wasn't something, and they handed me out a Herald."

"I hope the Herald is full of good news," I said.

"Can't say it is. D—d bad news."

"Political," I inquired, "or commercial?"

"Oh, hang politics! It's business, sir. There ain't any business. It's all gone to,"—and Mr. Ruck became profane. "Nine failures in one day. What do you say to that?"

"I hope they haven't injured you," I said.

"Well, they haven't helped me much. So many houses on fire, that's all. If they happen to take place in your own street, they don't increase the value of your property. When mine catches, I suppose they'll write and tell me—one of these days, when they've got nothing else to do. I didn't get a blessed letter this morning; I suppose they think I'm having such a good time over here it's a pity to disturb me. If I could attend to business for about half an hour, I'd find out something. But I can't, and it's no use talking. The state of my health was never so unsatisfactory as it was about five o'clock this morning."

"I am very sorry to hear that," I said, "and I recommend you strongly not to think of business."

"I don't," Mr. Ruck replied. "I'm thinking of cathedrals; I'm thinking of the beauties of nature. Come," he went on, turning round on the bench and leaning his elbow on the parapet, "I'll think of those mountains over there; they *are* pretty, certainly Can't you get over there?"

"Over where?"

"Over to those hills. Don't they run a train right up?"

"You can go to Chamouni," I said. "You can go to Grindelwald and Zermatt and fifty other places. You can't go by rail, but you can drive."

"All right, we'll drive—and not in a one-horse concern, either. Yes, Chamouni is one of the places we put down. I hope there are a few nice shops in Chamouni." Mr. Ruck spoke with a certain quickened emphasis, and in a tone more explicitly humorous than he commonly employed. I thought he was excited, and yet he had not the appearance of excitement. He looked like a man who has simply taken, in the face of disaster, a sudden, somewhat imaginative, resolution not to "worry." He presently twisted himself about on his bench again and began to watch for his companions. "Well, they *are* walking round," he resumed; "I guess they've hit on something, somewhere. And they've got a carriage waiting outside of that archway, too. They seem to do a big business in archways here, don't they. They like to have a carriage to carry home the things—those ladies of mine. Then they're sure they've got them." The ladies, after this, to do them justice, were not very long in appearing. They came toward us, from under the archway to which Mr. Ruck had somewhat invidiously alluded, slowly and with a rather exhausted step and expression. My companion looked at them a moment, as they advanced. "They're tired," he said softly. "When they're tired, like that, it's very expensive."

"Well," said Mrs. Ruck, "I'm glad you've had some company." Her husband looked at her, in silence, through narrowed eyelids, and I suspected that this gracious observation on the lady's part was prompted by a restless conscience.

Miss Sophy glanced at me with her little straightforward air of defiance. "It would have been more proper if *we* had had the company. Why didn't you come after us, instead of sitting there?" she asked of Mr. Ruck's companion.

"I was told by your father," I explained, "that you were engaged in sacred rites." Miss Ruck was not gracious, though I doubt whether it was because her conscience was better than her mother's.

"Well, for a gentleman there is nothing so sacred as ladies' society," replied Miss Ruck, in the manner of a person accustomed to giving neat retorts.

"I suppose you refer to the cathedral," said her mother. "Well, I must say, we didn't go back there. I don't know what it may be of a Sunday, but it gave me a chill."

"We discovered the loveliest little lace-shop," observed the young girl, with a serenity that was superior to bravado.

Her father looked at her a while; then turned about again, leaning on the parapet, and gazed away at the "hills."

"Well, it was certainly cheap," said Mrs. Ruck, also contemplating the Alps.

"We are going to Chamouni," said her husband. "You haven't any occasion for lace at Chamouni."

"Well, I'm glad to hear you have decided to go somewhere," rejoined his wife. "I don't want to be a fixture at a boarding-house."

"You can wear lace anywhere," said Miss Ruck, "if you put it on right. That's the great thing, with lace. I don't think they know how to wear lace in Europe. I know how I mean to wear mine; but I mean to keep it till I get home."

Her father transferred his melancholy gaze to her elaborately-appointed little person; there was a great deal of very new-looking detail in Miss Ruck's appearance. Then, in a tone of voice quite out of consonance with his facial despondency, "Have you purchased a great deal?" he inquired.

"I have purchased enough for you to make a fuss about."

"He can't make a fuss about that," said Mrs. Ruck.

"Well, you'll see!" declared the young girl with a little sharp laugh.

But her father went on, in the same tone: "Have you got it in your pocket? Why don't you put it on—why don't you hang it round you?"

"I'll hang it round *you*, if you don't look out!" cried Miss Sophy.

"Don't you want to show it to this gentleman?" Mr. Ruck continued.

"Mercy, how you do talk about that lace?" said his wife.

"Well, I want to be lively. There's every reason for it; we're going to Chamouni."

"You're restless; that's what's the matter with you." And Mrs. Ruck got up.

"No, I ain't," said her husband. "I never felt so quiet; I feel as peaceful as a little child."

Mrs. Ruck, who had no sense whatever of humour, looked at her daughter and at me. "Well, I hope you'll improve," she said.

"Send in the bills," Mr. Ruck went on, rising to his feet. "Don't hesitate, Sophy. I don't care what you do now. In for a penny, in for a pound."

Miss Ruck joined her mother, with a little toss of her head, and we followed the ladies to the carriage. "In your place," said Miss Sophy to her father, "I wouldn't talk so much about pennies and pounds before strangers."

Poor Mr. Ruck appeared to feel the force of this observation, which, in the consciousness of a man who had never been "mean," could hardly fail to strike a responsive chord. He coloured a little, and he was silent; his companions got into their vehicle, the front seat of which was adorned with a large parcel. Mr. Ruck gave the parcel a little poke with his umbrella, and then, turning to me with a rather grimly penitential smile, "After all," he said, "for the ladies that's the principal interest."

VII.

Old M. Pigeonneau had more than once proposed to me to take a walk, but I had hitherto been unable to respond to so alluring an invitation. It befell, however, one afternoon, that I perceived him going forth upon a desultory stroll, with a certain lonesomeness of demeanour that attracted my sympathy. I hastily overtook him, and passed my hand into his venerable arm, a proceeding which produced in the good old man so jovial a sense of comradeship that he ardently proposed we should bend our steps to the English Garden; no locality less festive was worthy of the occasion. To the English Garden, accordingly, we went; it lay beyond the bridge, beside the lake. It was very pretty and very animated; there was a band playing in the middle, and a considerable number of persons sitting under the small trees, on benches and little chairs, or strolling beside the blue water. We joined the strollers, we observed our companions, and conversed on obvious topics. Some of these last, of course, were the pretty women who embellished the scene, and who, in the light of M. Pigeonneau's comprehensive criticism, appeared surprisingly numerous. He seemed bent upon our making up our minds as to which was the prettiest, and as this was an innocent game I consented to play at it.

Suddenly M. Pigeonneau stopped, pressing my arm with the liveliest emotion. "La voilà, la voilà, the prettiest!" he quickly murmured, "coming toward us, in a blue dress, with the other." It was at the other I was looking, for the other, to my surprise, was our interesting fellow-pensioner, the daughter of a vigilant mother. M. Pigeonneau, meanwhile, had redoubled his exclamations; he had recognised Miss Sophy Ruck. "Oh, la belle rencontre, nos aimables convives; the prettiest girl in the world, in effect!"

We immediately greeted and joined the young ladies, who, like ourselves, were walking arm in arm and enjoying the scene.

"I was citing you with admiration to my friend, even before I had recognised you," said M. Pigeonneau to Miss Ruck.

"I don't believe in French compliments," remarked this young lady, presenting her back to the smiling old man.

"Are you and Miss Ruck walking alone?" I asked of her companion. "You had better accept of M. Pigeonneau's gallant protection, and of mine."

Aurora Church had taken her hand out of Miss Ruck's arm; she looked at me, smiling, with her head a little inclined, while, upon her shoulder, she made her open parasol revolve. "Which is most improper,—to walk alone or to walk with gentlemen? I wish to do what is most improper."

"What mysterious logic governs your conduct?" I inquired.

"He thinks you can't understand him when he talks like that," said Miss Ruck. "But I do understand you, always!"

"So I have always ventured to hope, my dear Miss Ruck."

"Well, if I didn't, it wouldn't be much loss," rejoined this young lady.

"Allons, en marche!" cried M. Pigeonneau, smiling still, and undiscouraged by her inhumanity. "Let us make together the tour of the garden." And he imposed his society upon Miss Ruck with a respectful, elderly grace which was evidently unable to see anything in her reluctance but modesty, and was sublimely conscious of a mission to place modesty at its ease. This ill-assorted couple walked in front, while Aurora Church and I strolled along together.

"I am sure this is more improper," said my companion; "this is delightfully improper. I don't say that as a compliment to you," she added. "I would say it to any man, no matter how stupid."

"Oh, I am very stupid," I answered, "but this doesn't seem to me wrong."

"Not for you, no; only for me. There is nothing that a man can do that is wrong, is there? *En morale,* you know, I mean. Ah, yes, he can steal; but I think there is nothing else, is there?"

"I don't know. One doesn't know those things until after one has done them. Then one is enlightened."

"And you mean that you have never been

enlightened? You make yourself out very good."

"That is better than making one's self out bad, as you do."

The young girl glanced at me a moment, and then, with her charming smile, "That's one of the consequences of a false position."

"Is your position false?" I inquired, smiling too at this large formula.

"Distinctly so."

"In what way?"

"Oh, in every way. For instance, I have to pretend to be a *jeune fille*. I am not a jeune fille; no American girl is a jeune fille; an American girl is an intelligent, responsible creature. I have to pretend to be very innocent, but I am not very innocent."

"You don't pretend to be very innocent; you pretend to be—what shall I call it?—very wise."

"That's no pretence. I am wise."

"You are not an American girl," I ventured to observe.

My companion almost stopped, looking at me; there was a little flush in her cheek. "Voilà!" she said. "There's my false position. I want to be an American girl, and I'm not."

"Do you want me to tell you?" I went on. "An American girl wouldn't talk as you are talking now."

"Please tell me," said Aurora Church, with expressive eagerness. "How would she talk?"

"I can't tell you all the things an American girl would say, but I think I can tell you the things she wouldn't say. She wouldn't reason out her conduct, as you seem to me to do."

Aurora gave me the most flattering attention. "I see. She would be simpler. To do very simple things that are not at all simple—that is the American girl!"

I permitted myself a small explosion of hilarity. "I don't know whether you are a French girl, or what you are," I said, "but you are very witty."

"Ah, you mean that I strike false notes!" cried Aurora Church, sadly. "That's just what I want to avoid. I wish you would always tell me."

The conversational union between Miss Ruck and her neighbour, in front of us, had evidently not become a close one. The young lady suddenly turned round to us with a question: "Don't you want some ice cream?"

"*She* doesn't strike false notes," I murmured.

There was a kind of pavilion or kiosk, which served as a café, and at which the delicacies procurable at such an establishment were dispensed. Miss Ruck pointed to the little green tables and chairs which were set out on the gravel; M. Pigeonneau, fluttering with a sense of dissipation, seconded the proposal, and we presently sat down and gave our order to a nimble attendant. I managed again to place myself next to Aurora Church; our companions were on the other side of the table.

My neighbour was delighted with our situation. "This is best of all," she said. "I never believed I should come to a café with two strange men! Now, you can't persuade me this isn't wrong."

"To make it wrong we ought to see your mother coming down that path."

"Ah, my mother makes everything wrong," said the young girl, attacking with a little spoon in the shape of a spade the apex of a pink ice. And then she returned to her idea of a moment before: "You must promise to tell me—to warn me in some way—whenever I strike a false note. You must give a little cough, like that—ahem!"

"You will keep me very busy, and people will think I am in a consumption."

"*Voyons*," she continued, "why have you never talked to me more? Is that a false note? Why haven't you been 'attentive?' That's what American girls call it; that's what Miss Ruck calls it."

I assured myself that our companions were out of ear-shot, and that Miss Ruck was much occupied with a large vanilla cream. "Because you are always entwined with that young lady. There is no getting near you."

Aurora looked at her friend while the latter devoted herself to her ice. "You wonder why I like her so much, I suppose. So does mamma; elle s'y perd. I don't like her particularly; je n'en suis pas folle. But she gives me information; she tells me about America. Mamma has always tried to prevent my knowing anything about it, and I am all the more curious. And then Miss Ruck is very fresh."

"I may not be so fresh as Miss Ruck," I said, "but in future, when you want information, I recommend you to come to me for it."

"Our friend offers to take me to America; she

invites me to go back with her, to stay with her. You couldn't do that, could you?" And the young girl looked at me a moment. "*Bon*, a false note! I can see it by your face; you remind me of a *maître de piano*."

"You overdo the character—the poor American girl," I said. "Are you going to stay with that delightful family?"

"I will go and stay with any one that will take me or ask me. It's a real *nostalgie*. She says that in New York—in Thirty-Seventh Street—I should have the most lovely time."

"I have no doubt you would enjoy it."

"Absolute liberty to begin with."

"It seems to me you have a certain liberty here," I rejoined.

"Ah, *this?* Oh, I shall pay for this. I shall be punished by mamma, and I shall be lectured by Madame Galopin."

"The wife of the pasteur?"

"His *digne épouse*. Madame Galopin, for mamma, is the incarnation of European opinion. That's what vexes me with mamma, her thinking so much of people like Madame Galopin. Going to see Madame Galopin—mamma calls that being in European society. European society! I'm so sick of that expression; I have heard it since I was six years old. Who is Madame Galopin—who thinks anything of her here? She is nobody; she is perfectly third-rate. If I like America better than mamma, I also know Europe better."

"But your mother, certainly," I objected, a trifle timidly, for my young lady was excited, and had a charming little passion in her eye—"your mother has a great many social relations all over the continent."

"She thinks so, but half the people don't care for us. They are not so good as we, and they know it—I'll do them that justice—and they wonder why we should care for them. When we are polite to them, they think the less of us; there are plenty of people like that. Mamma thinks so much of them simply because they are foreigners. If I could tell you all the dull, stupid, second-rate people I have had to talk to, for no better reason than that they were *de leur pays!*—Germans, French, Italians, Turks, everything. When I complain, mamma always says that at any rate it's practice in the language. And she makes so much of the English, too; I don't know what that's practice in."

Before I had time to suggest an hypothesis, as regards this latter point, I saw something that made me rise, with a certain solemnity, from my chair. This was nothing less than the neat little figure of Mrs. Church—a perfect model of the *femme comme il faut*—approaching our table with an impatient step, and followed most unexpectedly in her advance by the pre-eminent form of Mr. Ruck. She had evidently come in quest of her daughter, and if she had commanded this gentleman's attendance, it had been on no softer ground than that of his unenvied paternity to her guilty child's accomplice. My movement had given the alarm, and Aurora Church and M. Pigeonneau got up; Miss Ruck alone did not, in the local phrase, derange herself. Mrs.

Church, beneath her modest little bonnet, looked very serious, but not at all fluttered; she came straight to her daughter, who received her with a smile, and then she looked all round at the rest of us, very fixedly and tranquilly, without bowing. I must do both these ladies the justice to mention that neither of them made the least little "scene."

"I have come for you, dearest," said the mother.

"Yes, dear mamma."

"Come for you—come for you," Mrs. Church repeated, looking down at the relics of our little feast. "I was obliged to ask Mr. Ruck's assistance. I was puzzled; I thought a long time."

"Well, Mrs. Church, I was glad to see you puzzled once in your life!" said Mr. Ruck, with friendly jocosity. "But you came pretty straight for all that. I had hard work to keep up with you."

"We will take a cab, Aurora," Mrs. Church went on, without heeding this pleasantry—"a closed one. Come, my daughter."

"Yes, dear mamma." The young girl was blushing, yet she was still smiling; she looked round at us all, and, as her eyes met mine, I thought she was beautiful. "Good-bye," she said to us. "I have had a *lovely time*."

"We must not linger," said her mother; "it is five o'clock. We are to dine, you know, with Madame Galopin."

"I had quite forgotten," Aurora declared. "That will be charming."

"Do you want me to assist you to carry her back, ma'am?" asked Mr. Ruck.

Mrs. Church hesitated a moment, with her serene

little gaze. "Do you prefer, then, to leave your daughter to finish the evening with these gentlemen?"

Mr. Ruck pushed back his hat and scratched the top of his head. "Well, I don't know. How would you like that, Sophy?"

"Well, I never!" exclaimed Sophy, as Mrs. Church marched off with her daughter.

VIII.

I HAD half expected that Mrs. Church would make me feel the weight of her disapproval of my own share in that little act of revelry in the English Garden. But she maintained her claim to being a highly reasonable woman—I could not but admire the justice of this pretension—by recognising my irresponsibility. I had taken her daughter as I found her, which was, according to Mrs. Church's view, in a very equivocal position. The natural instinct of a young man, in such a situation, is not to protest but to profit; and it was clear to Mrs. Church that I had had nothing to do with Miss Aurora's appearing in public under the insufficient chaperonage of Miss Ruck. Besides, she liked to converse, and she apparently did me the honour to believe that of all the members of the Pension Beaurepas I had the most cultivated understanding. I found her in the salon a couple of evenings after the incident I have just narrated, and I approached her with a view of making my peace with her, if this should prove necessary. But Mrs. Church was as gracious as I could have desired; she put her marker into her book, and folded her plump little hands on the cover. She made no specific allusion to the English Garden; she embarked, rather, upon those general considerations in which her refined intellect was so much at home.

"Always at your studies, Mrs. Church," I ventured to observe.

"Que voulez-vous? To say studies is to say too much; one doesn't study in the parlour of a boarding-house. But I do what I can; I have always done what I can. That is all I have ever claimed."

"No one can do more, and you seem to have done a great deal."

"Do you know my secret?" she asked, with an air of brightening confidence. And she paused a moment before she imparted her secret—"To care only for the *best!* To do the best, to know the best—to have, to desire, to recognise, only the best. That's what I have always done, in my quiet little way. I have gone through Europe on my devoted little errand, seeking, seeing, heeding, only the best. And it has not been for myself alone; it has been for my daughter. My daughter has had the best. We are not rich, but I can say that."

"She has had you, madam," I rejoined finely.

"Certainly, such as I am, I have been devoted. We have got something everywhere; a little here, a little there. That's the real secret—to get something everywhere; you always can if you *are* devoted. Sometimes it has been a little music, sometimes a little deeper insight into the history of art; every little counts you know. Sometimes it has been just a glimpse, a view, a lovely landscape, an impression. We have always been on the look-out. Sometimes it has been a valued friendship, a delightful social tie."

"Here comes the 'European society,' the poor daughter's bugbear," I said to myself. "Certainly," I remarked aloud—I admit, rather perversely—"if you have lived a great deal in *pensions*, you must have got acquainted with lots of people."

Mrs. Church dropped her eyes a moment; and then, with considerable gravity, "I think the European pension system in many respects remarkable, and in some satisfactory. But of the friendships that we have formed, few have been contracted in establishments of this kind."

"I am sorry to hear that!" I said, laughing.

"I don't say it for you, though I might say it for some others. We have been interested in European *homes*."

"Oh, I see!"

"We have the *éntree* of the old Genevese society. I like its tone. I prefer it to that of Mr. Ruck," added Mrs. Church, calmly; "to that of Mrs. Ruck and Miss Ruck—of Miss Ruck, especially."

"Ah, the poor Rucks haven't any tone at all," I said. "Don't take them more seriously than they take themselves."

"Tell me this," my companion rejoined, "are they fair examples?"

"Examples of what?"

"Of our American tendencies."

"'Tendencies' is a big word, dear lady; tendencies are difficult to calculate. And you shouldn't abuse those good Rucks, who have been very kind to your daughter. They have invited her to go and stay with them in Thirty-Seventh Street."

"Aurora has told me. It might be very serious."

"It might be very droll," I said.

"To me," declared Mrs. Church, "it is simply terrible. I think we shall have to leave the Pension Beaurepas. I shall go back to Madame Chamousset."

"On account of the Rucks?" I asked.

"Pray, why don't they go themselves? I have given them some excellent addresses—written down the very hours of the trains. They were going to Appenzell; I thought it was arranged."

"They talk of Chamouni now," I said; "but they are very helpless and undecided."

"I will give them some Chamouni addresses. Mrs. Ruck will send a *chaise à porteurs;* I will give her the name of a man who lets them lower than you get them at the hotels. After that they *must* go."

"Well, I doubt," I observed, "whether Mr. Ruck will ever really be seen on the Mer de Glace—in a high hat. He's not like you; he doesn't value his European privileges. He takes no interest. He regrets Wall Street, acutely. As his wife says, he is very restless, but he has no curiosity about Chamouni. So you must not depend too much on the effect of your addresses."

"Is it a frequent type?" asked Mrs. Church, with an air of self-control.

"I am afraid so. Mr. Ruck is a broken-down man of business. He is broken-down in health, and I suspect he is broken down in fortune. He has spent his whole life in buying and selling; he knows how to do nothing else. His wife and daughter have spent their lives, not in selling, but in buying; and they, on their side, know how to do nothing else. To get something in a shop that they can put on their backs—that is their one idea; they haven't another in their heads. Of course they spend no end of money, and they do it with an implacable persistence, with a mixture of audacity and of cunning. They do it in his teeth and they do it behind his back; the mother protects the daughter, and the daughter eggs on the mother. Between them they are bleeding him to death."

"Ah, what a picture!" murmured Mrs. Church. "I am afraid they are very—uncultivated."

"I share your fears. They are perfectly ignorant; they have no resources. The vision of fine clothes occupies their whole imagination. They have not an idea—even a worse one—to compete with it. Poor Mr. Ruck, who is extremely good-natured and soft, seems to me a really tragic figure. He is getting bad news every day from home; his business is going to the dogs. He is unable to stop it; he has to stand and watch his fortunes ebb. He has been used to doing things in a big way, and he feels 'mean' if he makes a fuss about bills. So the ladies keep sending them in."

"But haven't they common sense? Don't they know they are ruining themselves?"

"They don't believe it. The duty of an American husband and father is to keep them going. If he asks them how, that's his own affair. So, by way of not being mean, of being a good American husband and father, poor Ruck stands staring at bankruptcy."

Mrs. Church looked at me a moment, in quickened meditation. "Why, if Aurora were to go to stay with them, she might not even be properly fed!"

"I don't, on the whole, recommend," I said, laughing, "that your daughter should pay a visit to Thirty-Seventh Street."

"Why should I be subjected to such trials—so sadly *éprouvée?* Why should a daughter of mine like that dreadful girl?"

"*Does* she like her?"

"Pray, do you mean," asked my companion, softly, "that Aurora is a hypocrite?"

I hesitated a moment. "A little, since you ask me. I think you have forced her to be."

Mrs. Church answered this possibly presumptuous charge with a tranquil, candid exultation. "I never force my daughter!"

"She is nevertheless in a false position," I rejoined. "She hungers and thirsts to go back to her own country; she wants to 'come' out in New York, which is certainly, socially speaking, the El Dorado of young ladies. She likes any one, for the moment, who will talk to her of that, and serve as a connecting-link with her native shores. Miss Ruck performs this agreeable office."

"Your idea is, then, that if she were to go with Miss Ruck to America she would drop her afterwards."

I complimented Mrs. Church upon her logical mind, but I repudiated this cynical supposition. "I can't imagine her—when it should come to the point—embarking with the famille Ruck. But I wish she might go, nevertheless."

Mrs. Church shook her head serenely, and

smiled at my inappropriate zeal. "I trust my poor child may never be guilty of so fatal a mistake. She is completely in error; she is wholly unadapted to the peculiar conditions of American life. It would not please her. She would not sympathise. My daughter's ideal is not the ideal of the class of young women to which Miss Ruck belongs. I fear they are very numerous; they give the tone—they give the tone."

"It is you that are mistaken," I said; "go home for six months and see."

"I have not, unfortunately, the means to make costly experiments. My daughter has had great advantages—rare advantages—and I should be very sorry to believe that *au fond* she does not appreciate them. One thing is certain: I must remove her from this pernicious influence. We must part company with this deplorable family. If Mr. Ruck and his ladies cannot be induced to go to Chamouni—a journey that no traveller with the smallest self-respect would omit—my daughter and I shall be obliged to retire. We shall go to Dresden."

"To Dresden?"

"The capital of Saxony. I had arranged to go there for the autumn, but it will be simpler to go immediately. There are several works in the gallery with which my daughter has not, I think, sufficiently familiarised herself; it is especially strong in the seventeenth century schools."

As my companion offered me this information I perceived Mr. Ruck come lounging in, with his hands in his pockets, and his elbows making acute angles. He had his usual anomalous appearance of both seeking and avoiding society, and he wandered obliquely toward Mrs. Church, whose last words he had overheard. "The seventeenth century schools," he said, slowly, as if he were weighing some very small object in a very large pair of scales. "Now, do you suppose they *had* schools at that period?"

Mrs. Church rose with a good deal of precision, making no answer to this incongruous jest. She clasped her large volume to her neat little bosom, and she fixed a gentle, serious eye upon Mr. Ruck.

"I had a letter this morning from Chamouni," she said.

"Well," replied Mr. Ruck, "I suppose you've got friends all over."

"I have friends at Chamouni, but they are leaving. To their great regret." I had got up, too; I listened to this statement, and I wondered. I am almost ashamed to mention the subject of my agitation. I asked myself whether this was a sudden improvisation, consecrated by maternal devotion; but this point has never been elucidated. "They are giving up some charming rooms; perhaps you would like them. I would suggest your telegraphing. The weather is glorious," continued Mrs. Church, "and the highest peaks are now perceived with extraordinary distinctness."

Mr. Ruck listened, as he always listened, respectfully. "Well," he said, "I don't know as I want to go up Mount Blank. That's the principal attraction, isn't it?"

"There are many others. I thought I would offer you an—an exceptional opportunity."

"Well," said Mr. Ruck, "you're right down

friendly. But I seem to have more opportunities than I know what to do with. I don't seem able to take hold."

"It only needs a little decision," remarked Mrs. Church, with an air which was an admirable example of this virtue. "I wish you good-night, sir." And she moved noiselessly away.

Mr. Ruck, with his long legs apart, stood staring after her; then he transferred his perfectly quiet eyes to me. "Does she own a hotel over there?" he asked. "Has she got any stock in Mount Blank?"

IX.

THE next day Madame Beaurepas handed me, with her own elderly fingers, a missive, which proved to be a telegram. After glancing at it, I informed her that it was apparently a signal for my departure; my brother had arrived in England, and proposed to me to meet him there; he had come on business and was to spend but three weeks in Europe. "But my house empties itself!" cried the old woman. "The famille Ruck talks of leaving me, and Madame Church *nous fait la révérence*."

"Mrs. Church is going away?"

"She is packing her trunk; she is a very extraordinary person. Do you know what she asked me this morning? To invent some combination by which the famille Ruck should move away. I informed her that I was not an inventor. That poor famille Ruck! 'Oblige me by getting rid of them,' said Madame Church, as she would have asked Célestine to remove a dish of cabbage. She speaks as if the world were made for Madame Church. I intimated to her that if she objected to the company there was a very simple remedy; and at present *elle fait ses paquets*."

"She really asked you to get the Rucks out of the house?"

"She asked me to tell them that their rooms had been let, three months ago, to another family. She has an *aplomb!*"

Mrs. Church's aplomb caused me considerable diversion; I am not sure that it was not, in some degree, to laugh over it at my leisure that I went out into the garden that evening to smoke a cigar. The night was dark and not particularly balmy, and most of my fellow-pensioners, after dinner, had remained in-doors. A long straight walk conducted from the door of the house to the ancient grille that I have described, and I stood here for some time, looking through the iron bars at the silent empty street. The prospect was not entertaining, and I presently turned away. At this moment I saw, in the distance, the door of the house open and throw a shaft of lamplight into the darkness. Into the lamplight there stepped the figure of a female, who presently closed the door behind her. She disappeared in the dusk of the garden, and I had seen her but for an instant, but I remained under the impression that Aurora Church, on the eve of her departure, had come out for a meditative stroll.

I lingered near the gate, keeping the red tip of my cigar turned toward the house, and before long a young lady emerged from among the shadows of the trees and encountered the light of a lamp that stood just outside the gate. It was in fact Aurora Church, but she seemed more bent upon conversation than upon meditation. She stood a moment looking at me, and then she said,—

"Ought I to retire—to return to the house?"

"If you ought, I should be very sorry to tell you so," I answered.

"But we are all alone; there is no one else in the garden."

"It is not the first time that I have been alone with a young lady. I am not at all terrified."

"Ah, but I?" said the young girl. "I have never been alone"—then, quickly, she interrupted herself. "Good, there's another false note!"

"Yes, I am obliged to admit that one is very false."

She stood looking at me. "I am going away to-morrow; after that there will be no one to tell me."

"That will matter little," I presently replied. "Telling you will do no good."

"Ah, why do you say that?" murmured Aurora Church.

I said it partly because it was true; but I said it for other reasons, as well, which it was hard to define. Standing there bare-headed, in the night air, in the vague light, this young lady looked extremely interesting; and the interest of her appearance was not diminished by a suspicion on my own part that she had come into the garden knowing me to be there. I thought her a charming girl, and I felt very sorry for her; but as I looked at her, the terms in which Madame Beaurepas had ventured to characterise her recurred to me with a certain force. I had professed a contempt for them at the time, but it now came into my head that perhaps this unfortunately situated, this insidiously mutinous, young creature was looking out for a preserver. She was certainly not a girl to throw herself at a man's head, but it was possible that in her intense—her almost morbid—desire to put into effect an ideal which was perhaps after all charged with as many fallacies as her mother affirmed, she might do something reckless and irregular—something in which a sympathetic compatriot, as yet unknown, would find his profit. The image, unshaped though it was, of this sympathetic compatriot filled me with a sort of envy. For some moments I was silent, conscious of these things, and then I answered her question. "Because some things—some differences—are felt, not learned. To you liberty is not natural; you are like a person who has bought a repeater, and, in his satisfaction, is constantly making it sound. To a real American girl her liberty is a very vulgarly-ticking old clock."

"Ah, you mean, then," said the poor girl, "that my mother has ruined me?"

"Ruined you?"

"She has so perverted my mind that when I try to be natural I am necessarily immodest."

"That again is a false note," I said, laughing.

She turned away. "I think you are cruel."

"By no means," I declared; "because, for my own taste, I prefer you as—as——"

I hesitated, and she turned back. "As what?"

"As you are."

She looked at me a while again, and then she said, in a little reasoning voice that reminded me of her mother's, only that it was conscious and studied, "I was not aware that I am under any particular obligation to please you!" And then she gave a clear laugh, quite at variance with her voice.

"Oh, there is no obligation," I said, "but one has preferences. I am very sorry you are going away."

"What does it matter to you? You are going yourself."

"As I am going in a different direction, that makes all the greater separation."

She answered nothing; she stood looking through the bars of the tall gate at the empty, dusky street. "This grille is like a cage," she said at last.

"Fortunately, it is a cage that will open." And I laid my hand on the lock.

"Don't open it," and she pressed the gate back. "If you should open it I would go out—and never return."

"Where should you go?"

"To America."

"Straight away?"

"Somehow or other. I would go to the American consul. I would beg him to give me money—to help me."

I received this assertion without a smile; I was not in a smiling humour. On the contrary, I felt singularly excited, and I kept my hand on the lock of the gate. I believed (or I thought I believed) what my companion said, and I had—absurd as it may appear—an irritated vision of her throwing herself upon consular sympathy. It seemed to me, for a moment, that to pass out of that gate with this yearning, straining young creature would be to pass into some mysterious felicity. If I were only a hero of romance, I would offer, myself, to take her to America.

In a moment more, perhaps, I should have persuaded myself that I was one, but at this juncture I heard a sound that was not romantic. It proved to be the very realistic tread of Célestine, the cook, who stood grinning at us as we turned about from our colloquy.

"I ask *bien pardon*," said Célestine. "The mother of mademoiselle desires that mademoiselle should come in immediately. M. le Pasteur Galopin has come to make his adieux to *ces dames*."

Aurora gave me only one glance, but it was a touching one. Then she slowly departed with Célestine.

The next morning, on coming into the garden, I found that Mrs. Church and her daughter had departed. I was informed of this fact by old M. Pigeonneau, who sat there under a tree, having his coffee at a little green table.

"I have nothing to envy you," he said; "I had the last glimpse of that charming Miss Aurora."

"I had a very late glimpse," I answered, "and it was all I could possibly desire."

"I have always noticed," rejoined M. Pigeonneau, "that your desires are more moderate than mine. Que voulez-vous? I am of the old school. Je crois que la race se perd. I regret the departure of that young girl: she had an enchanting smile. Ce sera une femme d'esprit. For the mother, I can console myself. I am not sure that *she* was a femme d'esprit, though she wished to pass for one. Round, rosy, *potelée*, she yet had not the temperament of her appearance; she was a *femme austère*. I have often noticed that contradiction in American ladies. You see a plump little woman, with a speaking eye and the contour and complexion of a ripe peach, and if you venture to conduct yourself in the smallest degree in accordance with these *indices,* you discover a species of Methodist—of what do you call it?—of Quakeress. On the other hand, you encounter a tall, lean, angular person, without colour, without grace, all elbows and knees, and you find it's a nature of the tropics! The women of duty look like coquettes, and the others look like alpenstocks! However, we have still the handsome Madame Ruck—a real *femme de Rubens, celle-là.* It is very true that to talk to her one must know the Flemish tongue!"

I had determined, in accordance with my brother's telegram, to go away in the afternoon; so that, having various duties to perform, I left M. Pigeonneau to his international comparisons. Among other things, I went in the course of the morning to the banker's, to draw money for my journey, and there I found Mr. Ruck, with a pile of crumpled letters in his lap, his chair tipped back and his eyes gloomily fixed on the fringe of the green plush table-cloth. I timidly expressed the hope that he had got better news from home; whereupon he gave me a look in which, considering his provocation, the absence of irritation was conspicuous.

He took up his letters in his large hand, and crushing them together held it out to me. "That epistolary matter," he said, "is worth about five cents. But I guess," he added, rising, "I have taken it in by this time." When I had drawn my money, I asked him to come and breakfast with me at the little *brasserie,* much favoured by students, to which I used to resort in the old town. "I couldn't eat, sir," he said, "I couldn't eat. Bad news takes away the appetite. But I guess I'll go with you, so that I needn't go to table down there at the pension. The old woman down there is always accusing me of turning up my nose at her food. Well, I guess I shan't turn up my nose at anything now."

We went to the little brasserie, where poor Mr. Ruck made the lightest possible breakfast. But if he ate very little, he talked a great deal; he talked about business, going into a hundred details in which I was quite unable to follow him. His talk was not angry nor bitter; it was a long, meditative, melancholy monologue; if it had been a trifle less incoherent I should almost have called it philosophic. I was very sorry for him; I wanted to do something for him, but the only thing I could do was, when we had breakfasted, to see him safely back to the Pension Beaurepas. We went across the Treille and down the Corraterie, out of which we turned into the Rue du Rhône. In this latter street, as all the world knows, are many of those brilliant jewellers' shops for which Geneva is famous. I always admired their glittering windows, and never passed them without a lingering glance. Even on this occasion, preoccupied as I was with my impending departure and with my companion's troubles, I suffered my eyes to wander along the precious tiers that flashed and twinkled behind the huge, clear plates of glass. Thanks to this inveterate habit, I made a discovery. In the largest and most brilliant of these establishments I perceived two ladies, seated before the counter with an air of absorption which sufficiently proclaimed their identity.

I hoped my companion would not see them, but as we came abreast of the door, a little beyond, we found it open to the warm summer air. Mr. Ruck happened to glance in, and he immediately recognised his wife and daughter. He slowly stopped, looking at them; I wondered what he would do. The salesman was holding up a bracelet before them, on its velvet cushion, and flashing it about in an irresistible manner.

Mr. Ruck said nothing, but he presently went in, and I did the same.

"It will be an opportunity," I remarked, as cheerfully as possible, "for me to bid good-bye to the ladies."

They turned round when Mr. Ruck came in, and looked at him without confusion. "Well, you had better go home to breakfast," remarked his wife. Miss Sophy made no remark, but she took the bracelet from the attendant and gazed at it very fixedly. Mr. Ruck seated himself on an empty stool and looked round the shop.

"Well, you have been here before," said his wife; "you were here the first day we came."

Miss Ruck extended the precious object in her hands towards me. "Don't you think that sweet?" she inquired.

I looked at it a moment. "No, I think it's ugly."

She glanced at me a moment, incredulous. "Well, I don't believe you have any taste."

"Why, sir, it's just lovely," said Mrs. Ruck.

"You'll see it some day on me, any way," her daughter declared.

"No, he won't," said Mr. Ruck quietly.

"It will be his own fault, then," Miss Sophy observed.

"Well, if we are going to Chamouni we want to get something here," said Mrs. Ruck. "We may not have another chance."

Mr. Ruck was still looking round the shop, whistling in a very low tone. "We ain't going to Chamouni. We are going to New York city, straight."

"Well, I'm glad to hear that," said Mrs. Ruck. "Don't you suppose we want to take something home?"

"If we are going straight back I must have that bracelet," her daughter declared. "Only I don't want a velvet case; I want a satin case."

"I must bid you good-bye," I said to the ladies. "I am leaving Geneva in an hour or two."

"Take a good look at that bracelet, so you'll know it when you see it," said Miss Sophy.

"She's bound to have something," remarked her mother, almost proudly.

Mr. Ruck was still vaguely inspecting the shop; he was still whistling a little. "I am afraid he is not at all well," I said, softly, to his wife.

She twisted her head a little, and glanced at him. "Well, I wish he'd improve!" she exclaimed.

"A satin case, and a nice one!" said Miss Ruck to the shopman.

I bade Mr. Ruck good-bye. "Don't wait for me," he said, sitting there on his stool, and not meeting my eye. "I've got to see this thing through."

I went back to the Pension Beaurepas, and when, an hour later, I left it with my luggage, the family had not returned.

A BUNDLE OF LETTERS.

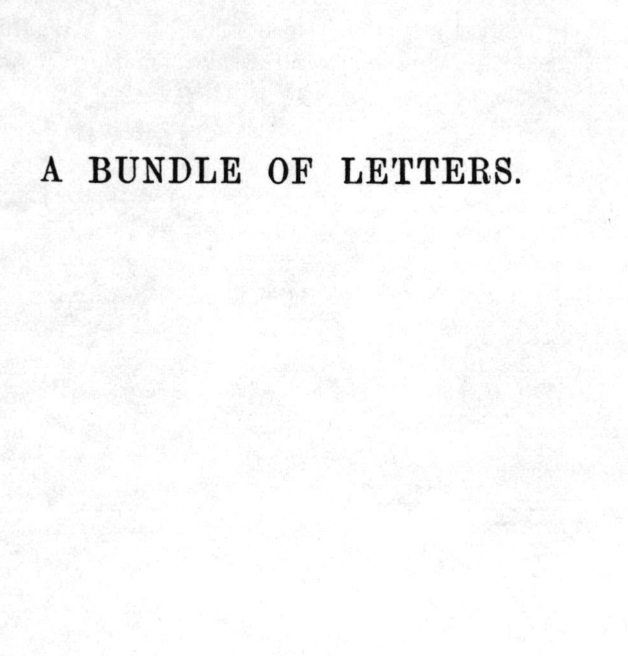

A BUNDLE OF LETTERS.

I.

From Miss MIRANDA HOPE, *in Paris, to Mrs.* ABRAHAM C. HOPE, *at Bangor, Maine.*

SEPTEMBER 5*th*, 1879.

MY DEAR MOTHER—

I HAVE kept you posted as far as Tuesday week last, and, although my letter will not have reached you yet, I will begin another, before my news accumulates too much. I am glad you show my letters round in the family, for I like them all to know what I am doing, and I can't write to every one, though I try to answer all reasonable expectations. But there are a great many unreasonable ones, as I suppose you know—not yours, dear mother, for I am bound to say that you never required of me more than was natural. You see you are reaping your reward: I write to you before I write to any one else.

There is one thing, I hope—that you don't show any of my letters to William Platt. If he wants to see any of my letters, he knows the right way to go to work. I wouldn't have him see one of these letters, written for circulation in the family, for anything in the world. If he wants one for himself, he has got to write to me first. Let him write to me first, and then I will see about answering him. You can show him this if you like; but if you show him anything more, I will never write to you again.

I told you in my last about my farewell to England, my crossing the channel, and my first impressions of Paris. I have thought a great deal about that lovely England since I left it, and all the famous historic scenes I visited; but I have come to the conclusion that it is not a country in which I should care to reside. The position of woman does not seem to me at all satisfactory, and that is a point, you know, on which I feel very strongly. It seems to me that in England they play a very faded-out part, and those with whom I conversed had a kind of depressed and humiliated tone; a little dull, tame look, as if they were used to being snubbed and bullied, which made me want to give them a good shaking. There are a great many people—and a great many things, too—over here that I should like to perform that operation upon. I should like to shake the starch out of some of them, and the dust out of the others. I know fifty girls in Bangor that come much more up to my notion of the stand a truly noble woman should take, than those young ladies in England. But they had a most lovely way of speaking (in England), and the men are *remarkably handsome.* (You can show this to William Platt, if you like.)

I gave you my first impressions of Paris, which quite came up to my expectations, much as I had heard and read about it. The objects of interest are extremely numerous, and the climate is remarkably cheerful and sunny. I should say the position of woman here was considerably higher, though by no means coming up to the American standard. The manners of the people are in some respects extremely peculiar, and I feel at last that I am indeed in *foreign parts.* It is, however, a truly elegant city (very superior to New York), and I have spent a great deal of time in visiting the various monuments and palaces. I won't give you an account of all my wanderings, though I have been most indefatigable; for I am keeping, as I told you before, a most *exhaustive* journal, which I will allow you the *privilege* of reading on my return to Bangor. I am getting on remarkably well, and I must say I am sometimes surprised at my universal good fortune. It only shows what a little energy and common-sense will accomplish. I have discovered none of these objections to a young lady travelling in Europe by herself, of which we heard so much before I left, and I don't expect I ever shall, for I certainly don't mean to look for them. I know what I want and I always manage to get it.

I have received a great deal of politeness—some of it really most pressing, and I have experienced no drawbacks whatever. I have made a great many pleasant acquaintances in travelling round (both ladies and gentlemen), and had a great many most interesting talks. I have collected a great deal of information, for which I refer you to my journal. I assure you my journal is going to be a splendid thing. I do just exactly as I do in Bangor, and I find I do perfectly right; and at any rate, I don't care if I don't. I didn't come to Europe to lead a merely conventional life; I could do that at Bangor. You know I never *would* do it at Bangor, so it isn't likely I am going to make myself miserable over here. So long as I accomplish what I desire, and make my money hold out, I shall regard the thing as a success. Sometimes I feel rather lonely, especially in the evening; but I generally manage to interest myself in something or in some one. In the evening I usually read up about the objects of interest I have visited during the day, or I post up my journal. Sometimes I go to the theatre; or else I play the piano in the public parlour. The public parlour at the hotel isn't much; but the piano is better than that fearful old thing at the Sebago House. Sometimes I go downstairs and talk to the lady who keeps the books—a French lady, who is remarkably polite. She is very pretty, and always wears a black dress, with the most beautiful fit; she speaks a little English; she tells me she had to learn it in order to converse with the Americans who come in such numbers to this hotel. She has given me a great deal of information about the position of woman in France, and much of it is very encouraging. But she has told me at the same time some things that I should not like to write to you (I am hesitating even about putting them into my journal), especially if my letters are to be handed round in the family. I assure you they appear to talk about things here that we never think of mentioning at Bangor, or even of thinking about. She seems to think she can tell me everything, because I told her I was travelling for general culture. Well, I *do* want to know so much that it seems sometimes as if I wanted to know everything; and yet there are some things that I think I don't want to know. But, as a general thing, everything is intensely interesting; I don't mean only everything that this French lady tells me, but everything I see and hear for myself. I feel really as if I should gain all I desire.

I meet a great many Americans, who, as a general thing, I must say, are not as polite to me as the people over here. The people over here—especially the gentlemen—are much more what I should call *attentive*. I don't know whether Americans are more *sincere*; I haven't yet made up my mind about that. The only drawback I experience is when Americans sometimes express surprise that I should be travelling round alone; so you see it doesn't come from Europeans. I always have my answer ready: "For general culture, to acquire the languages, and to see Europe for myself;" and that generally seems to satisfy them. Dear mother, my money holds out very well, and it *is* real interesting.

II.

From the Same to the Same.

SEPTEMBER 16th.

SINCE I last wrote to you I have left that hotel, and come to live in a French family. It's a kind of boarding-house combined with a kind of school; only it's not like an American boarding-house, nor like an American school either. There are four or five people here that have come to learn the language—not to take lessons, but to have an opportunity for conversation. I was very glad to come to such a place, for I had begun to realise that I was not making much progress with the French. It seemed to me that I should feel ashamed to have spent two months in Paris, and not to have acquired more insight into the language. I had always heard so much of French conversation, and I found I was having no more opportunity to practise it than if I had remained at Bangor. In fact, I used to hear a great deal more at Bangor, from those French Canadians that came down to cut the ice, than I saw I should ever hear at that hotel. The lady that kept the books seemed to want so much to talk to me in English (for the sake of practice, too, I suppose), that I couldn't bear to let her know I didn't like it. The chambermaid was Irish, and all the waiters were German, so that I never heard a word of French spoken. I suppose you might hear a great deal in the shops; only, as I don't buy anything—I prefer to spend my money for purposes of culture—I don't have that advantage.

I have been thinking some of taking a teacher, but I am well acquainted with the grammar already, and teachers always keep you bothering over the verbs. I was a good deal troubled, for I felt as if I didn't want to go away without having, at least, got a general idea of French conversation. The theatre gives you a good deal of insight, and, as I told you in my last, I go a good deal to places of amusement. I find no difficulty whatever in going to such places alone, and am always treated with the politeness which, as I told you before, I encounter everywhere. I see plenty of other ladies alone (mostly French), and they generally seem to be enjoying themselves as much as I. But, at the theatre, every one talks so fast that I can scarcely make out what they say; and, besides, there are a great many vulgar expressions which it is unnecessary to learn. But it was the theatre, nevertheless, that put me on the track. The very next day after I wrote to you last, I went to the Palais Royal, which is one of the principal theatres in Paris. It is very small, but it is very celebrated, and in my guide-book it is marked with *two stars*, which is a sign of importance attached only to *first-class* objects of interest. But after I had been there half an hour I found I couldn't understand a single word of the play, they gabbled it off so fast, and they made use of such peculiar expressions. I felt a good deal disappointed and troubled—I was afraid I shouldn't gain all I had come for. But while I was thinking it over—thinking what I *should* do—I heard two gentlemen talking behind me. It was between the acts, and I couldn't help listening to what they said. They were talking English, but I guess they were Americans.

"Well," said one of them, "it all depends on what you are after. I'm after French; that's what I'm after."

"Well," said the other, "I'm after Art."

"Well," said the first, "I'm after Art too; but I'm after French most."

Then, dear mother, I am sorry to say the second one swore a little. He said, "Oh, damn French!"

"No, I won't damn French," said his friend. "I'll acquire it—that's what I'll do with it. I'll go right into a family."

"What family'll you go into?"

"Into some French family. That's the only way to do—to go to some place where you can talk. If you're after Art, you want to stick to the galleries; you want to go right through the Louvre, room by room; you want to take a room a day, or something of that sort. But, if you want to acquire French, the thing is to look out for a family. There are lots of French families here that take you to board and teach you. My second cousin—that young lady I told you about—she got in with a crowd like that, and they booked her right up in three months. They just took her right in and they talked to her. That's what they do to you; they set you right down and they talk *at* you. You've got to understand them; you can't help yourself. That family my cousin was with has moved away somewhere, or I should try and get in with them. They were very smart people, that family; after she left, my cousin corresponded with them in French. But I mean to find some other crowd, if it takes a lot of trouble!"

I listened to all this with great interest, and when he spoke about his cousin I was on the point of turning around to ask him the address of the family that she was with; but the next moment he said they had moved away; so I sat still. The other gentleman, however, didn't seem to be affected in the same way as I was.

"Well," he said, "you may follow up that if you like; I mean to follow up the pictures. I don't believe there is ever going to be any considerable demand in the United States for French; but I can promise you that in about ten years there'll be a big demand for Art! And it won't be temporary either."

That remark may be very true, but I don't care anything about the demand; I want to know French for its own sake. I don't want to think I have been all this while without having gained an insight .... The very next day, I asked the lady who kept the books at the hotel whether she knew of any family that could take me to board and give me the benefit of their conversation. She instantly threw up her hands, with several little shrill cries (in their French way, you know), and told me that her dearest friend kept a regular place of that kind. If she had known I was looking out for such a place she would have told me before; she had not spoken of it herself, because she didn't wish to injure the hotel by being the cause of my going way. She told me this was a charming family, who had often received American ladies (and others as well) who wished to follow up the language, and she was sure I should be delighted with them. So she gave me their address, and offered to go with me to introduce me. But I was in such a hurry that I went off by myself, and I had no trouble in finding these good people. They were delighted to receive me, and I was very much pleased with what I saw of them. They seemed to have plenty of conversation, and there will be no trouble about that.

I came here to stay about three days ago, and by this time I have seen a great deal of them. The price of board struck me as rather high; but I must remember that a quantity of conversation is thrown in. I have a very pretty little room—without any carpet, but with seven mirrors, two clocks, and five curtains. I was rather disappointed after I arrived to find that there are several other Americans here for the same purpose as myself. At least there are three Americans and two English people; and also a German gentleman. I am afraid, therefore, our conversation will be rather mixed, but I have not yet time to judge. I try to talk with Madame de Maisonrouge all I can (she is the lady of the house, and the *real* family consists only of herself and her two daughters). They are all most elegant, interesting women, and I am sure we shall become intimate friends. I will write you more about them in my next. Tell William Platt I don't care what he does.

III.

From Miss VIOLET RAY, *in Paris, to* Miss AGNES RICH, *in New York.*

September 21*st.*

WE had hardly got here when father received a telegram saying he would have to come right back to New York. It was for something about his business—I don't know exactly what; you know I never understand those things, never want to. We had just got settled at the hotel, in some charming rooms, and mother and I, as you may imagine, were greatly annoyed. Father is extremely fussy, as you know, and his first idea, as soon as he found he should have to go back, was that we should go back with him. He declared he would never leave us in Paris alone, and that we must return and come out again. I don't know what he thought would happen to us; I suppose he thought we should be too extravagant. It's father's theory that we are always running up bills, whereas a little observation would show him that we wear the same old *rags* FOR MONTHS. But father has no observation; he has nothing but theories. Mother and I, however, have, fortunately, a great deal of *practice*, and we succeeded in making him understand that we wouldn't budge from Paris, and that we would rather be chopped into small pieces than cross that dreadful ocean again. So, at last, he decided to go back alone, and to leave us here for three months. But, to show you how fussy he is, he refused to let us stay at the hotel, and insisted that we should go into a *family*. I don't know what put such an idea into his head, unless it was some advertisement that he saw in one of the American papers that are published here.

There are families here who receive American and English people to live with them, under the pretence of teaching them French. You may imagine what people they are—I mean the families themselves. But the Americans who choose this peculiar manner of seeing Paris must be actually just as bad. Mother and I were horrified, and declared that *main force* should not remove us from the hotel. But father has a way of arriving at his ends which is more efficient than violence. He worries and fusses; he "nags," as we used to say at school; and, when mother and I are quite worn out, his triumph is assured. Mother is usually worn out more easily than I, and she ends by siding with father; so that, at last, when they combine their forces against poor little me, I have to succumb. You should have heard the way father went on about this "family" plan; he talked to every one he saw about it; he used to go round to the banker's and talk to the people there—the people in the post-office; he used to try and exchange ideas about it with the waiters at the hotel. He said it would be more safe, more respectable, more economical; that I should perfect my French; that mother would learn how a French household is conducted; that he should feel more easy, and five hundred reasons more. They were none of them good, but that made no difference. It's all humbug, his talking about economy, when every one knows that business in America has completely recovered, that the prostration is all over, and that *immense fortunes* are being made. We have been economising for the last five years, and I supposed we came abroad to reap the benefits of it.

As for my French, it is quite as perfect as I want it to be. (I assure you I am often surprised at my own fluency, and, when I get a little more practice in the genders and the idioms, I shall do very well in this respect.) To make a long story short, however, father carried his point, as usual; mother basely deserted me at the last moment, and, after holding out alone for three days, I told them to do with me what they pleased! Father lost three steamers in succession by remaining in Paris to argue with me. You know he is like the schoolmaster in Goldsmith's "Deserted Village"—"e'en though vanquished, he would argue still." He and mother went to look at some seventeen families (they had got the addresses somewhere), while I retired to my sofa, and would have nothing to do with it. At last they made arrangements, and I was transported to the establishment from which I now write you. I write you from the bosom of a Parisian ménage—from the depths of a second-rate boarding-house.

Father only left Paris after he had seen us what

he calls comfortably settled here, and had informed Madame de Maisonrouge (the mistress of the establishment—the head of the "family") that he wished my French pronunciation especially attended to. The pronunciation, as it happens, is just what I am most at home in; if he had said my genders or my idioms there would have been some sense. But poor father has no tact, and this defect is especially marked since he has been in Europe. He will be absent, however, for three months, and mother and I shall breathe more freely; the situation will be less intense. I must confess that we breathe more freely than I expected, in this place, where we have him for about a week. I was sure, before we came, that it would prove to be an establishment of the *lowest description;* but I must say that, in this respect, I am agreeably disappointed. The French are so clever that they know even how to manage a place of this kind. Of course it is very disagreeable to live with strangers, but as, after all, if I were not staying with Madame de Maisonrouge I should not be living in the Faubourg St.-Germain, I don't know that from the point of view of exclusiveness it is any great loss to be here.

Our rooms are very prettily arranged, and the table is remarkably good. Mamma thinks the whole thing—the place and the people, the manners and customs—very amusing; but mamma is very easily amused. As for me, you know, all that I ask is to be let alone, and not to have people's society *forced upon me.* I have never wanted for society of my own choosing, and, so long as I retain possession of my faculties, I don't suppose I ever shall. As I said, however, the place is very well managed, and I succeed in doing as I please, which, you know, is my most cherished pursuit. Madame de Maisonrouge has a great deal of tact—much more than poor father. She is what they call here a *belle femme*, which means that she is a tall, ugly woman, with style. She dresses very well, and has a great deal of talk; but, though she is a very good imitation of a lady, I never see her behind the dinner-table, in the evening, smiling and bowing, as the people come in, and looking all the while at the dishes and the servants, without thinking of a *dame de comptoir* blooming in a corner of a shop or a restaurant. I am sure that, in spite of her fine name, she was once a *dame de comptoir*. I am also sure that, in spite of her smiles and the pretty things she says to every one, she hates us all, and would like to murder us. She is a hard, clever Frenchwoman, who would like to amuse herself and enjoy her Paris, and she must be bored to death at passing all her time in the midst of stupid English people who mumble broken French at her. Some day she will poison the soup or the *vin rouge*; but I hope that will not be until after mother and I shall have left her. She has two daughters, who, except that one is decidedly pretty, are meagre imitations of herself.

The "family," for the rest, consists altogether of our beloved compatriots, and of still more beloved Englanders. There is an Englishman here, with his sister, and they seem to be rather nice people. He is remarkably handsome, but excessively affected and patronising, especially to us Americans; and I hope to have a chance of biting his head off before long. The sister is very pretty, and, apparently, very nice; but, in costume, she is Britannia incarnate. There is a very pleasant little Frenchman—when they are nice they are charming—and a German doctor, a big, blond man, who looks like a great white bull; and two Americans, besides mother and me. One of them is a young man from Boston,—an æsthetic young man, who talks about its being "a real Corot day," etc., and a young woman—a girl, a female, I don't know what to call her—from Vermont, or Minnesota, or some such place. This young woman is the most extraordinary specimen of artless Yankeeism that I ever encountered; she is really too horrible. I have been three times to Clémentine about your underskirt, etc.

IV.

From LOUIS LEVERETT, *in Paris, to* HARVARD TREMONT, *in Boston.*

SEPTEMBER 25*th.*

MY DEAR HARVARD—

I HAVE carried out my plan, of which I gave you a hint in my last, and I only regret that I should not have done it before. It is human nature, after all, that is the most interesting thing in the world, and it only reveals itself to the truly earnest seeker. There is a want of earnestness in that life of hotels and railroad trains, which so many of our countrymen are content to lead in this strange Old World, and I was distressed to find how far I, myself, had been led along the dusty, beaten track. I had, however, constantly wanted to turn aside into more unfrequented ways; to plunge beneath the surface and see what I should discover. But the opportunity had always been missing; somehow, I never meet those opportunities that we hear about and read about—the things that happen to people in novels and biographies. And yet I am always on the watch to take advantage of any opening that may present itself; I am always looking out for experiences, for sensations—I might almost say for adventures.

The great thing is to *live*, you know—to feel, to be conscious of one's possibilities; not to pass through life mechanically and insensibly, like a letter through the post-office. There are times, my dear Harvard, when I feel as if I were really capable of everything—*capable de tout*, as they say here—of the greatest excesses as well as the greatest heroism. Oh, to be able to say that one has lived—*qu'on a vécu,* as they say here—that idea exercises an indefinable attraction for me. You will, perhaps, reply, it is easy to say it; but the thing is to make people believe you! And, then, I don't want any second-hand, spurious sensations; I want the knowledge that leaves a trace—that leaves strange scars and stains and reveries behind it! But I am afraid I shock you, perhaps even frighten you.

If you repeat my remarks to any of the West Cedar Street circle, be sure you tone them down as your discretion will suggest. For yourself, you will know that I have always had an intense desire to see something of *real French life.* You are acquainted with my great sympathy with the French; with my natural tendency to enter into the French way of looking at life. I sympathise with the artistic temperament; I remember you used sometimes to hint to me that you thought my own temperament too artistic. I don't think that in Boston there is any real sympathy with the artistic temperament; we tend to make everything a matter of right and wrong. And in Boston one can't *live—on ne peut pas vivre,* as they say here. I don't mean one can't reside—for a great many people manage that, but one can't live, æsthetically —I may almost venture to say, sensuously. This is why I have always been so much drawn to the French, who are so æsthetic, so sensuous. I am so sorry that Théophile Gautier has passed away; I should have liked so much to go and see him, and tell him all that I owe him. He was living when I was here before; but, you know, at that time I was travelling with the Johnsons, who are not æsthetic, and who used to make me feel rather ashamed of my artistic temperament. If I had gone to see the great apostle of beauty, I should have had to go clandestinely—*en cachette*, as they say here; and that is not my nature; I like to do everything frankly, freely, *naïvement, au grand jour*. That is the great thing—to be free, to be frank, to be *naïf*. Doesn't Matthew Arnold say that somewhere—or is it Swinburne, or Pater?

When I was with the Johnsons everything was superficial; and, as regards life, everything was brought down to the question of right and wrong. They were too didactic; art should never be didactic; and what is life but an art? Pater has said that so well, somewhere. With the Johnsons I am afraid I lost many opportunities; the tone was gray and cottony, I might almost say woolly. But now, as I tell you, I have determined to take right hold for myself; to look right into European life, and judge it without Johnsonian prejudices. I have taken up my residence in a French family, in a real Parisian house. You see I have the courage of my opinions; I don't shrink from carrying out my theory that the great thing is to *live*.

You know I have always been intensely interested in Balzac, who never shrank from the reality, and whose almost *lurid* pictures of Parisian life have often haunted me in my wanderings through the old wicked-looking streets on the other side of the river. I am only sorry that my new friends—my French family—do not live in the old city—*au cœur du vieux Paris,* as they say here. They live only in the Boulevard Haussman, which is less picturesque; but in spite of this they have a great deal of the Balzac tone. Madame de Maisonrouge belongs to one of the oldest and proudest families in France; but she has had reverses which have compelled her to open an establishment in which a limited number of travellers, who are weary of the beaten track, who have the sense of local colour—she explains it herself, she expresses it so well—in short, to open a sort of boarding-house. I don't see why I should not, after all, use that expression, for it is the correlative of the term *pension bourgeoise,* employed by Balzac in the *Père Goriot.* Do you remember the *pension bourgeoise* of Madame Vauquer *née* de Conflans? But this establishment is not at all like that: and indeed it is not at all *bourgeois;* there is something distinguished, something aristocratic, about it. The Pension Vauquer was dark, brown, sordid, *graisseuse;* but this is in quite a different tone, with high, clear, lightly-draped windows, tender, subtle, almost morbid, colours, and furniture in elegant, studied, reed-like lines. Madame de Maisonrouge reminds me of Madame Hulot—do you remember "la belle Madame Hulot?"—in *Les Barents Pauvres.* She has a great charm; a little artificial, a little fatigued, with a little suggestion of hidden things in her life; but I have always been sensitive to the charm of fatigue, of duplicity.

I am rather disappointed, I confess, in the society I find here; it is not so local, so characteristic, as I could have desired. Indeed, to tell the truth, it is not local at all; but, on the other hand, it is cosmopolitan, and there is a great advantage in that. We are French, we are English, we are American, we are German; and, I believe, there are some Russians and Hungarians expected. I am much interested in the study of national types; in comparing, contrasting, seizing the strong points, the weak points, the point of view of each. It is interesting to shift one's point of view—to enter into strange, exotic ways of looking at life.

The American types here are not, I am sorry to say, so interesting as they might be, and, excepting myself, are exclusively feminine. We are *thin*, my dear Harvard; we are pale, we are sharp. There is something meagre about us; our line is wanting in roundness, our composition in richness. We lack temperament; we don't know how to live; *nous ne savons pas vivre*, as they say here. The American temperament is represented (putting myself aside, and I often think that my temperament is not at all American) by a young girl and her mother, and another young girl without her mother—without her mother or any attendant or appendage whatever. These young girls are rather curious types; they have a certain interest, they have a certain grace, but they are disappointing too; they don't go far; they don't keep all they promise; they don't satisfy the imagination. They are cold, slim, sexless; the physique is not generous, not abundant; it is only the drapery, the skirts and furbelows (that is, I mean in the young lady who has her mother) that are abundant. They are very different: one of them all elegance, all expensiveness, with an air of high fashion, from New York; the other a plain, pure, clear-eyed, straight-waisted, straight-stepping maiden from the heart of New England. And yet they are very much alike too—more alike than they would care to think themselves; for they eye each other with cold, mistrustful, deprecating looks. They are both specimens of the emancipated young American girl—practical, positive, passionless, subtle, and knowing, as you please, either too much or too little. And yet, as I say, they have a certain stamp, a certain grace; I like to talk with them, to study them.

The fair New Yorker is, sometimes, very amusing; she asks me if every one in Boston talks like me—if every one is as "intellectual" as your poor correspondent. She is for ever throwing Boston up at me; I can't get rid of Boston. The other one rubs it into me too; but in a different way; she seems to feel about it as a good Mahommedan feels toward Mecca, and regards it as a kind of focus of light for the whole human race. Poor little Boston, what nonsense is talked in thy name! But this New England maiden is, in her way, a strange type: she is travelling all over Europe alone—"to see it," she says, "for herself." For herself! What can that stiff, slim self of hers do with such sights, such visions! She looks at everything, goes everywhere, passes her way, with her clear, quiet eyes wide open; skirting the edge of obscene abysses without suspecting them; pushing through brambles without tearing her robe; exciting, without knowing it, the most injurious suspicions; and always holding her course, passionless, stainless, fearless, charmless! It is a little figure in which, after all, if you can get the right point of view, there is something rather striking.

By way of contrast, there is a lovely English girl, with eyes as shy as violets, and a voice as sweet! She has a sweet Gainsborough head, and a great Gainsborough hat, with a mighty plume in front of it, which makes a shadow over her quiet English eyes. Then she has a sage-green robe, "mystic, wonderful," all embroidered with subtle devices and flowers, and birds of tender tint; very straight and tight in front, and adorned behind, along the spine, with large, strange, iridescent buttons. The revival of taste, of the sense of beauty, in England, interests me deeply; what is there in a simple row of spinal buttons to make one dream—to *donnor à rêver*, as they say here? I think that a great æsthetic renascence is at hand, and that a great light will be kindled in England, for all the world to see. There are spirits there that I should like to commune with; I think they would understand me.

This gracious English maiden, with her clinging robes, her amulets and girdles, with something quaint and angular in her step, her carriage something mediæval and Gothic, in the details of her person and dress, this lovely Evelyn Vane (isn't it a beautiful name?) is deeply, delightfully picturesque. She is much a woman—*elle est bien femme*, as they say here; simpler, softer, rounder, richer than the young girls I spoke of just now. Not much talk—a great, sweet silence. Then the violet eye—the very eye itself seems to blush; the great shadowy hat, making the brow so quiet; the strange, clinging, clutching, pictured raiment! As I say, it is a very gracious, tender type. She has her brother with her, who is a beautiful, fair-haired, gray-eyed young Englishman. He is purely objective; and he, too, is very plastic.

V.

From Miranda Hope *to her* Mother.

September 26*th.*

You must not be frightened at not hearing from me oftener; it is not because I am in any trouble, but because I am getting on so well. If I were in any trouble I don't think I should write to you; I should just keep quiet and see it through myself. But that is not the case at present; and, if I don't write to you, it is because I am so deeply interested over here that I don't seem to find time. It was a real providence that brought me to this house, where, in spite of all obstacles, I am able to do much good work. I wonder how I find the time for all I do; but when I think that I have only got a year in Europe, I feel as if I wouldn't sacrifice a single hour.

The obstacles I refer to are the disadvantages I have in learning French, there being so many persons around me speaking English, and that, as you may say, in the very bosom of a French family. It seems as if you heard English everywhere; but I certainly didn't expect to find it in a place like this. I am not discouraged, however, and I talk

French all I can, even with the other English boarders. Then I have a lesson every day from Miss Maisonrouge (the elder daughter of the lady of the house), and French conversation every evening in the *salon*, from eight to eleven, with Madame herself, and some friends of hers that often come in. Her cousin, Mr. Verdier, a young French gentleman, is fortunately staying with her, and I make a point of talking with him as much as possible. I have *extra private lessons* from him, and I often go out to walk with him. Some night, soon, he is to accompany me to the opera. We have also a most interesting plan of visiting all the galleries in Paris together. Like most of the French, he converses with great fluency, and I feel as if I should really gain from him. He is remarkably handsome, and extremely polite—paying a great many compliments, which, I am afraid, are not always *sincere*. When I return to Bangor I will tell you some of the things he has said to me. I think you will consider them extremely curious, and very beautiful *in their way*.

The conversation in the parlour (from eight to eleven) is often remarkably brilliant, and I often wish that you, or some of the Bangor folks, could be there to enjoy it. Even though you couldn't understand it I think you would like to hear the way they go on; they seem to express so much. I sometimes think that at Bangor they don't express enough (but it seems as if over there, there was less to express). It seems as if, at Bangor, there were things that folks never *tried* to say; but here, I have learned from studying French that you have no idea what you *can* say, before you try. At Bangor they seem to give it up beforehand; they don't make any effort. (I don't say this in the least for William Platt, *in particular*.)

I am sure I don't know what they will think of me when I get back. It seems as if, over here, I had learned to come out with everything. I suppose they will think I am not sincere; but isn't it more sincere to come out with things than to conceal them? I have become very good friends with every one in the house—that is (you see, I *am* sincere), with *almost* every one. It is the most interesting circle I ever was in. There's a girl here, an American, that I don't like so much as the rest; but that is only because she won't let me. I should like to like her, ever so much, because she is most lovely and most attractive; but she doesn't seem to want to know me or to like me. She comes from New York, and she is remarkably pretty, with beautiful eyes and the most delicate features; she is also remarkably elegant—in this respect would bear comparison with any one I have seen over here. But it seems as if she didn't want to recognise me, or associate with me; as if she wanted to make a difference between us. It is like people they call "haughty" in books. I have never seen any one like that before—any one that wanted to make a difference; and at first I was right down interested, she seemed to me so like a proud young lady in a novel. I kept saying to myself all day, "haughty, haughty," and I wished she would keep on so. But she did keep on; she kept on too long; and then I began to feel hurt. I couldn't think what I have done, and I can't think yet. It's as if she had got some idea about me, or had heard some one say something. If some girls should behave like that I shouldn't make any account of it; but this one is so refined, and looks as if she might be so interesting if I once got to know her, that I think about it a good deal. I am bound to find out what her reason is—for of course she has got some reason; I am right down curious to know.

I went up to her to ask her the day before yesday; I thought that was the best way. I told her I wanted to know her better, and would like to come and see her in her room—they tell me she has got a lovely room—and that if she had heard anything against me, perhaps she would tell me when I came. But she was more distant than ever, and she just turned it off; said that she had never heard me mentioned, and that her room was too small to receive visitors. I suppose she spoke the truth, but I am sure she has got some reason, all the same. She has got some idea, and I am bound to find out before I go, if I have to ask everybody in the house. I *am* right down curious. I wonder if she doesn't think me refined—or if she had ever heard anything against Bangor? I can't think it is that. Don't you remember when Clara Barnard went to visit in New York, three years ago, how much attention she received? And you know Clara *is* Bangor, to the soles of her shoes. Ask William Platt—so long as he isn't a native—if he doesn't consider Clara Barnard refined.

Apropos, as they say here, of refinement, there is another American in the house—a gentleman from

Boston—who is just crowded with it. His name is Mr. Louis Leverett (such a beautiful name, I think), and he is about thirty years old. He is rather small, and he looks pretty sick; he suffers from some affection of the liver. But his conversation is remarkably interesting, and I delight to listen to him—he has such beautiful ideas. I feel as if it were hardly right, not being in French; but, fortunately, he uses a great many French expressions. It's in a different style from the conversation of Mr. Verdier—not so complimentary, but more intellectual. He is intensely fond of pictures, and has given me a great many ideas about them which I should never have gained without him; I shouldn't have known where to look for such ideas. He thinks everything of pictures; he thinks we don't make near enough of them. They seem to make a good deal of them here; but I couldn't help telling him the other day that in Bangor I really don't think we do.

If I had any money to spend I would buy some and take them back, to hang up. Mr. Leverett says it would do them good—not the pictures, but the Bangor folks. He thinks everything of the French, too, and says we don't make nearly enough of *them.* I couldn't help telling him the other day that at any rate they make enough of themselves. But it is very interesting to hear him go on about the French, and it is so much gain to me, so long as that is what I came for. I talk to him as much as I dare about Boston, but I do feel as if this were right down wrong—a stolen pleasure.

I can get all the Boston culture I want when I

go back, if I carry out my plan, my happy vision, of going there to reside. I ought to direct all my efforts to European culture now, and keep Boston to finish off. But it seems as if I couldn't help taking a peep now and then, in advance—with a Bostonian. I don't know when I may meet one again; but if there are many others like Mr. Leverett there, I shall be certain not to want when I carry out my dream. He is just as full of culture as he can live. But it seems strange how many different sorts there are.

There are two of the English who I suppose are very cultivated too; but it doesn't seem as if I could enter into theirs so easily, though I try all I can. I do love their way of speaking, and sometimes I feel almost as if it would be right to give up trying to learn French, and just try to learn to speak our own tongue as these English speak it. It isn't the things they say so much, though these are often rather curious, but it is in the way they pronounce, and the sweetness of their voice. It seems as if they must *try* a good deal to talk like that; but these English that are here don't seem to try at all, either to speak or do anything else. They are a young lady and her brother. I believe they belong to some noble family. I have had a good deal of intercourse with them, because I have felt more free to talk to them than to the Americans—on account of the language. It seems as if in talking with them I was almost learning a new one.

I never supposed, when I left Bangor, that I was coming to Europe to learn *English!* If I do learn it, I don't think you will understand me when I get back, and I don't think you'll like it much. I should be a good deal criticised if I spoke like that at Bangor. However, I verily believe Bangor is the most critical place on earth; I have seen nothing like it over here. Tell them all I have come to the conclusion that they are *a great deal too fastidious.* But I was speaking about this English young lady and her brother. I wish I could put them before you. She is lovely to look at; she seems so modest and retiring. In spite of this, however, she dresses in a way that attracts great attention, as I couldn't help noticing when one day I went out to walk with her. She was ever so much looked at; but she didn't seem to notice it, until at last I couldn't help calling attention to it. Mr. Leverett thinks everything of it; he calls it the "costume of the future." I should call it rather the costume of the past—you know the English have such an attachment to the past. I said this the other day to Madame de Maisonrouge—that Miss Vane dressed in the costume of the past. *De l'an passé, vous voulez dire?* said Madame, with her little French laugh (you can get William Platt to translate this, he used to tell me he knew so much French).

You know I told you, in writing some time ago, that I had tried to get some insight into the position of woman in England, and, being here with Miss Vane, it has seemed to me to be a good opportunity to get a little more. I have asked her a great deal about it; but she doesn't seem able to give me much information. The first time I asked her she told me the position of a lady depended upon the rank of her father, her eldest brother, her husband, etc.

She told me her own position was very good, because her father was some relation—I forget what—to a lord. She thinks everything of this; and that proves to me that the position of woman in her country cannot be satisfactory; because, if it were, it wouldn't depend upon that of your relations, even your nearest. I don't know much about lords, and it does try my patience (though she is just as sweet as she can live) to hear her talk as if it were a matter of course that I should.

I feel as if it were right to ask her as often as I can if she doesn't consider every one equal; but she always says she doesn't, and she confesses that she doesn't think she is equal to "Lady Something-or-other," who is the wife of that relation of her father. I try and persuade her all I can that she is; but it seems as if she didn't want to be persuaded; and when I ask her if Lady So-and-so is of the same opinion (that Miss Vane isn't her equal), she looks so soft and pretty with her eyes, and says, "Of course she is!" When I tell her that this is right down bad for Lady So-and-so, it seems as if she wouldn't believe me, and the only answer she will make is that Lady So-and-so is "extremely nice." I don't believe she is nice at all; if she were nice, she wouldn't have such ideas as that. I tell Miss Vane that at Bangor we think such ideas vulgar; but then she looks as though she had never heard of Bangor. I often want to shake her, though she *is* so sweet. If she isn't angry with the people who make her feel that way, I am angry for her. I am angry with her brother, too, for she is evidently very much afraid of him, and this gives me some further insight into the subject. She thinks everything of her brother, and thinks it natural that she should be afraid of him, not only physically (for this *is* natural as he is enormously tall and strong, and has very big fists), but morally and intellectually. She seems unable, however, to take in any argument, and she makes me realise what I have often heard—that if you are timid nothing will reason you out of it.

Mr. Vane, also (the brother), seems to have the same prejudices, and when I tell him, as I often think it right to do, that his sister is not his subordinate, even if she does think so, but his equal, and, perhaps in some respects his superior, and that if my brother, in Bangor, were to treat me as he treats this poor young girl, who has not spirit enough to see the question in its true light, there would be an indignation-meeting of the citizens, to protest against such an outrage to the sanctity of womanhood—when I tell him all this, at breakfast or dinner, he bursts out laughing so loud that all the plates clatter on the table.

But at such a time as this there is always one person who seems interested in what I say—a German gentleman, a professor, who sits next to me at dinner, and whom I must tell you more about another time. He is very learned, and has a great desire for information; he appreciates a great many of my remarks, and, after dinner, in the salon, he often comes to me to ask me questions about them. I have to think a little, sometimes, to know what I did say, or what I do think. He takes you right up where you left off, and he is almost as fond of discussing things as William Platt is. He is splendidly educated, in the German style, and he told me the other day that he was an "intellectual broom." Well, if he is, he sweeps clean; I told him that. After he has been talking to me I feel as if I hadn't got a speck of dust left in my mind anywhere. It's a most delightful feeling. He says he's an observer; and I am sure there is plenty over here to observe. But I have told you enough for to-day. I don't know how much longer I shall stay here; I am getting on so fast that it sometimes seems as if I shouldn't need all the time I have laid out. I suppose your cold weather has promptly begun, as usual; it sometimes makes me envy you. The fall weather here is very dull and damp, and I feel very much as if I should like to be braced up.

VI.

From Miss Evelyn Vane, *in Paris, to the* Lady Augusta Fleming, *at Brighton.*

Paris, *September* 30*th.*

Dear Lady Augusta—

I am afraid I shall not be able to come to you on January 7th, as you kindly proposed at Homburg. I am so very, very sorry; it is a great disappointment to me. But I have just heard that it has been settled that mamma and the children are coming abroad for a part of the winter, and mamma wishes me to go with them to Hyères, where Georgina has been ordered for her lungs. She has not been at all well these three months, and now that the damp weather has begun she is very poorly indeed; so that last week papa decided to have a consultation, and he and mamma went with her up to town and saw some three or four doctors. They all of them ordered the south of France, but they didn't agree about the place; so that mamma herself decided for Hyères, because it is the most economical. I believe it is very dull, but I hope it will do Georgina good. I am afraid, however, that nothing will do her good until she consents to take more care of herself; I am afraid she is very wild and wilful, and mamma tells me that all this month it has taken papa's positive orders to make her stop in-doors. She is very cross (mamma writes me) about coming abroad, and doesn't seem at all to mind the expense that papa has been put to,—talks very ill-naturedly about losing the hunting, etc. She expected to begin to hunt in December, and wants to know whether anybody keeps hounds at Hyères. Fancy a girl wanting to follow the hounds when her lungs are so bad! But I dare say that when she gets there she will be glad enough to keep quiet, as they say that the heat is intense. It may cure Georgina, but I am sure it will make the rest of us very ill.

Mamma, however, is only going to bring Mary and Gus and Fred and Adelaide abroad with her; the others will remain at Kingscote until February (about the 3d), when they will go to Eastbourne for a month with Miss Turnover, the new governess, who has turned out such a very nice person. She is going to take Miss Travers, who has been with us so long, but who is only qualified for the younger children, to Hyères, and I believe some of the Kingscote servants. She has perfect confidence in Miss T.; it is only a pity she has such an odd name. Mamma thought of asking her if she would mind taking another when she came; but papa thought she might object. Lady Battledown makes all her governesses take the same name; she gives £5 more a year for the purpose. I forget what it is she calls them; I think it's Johnson (which to me always suggests a lady's maid). Governesses shouldn't have too pretty a name; they shouldn't have a nicer name than the family.

I suppose you heard from the Desmonds that I did not go back to England with them. When it began to be talked about that Georgina should be taken abroad, mamma wrote to me that I had better stop in Paris for a month with Harold, so that she could pick me up on their way to Hyères. It saves the expense of my journey to Kingscote and back, and gives me the opportunity to "finish" a little, in French.

You know Harold came here six weeks ago, to get up his French for those dreadful examinations that he has to pass so soon. He came to live with some French people that take in young men (and others) for this purpose; it's a kind of coaching place, only kept by women. Mamma had heard it was very nice; so she wrote to me that I was to come and stop here with Harold. The Desmonds brought me and made the arrangement, or the bargain, or whatever you call it. Poor Harold was naturally not at all pleased; but he has been very kind, and has treated me like an angel. He is getting on beautifully with his French; for though I don't think the place is so good as papa supposed, yet Harold is so immensely clever that he can scarcely help learning. I am afraid I learn much less, but, fortunately, I have not to pass an examination—except if mamma takes it into her head to examine me. But she will have so much to think of with Georgina that I hope this won't occur to her. If it does, I shall be, as Harold says, in a dreadful funk.

This is not such a nice place for a girl as for a young man, and the Desmonds thought it *exceedingly odd* that mamma should wish me to come here. As Mrs. Desmond said, it is because she is so very unconventional. But you know Paris is so very amusing, and if only Harold remains good-natured about it, I shall be content to wait for the caravan (that's what he calls mamma and the children). The person who keeps the establishment, or whatever they call it, is rather odd, and *exceedingly foreign;* but she is wonderfully civil, and is perpetually sending to my door to see if I want anything. The servants are not at all like English servants, and come bursting in, the footman (they have only one) and the maids alike, at all sorts of hours, in the *most sudden way.* Then when one rings, it is half an hour before they come. All this is very uncomfortable, and I daresay it will be worse at Hyères. There, however, fortunately, we shall have our own people.

There are some very odd Americans here, who keep throwing Harold into fits of laughter. One is a dreadful little man who is always sitting over the fire, and talking about the colour of the sky. I don't believe he ever saw the sky except through the window-pane. The other day he took hold of my frock (that green one you thought so nice at Homburg) and told me that it reminded him of the texture of the Devonshire turf. And then he talked for half an hour about the Devonshire turf, which I thought such a very extraordinary subject. Harold says he is mad. It is very strange to be living in this way, with people one doesn't know.

I mean that one doesn't know as one knows them in England.

The other Americans (beside the madman) are two girls, about my own age, one of whom is rather nice. She has a mother; but the mother is always sitting in her bed-room, which seems so very odd. I should like mamma to ask them to Kingscote, but I am afraid mamma wouldn't like the mother, who is rather vulgar. The other girl is rather vulgar too, and is travelling about quite alone. I think she is a kind of schoolmistress; but the other girl (I mean the nicer one, with the mother) tells me she is more respectable than she seems. She has, however, the most extraordinary opinions—wishes to do away with the aristocracy, thinks it wrong that Arthur should have Kingscote when papa dies, etc. I don't see what it signifies to her that poor Arthur should come into the property, which will be so delightful—except for papa dying. But Harold says she is mad. He chaffs her tremendously about her radicalism, and he is so immensely clever that she can't answer him, though she is rather clever, too.

There is also a Frenchman, a nephew, or cousin, or something, of the person of the house, who is extremely nasty; and a German professor, or doctor, who eats with his knife and is a great bore. I am so very sorry about giving up my visit. I am afraid you will never ask me again.

VII.

From LÉON VERDIER *in Paris, to* PROSPER GOBAIN, *at Lille.*

September 28th.

MY DEAR PROSPER—

IT is a long time since I have given you of my news, and I don't know what puts it into my head to-night to recall myself to your affectionate memory. I suppose it is that when we are happy the mind reverts instinctively to those with whom formerly we shared our exaltations and depressions, and *je t'en ai trop dit, dans le bon temps, mon gros Prosper*, and you always listened to me too imperturbably, with your pipe in your mouth, your waistcoat unbuttoned, for me not to feel that I can count upon your sympathy to-day. *Nous en sommes nous flanquées, des confidences*—in those happy days when my first thought in seeing an adventure *poindre à l'horizon* was of the pleasure I should have in relating it to the great Prosper. As I tell thee, I am happy; decidedly, I am happy, and from this affirmation I fancy you can construct the rest. Shall I help thee a little? Take three adorable girls . . . three, my good Prosper—the mystic number—neither more nor less. Take them and place thy insatiable little Léon in the midst of them! Is the situation sufficiently indicated, and do you apprehend the motives of my felicity?

You expected, perhaps, I was going to tell you that I had made my fortune, or that the Uncle Blondeau had at last decided to return into the breast of nature, after having constituted me his universal legatee. But I needn't remind you that women are always for something in the happiness of him who writes to thee—for something in his happiness, and for a good deal more in his misery. But don't let me talk of misery now; time enough when it comes; *ces demoiselles* have gone to join the serried ranks of their amiable predecessors. Excuse me—I comprehend your impatience. I will tell you of whom *ces demoiselles* consist.

You have heard me speak of my *cousine* de Maisonrouge, that *grande belle femme,* who, after having married, *en secondes noces*—there had been, to tell the truth, some irregularity about her first union—a venerable relic of the old noblesse of Poitou, was left, by the death of her husband, complicated by the indulgence of expensive tastes on an income of 17,000 francs, on the pavement of Paris, with two little demons of daughters to bring up in the path of virtue. She managed to bring them up; my little cousins are rigidly virtuous. If you ask me how she managed it, I can't tell you; it's no business of mine, and, *à fortiori,* none of yours. She is now fifty years old (she confesses to thirty-seven), and her daughters, whom she has never been able to marry, are respectively twenty-seven and twenty-three (they confess to twenty and to seventeen).

Three years ago she had the thrice-blessed idea of opening a sort of *pension* for the entertainment and instruction of the blundering barbarians who come to Paris in the hope of picking up a few stray particles of the language of Voltaire—or of Zola. The idea *lui a porté bonheur;* the shop does a very good business. Until within a few months ago it was carried on by my cousins alone; but lately the need of a few extensions and embellishments has caused itself to be felt. My cousin has undertaken them, regardless of expense; she has asked me to come and stay with her—board and lodging gratis—and keep an eye on the grammatical eccentricities of her *pensionnaires.* I am the extension, my good Prosper; I am the embellishment! I live for nothing, and I straighten up the accent of the prettiest English lips. The English lips are not all pretty, heaven knows, but enough of them are so to make it a gaining bargain for me.

Just now, as I told you, I am in daily conversation with three separate pairs. The owner of one of them has private lessons; she pays extra. My cousin doesn't give me a sou of the money; but I make bold, nevertheless, to say that my trouble is remunerated. But I am well, very well, with the proprietors of the two other pairs. One of them is a little Anglaise, of about twenty—a little *figure de keepsake;* the most adorable miss that you ever, or at least that I ever, beheld. She is decorated all over with beads and bracelets and embroidered dandelions; but her principal decoration consists of the softest little gray eyes in the world, which rest upon you with a profundity of confidence—a confidence that I really feel some compunction in betraying. She has a tint as white as this sheet of paper, except just in the middle of each cheek, where it passes into the purest and most transparent, most liquid, carmine. Occasionally this rosy fluid overflows into the rest of her face—by which I mean that she blushes—as softly as the mark of your breath on the window-pane.

Like every Anglaise, she is rather pinched and prim in public; but it is very easy to see that when no one is looking *elle ne demande qu'à se laisser aller!* Whenever she wants it I am always there, and I have given her to understand that she can count upon me. I have every reason to believe that she appreciates the assurance, though I am bound in honesty to confess that with her the situation is a little less advanced than with the others. *Que voulez-vous?* The English are heavy, and the Anglaises move slowly, that's all. The movement, however, is perceptible, and once this fact is established I can let the pottage simmer. I can give her time to arrive, for I am over-well occupied with her *concurrentes.* *Celles-ci* don't keep me waiting, *par exemple!*

These young ladies are Americans, and you know that it is the national character to move fast. "All right—go ahead!" (I am learning a great deal of English, or, rather, a great deal of American.) They go ahead at a rate that sometimes makes it difficult for me to keep up. One of them is prettier than the other; but this latter (the one that takes the private lessons) is really *une fille prodigieuse.* *Ah, par exemple, elle brûle ses vaisseux celle-la!* She threw herself into my arms the very first day, and I almost owed her a grudge for having deprived me of that pleasure of gradation, of carrying the defences, one by one, which is almost as great as that of entering the place.

Would you believe that at the end of exactly twelve minutes she gave me a rendezvous? It is true it was in the Galerie d'Apollon, at the Louvre; but that was respectable for a beginning, and since then we have had them by the dozen; I have ceased to keep the account. *Non, c'est une fille qui me dépasse.*

The little one (she has a mother somewhere, out of sight, shut up in a closet or a trunk) is a good deal prettier, and, perhaps, on that account *elle y met plus de façons.* She doesn't knock about Paris with me by the hour; she contents herself with long interviews in the *petit salon,* with the curtains half-drawn, beginning at about three o'clock, when every one is *à la promenade.* She is admirable, this little one; a little too thin, the bones rather accentuated, but the detail, on the whole, most satisfactory. And you can say anything to her. She takes the trouble to appear not to understand, but her conduct, half an hour afterwards, reassures you completely—oh, completely!

However, it is the tall one, the one of the private lessons, that is the most remarkable. These private lessons, my good Prosper, are the most brilliant invention of the age, and a real stroke of genius on the part of Miss Miranda! They also take place in the *petit salon,* but with the doors tightly closed, and with explicit directions to every one in the house that we are not to be disturbed. And we are not, my good Prosper; we are not! Not a sound, not a shadow, interrupts our felicity. My *cousine* is really admirable; the shop deserves to succeed. Miss Miranda is tall and rather flat; she is too pale; she hasn't the adorable *rougeurs* of the little Anglaise. But she has bright, keen, inquisitive eyes, superb teeth, a nose modelled by a sculptor, and a way of holding up her head and looking every one in the face, which is the most finished piece of impertinence I ever beheld. She is making the *tour du monde,* entirely alone, without even a soubrette to carry the ensign, for the purpose of seeing for herself *à quoi s'en tenir sur les hommes et les choses*—on *les hommes* particularly. *Dis donc,* Prosper, it must be a *drôle de pays* over there, where young persons animated by this ardent curiosity are manufactured! If we should turn the tables, some day, thou and I, and go over and see it for ourselves. It is as well that we should go and find them *chez elles,* as that they should come out here after us. *Dis donc, mon gros Prosper.* . . .

VIII.

From DR. RUDOLF STAUB, *in Paris, to* DR. JULIUS HIRSCH, *at Göttingen.*

MY DEAR BROTHER IN SCIENCE—

I RESUME my hasty notes, of which I sent you the first instalment some weeks ago. I mentioned then that I intended to leave my hotel, not finding it sufficiently local and national. It was kept by a Pomeranian, and the waiters, without exception, were from the Fatherland. I fancied myself at Berlin, Unter den Linden, and I reflected that, having taken the serious step of visiting the headquarters of the Gallic genius, I should try and project myself, as much as possible, into the circumstances which are in part the consequence and in part the cause of its irrepressible activity. It seemed to me that there could be no well-grounded knowledge without this preliminary operation of placing myself in relations, as slightly as possible modified by elements proceeding from a different combination of causes, with the spontaneous home-life of the country.

I accordingly engaged a room in the house of a lady of pure French extraction and education, who supplements the shortcomings of an income insufficient to the ever-growing demands of the Parisian system of sense-gratification, by providing food and lodging for a limited number of distinguished strangers. I should have preferred to have my room alone in the house, and to take my meals in a brewery, of very good appearance, which I speedily discovered in the same street; but this arrangement, though very lucidly proposed by myself, was not acceptable to the mistress of the establishment (a woman with a mathematical head), and I have consoled myself for the extra expense by fixing my thoughts upon the opportunity that conformity to the customs of the house gives me of studying the table-manners of my companions, and of observing the French nature at a peculiarly physiological moment, the moment when the satisfaction of the *taste,* which is the governing quality in its composition, produces a kind of exhalation, an intellectual transpiration, which, though light and perhaps invisible to a superficial spectator, is nevertheless appreciable by a properly adjusted instrument.

I have adjusted my instrument very satisfactorily (I mean the one I carry in my good, square German head), and I am not afraid of losing a single drop of this valuable fluid, as it condenses itself upon the plate of my observation. A prepared surface is what I need, and I have prepared my surface.

Unfortunately here, also, I find the individual native in the minority. There are only four French persons in the house—the individuals concerned in its management, three of whom are women, and one a man. This preponderance of the feminine element is, however, in itself characteristic, as I need not remind you what an abnormally-developed part this sex has played in French history. The remaining figure is apparently that of a man, but I hesitate to classify him so superficially. He appears to me less human than simian, and whenever I hear him talk I seem to myself to have paused in the street to listen to the shrill clatter of a hand-organ, to which the gambols of a hairy *homunculus* form an accompaniment.

I mentioned to you before that my expectation of rough usage, in consequence of my German nationality, had proved completely unfounded. No one seems to know or to care what my nationality is, and I am treated, on the contrary, with the civility which is the portion of every traveller who pays the bill without scanning the items too narrowly. This, I confess, has been something of a surprise to me, and I have not yet made up my mind as to the fundamental cause of the anomaly. My determination to take up my abode in a French interior was largely dictated by the supposition that I should be substantially disagreeable to its inmates. I wished to observe the different forms taken by the irritation that I should naturally produce; for it is under the influence of irritation that the French character most completely expresses itself. My presence, however, does not appear to operate as a stimulus, and in this respect I am materially disappointed. They treat me as they treat every one else; whereas, in order to be treated differently, I was resigned in advance to be treated worse. I have not, as I say, fully explained to myself this logical contradiction; but this is the explanation to which I tend. The French are so exclusively occupied with the idea of themselves, that in spite of the very definite image the German personality presented to them by the war of 1870, they have at present no distinct apprehension of its existence. They are not very sure that there are any Germans; they have already forgotten the convincing proofs of the fact that were presented to them nine years ago. A German was something disagreeable, which they determined to keep out of their conception of things. I therefore think that we are wrong to govern ourselves upon the hypothesis of the *revanche*; the French nature is too shallow for that large and powerful plant to bloom in it.

The English-speaking specimens, too, I have not been willing to neglect the opportunity to examine; and among these I have paid special attention to the American varieties, of which I find here several singular examples. The two most remarkable are a young man who presents all the characteristics of a period of national decadence; reminding me strongly of some diminutive Hellenised Roman of the third century. He is an illustration of the period of culture in which the faculty of appreciation has obtained such a preponderance over that of production that the latter sinks into a kind of rank sterility, and the mental condition becomes analogous to that of a malarious bog. I learn from him that there is an immense number of Americans exactly resembling him, and that the city of Boston, indeed, is almost exclusively composed of them. (He communicated this fact very proudly, as if it were greatly to the credit of his native country; little perceiving the truly sinister impression it made upon me.)

What strikes one in it is that it is a phenomenon to the best of my knowledge—and you know what my knowledge is—unprecedented and unique in the history of mankind; the arrival of a nation at an ultimate stage of evolution without having passed through the mediate one; the passage of the fruit, in other words, from crudity to rottenness, without the interposition of a period of useful (and ornamental) ripeness. With the Americans, indeed, the crudity and the rottenness are identical and simultaneous; it is impossible to say, as in the conversation of this deplorable young man, which is one and which is the other; they are inextricably mingled. I prefer the talk of the French *homunculus;* it is at least more amusing.

It is interesting in this manner to perceive, so largely developed, the germs of extinction in the so-called powerful Anglo-Saxon family. I find them in almost as recognisable a form in a young woman from the State of Maine, in the province of New England, with whom I have had a good deal of conversation. She differs somewhat from the young man I just mentioned, in that the faculty of production, of action, is, in her, less inanimate; she has more of the freshness and vigour that we suppose to belong to a young civilisation. But unfortunately she produces nothing but evil, and her tastes and habits are similarly those of a Roman lady of the lower Empire. She makes no secret of them, and has, in fact, elaborated a complete system of licentious behaviour. As the opportunities she finds in her own country do not satisfy her, she has come to Europe "to try" as she says, "for herself." It is the doctrine of universal experience professed with a cynicism that is really most extraordinary, and which, presenting itself in a young woman of considerable education, appears to me to be the judgment of a society.

Another observation which pushes me to the same induction—that of the premature vitiation of the American population—is the attitude of the Americans whom I have before me with regard to each other. There is another young lady here, who is less abnormally developed than the one I have just described, but who yet bears the stamp of this peculiar combination of incompleteness and effeteness. These three persons look with the greatest mistrust and aversion upon each other; and each has repeatedly taken me apart and assured me, secretly, that he or she only is the real, the genuine, the typical American. A type that has lost itself before it has been fixed—what can you look for from this?

Add to this that there are two young Englanders in the house, who hate all the Americans in a lump, making between them none of the distinctions and favourable comparisons which they insist upon, and you will, I think, hold me warranted in believing that, between precipitate decay and internecine enmities, the English-speaking family is destined to consume itself, and that with its decline the prospect of general pervasiveness, to which I alluded above, will brighten for the deep-lunged children of the Fatherland!

XI.

MIRANDA HOPE *to her* MOTHER.

October 22d.

DEAR MOTHER—

I AM off in a day or two to visit some new country; I haven't yet decided which. I have satisfied myself with regard to France, and obtained a good knowledge of the language. I have enjoyed my visit to Madame de Maisonrouge deeply, and feel as if I were leaving a circle of real friends. Everything has gone on beautifully up to the end, and every one has been as kind and attentive as if I were their own sister, especially Mr. Verdier, the French gentleman, from whom I have gained more than I ever expected (in six weeks), and with whom I have promised to *correspond.* So you can imagine me dashing off the most correct French letters; and, if you don't believe it, I will keep the rough draft to show you when I go back.

The German gentleman is also more interesting, the more you know him; it seems sometimes as if I could fairly drink in his ideas. I have found out why the young lady from New York doesn't like me! It is because I said one day at dinner that I *admired* to go to the Louvre. Well, when I first came, it seemed as if I *did* admire everything!

Tell William Platt his letter has come. I knew he would have to write, and I was bound I would make him! I haven't decided what country I will visit yet; it seems as if there were so many to choose from. But I shall take care to pick out a good one, and to meet plenty of fresh experiences.

Dearest mother, my money holds out, and it *is* most interesting!

THE END.

This book designed by
William B. Taylor
is a production of
Heron Books, London

Published by Heron Books, London
By arrangement with Macmillan & Co

Printed and bound by Hazell Watson & Viney Ltd,
Aylesbury, Bucks

Printed and bound in England

MYSTERIOUS PRESS
KU-114-195

On the Edge

BY THE SAME AUTHOR

Wobble to Death
The Detective Wore Silk Drawers
Abracadaver
Mad Hatter's Holiday
Invitation to a Dynamite Party
A Case of Spirits
Swing, Swing Together
Waxwork
The False Inspector Dew
Keystone
Rough Cider
Bertie and the Tinman
Butchers and Other Stories of Crime

1

Smiling serenely in the September sun, Rose Bell strolled along Regent Street. Mentally she was miles away, having her husband neutered like the cat. So she ignored the woman who rushed out of Swan & Edgar's making a beeline for the kerb to hail a taxi.

The woman stopped suddenly and spun around.

'Hey, when did they let *you* out?'

Rose blinked. She registered that the woman was blonde and about her own age. A mink coat was slung casually over her shoulders. It was in beautiful condition, practically screaming out to be touched. Their eyes locked.

Rose thought, I know her, but who is she?

Penetrating eyes. Intense green. Jungle green.

Antonia Ashton.

Ack-Ack.

The service nickname struck an odd note in peacetime 1946, but those eyes were unmistakable. In Fighter Command they'd started more scrambles than the siren.

'I can't believe it!'

Antonia came right up to her and grasped her arm.

'We've got to sit down and talk, darling. We can't just pass each other in the street.'

The first place they could find was the Black and White Milk Bar in Coventry Street. They perched on high stools under the strip lighting.

'It must be five years, at least.'

'Six.'

'Kettlesham Heath.'

'We were all completely mad.'

'We had to be.'

Antonia snapped open a gold cigarette case.

'Forgive me, darling, I spotted you straight away, but your name escapes me.'

'Rose.'

'Of course! Rose – don't tell me – Mason.'

'Not any longer.'

As Rose reached for the cigarette, Antonia leaned forward, fixed those disturbing eyes on her and lightly ran her finger down the back of her hand towards the wedding ring. 'Was it the man . . . or the money . . . or both?'

'Still smoking Abdullahs, then?'

'That's dodging the question.'

'Do you have a light?'

'Of course.' Antonia's eyes strayed to an army officer walking past the window. 'Kids?'

'No.'

'Nor me, touch wood. They're a tie, aren't they?' She produced a gold lighter and held the flame to each cigarette. 'God, this street has lost its charm. You couldn't move for GIs a year ago.'

Rose took a deep draught of smoke and immediately exhaled.

'In a hurry?'

'No, no.'

'Where were you going?'

'I heard there was a queue at Lilley & Skinner's. It was a mile long.'

'What were they like?'

'The shoes? Quite dinky. Platforms with ankle-straps. I couldn't have afforded them anyway.'

'With legs like yours you should have heels three inches high.'

'These?' Rose straightened them and looked. 'You always said potty things, Antonia, but you're a tonic.'

'They were the talk of 651 Squadron, and you know it.'

'Get away, if I'd known that, I'd have really larked around.'

'You?'

Antonia's eyes shone with amusement. Creases appeared at the ends of her mouth.

It was infectious. Rose started to giggle. She had to hold on to the counter to steady herself.

When two women laugh together, really laugh, nothing else matters. The rest of the world was switched off like the wireless.

'I don't know why you're laughing. You were no angel.'

'My contribution to the war effort.'

This started them off again. They took ages to subside and then Antonia made the effort to string together some intelligible words.

'Gorgeous men. I'd love to know what happened to them – the ones who came back, I mean. Rex Ballard, Johnny Dalton-Smith . . .'

'He was nice.'

'. . . and that Wing Commander who couldn't keep his hands to himself. What was his name, for heaven's sake? You remember. What a wolf! Wicked black moustache and so much brilliantine it made your eyes water. Barry someone.'

'Bell.'

'Yes! Barry Bell. Run like hell, it's Barry Bell – remember?'

'I remember.'

'God knows how he ended up.'

'Married to me.'

Antonia stared.

'Darling, are you serious? You *are*.'

Rose nodded. 'After the Battle of Britain I was posted to Hornchurch. They wanted someone who could drive.'

'It's coming back to me. Didn't we give you a rather special send-off? It *was* you, wasn't it, when we all got drunk as skunks and tied your bed to the CO's staff car?'

'And didn't even tell me, rotten lot.'

'You were out to the world, sweetie. Go on, what happened at Hornchurch?'

'When I reported to the adjutant, who do you think was the first fellow I met?'

'No – really?'

'If you remember, I was about the only girl he ignored at Kettlesham Heath apart from Peggy the fat one in the

NAAFI, but he said there was a reason. He said he'd been dying to ask me out and couldn't bring himself to the point.'

'Why not?'

'Because he was worried sick that I'd refuse.'

Antonia's eyes grew improbably wide. 'Barry?'

'That's what he said.'

'He worshipped you from afar? Barry? I don't mean to be personal, sweetie, but–'

'I know. I fell for it. The blue eyes, the Charles Boyer voice, the uniform, the DFC, the letter he left behind in case he was shot down. I suppose you had one, too.'

'At least you got him to the altar, which is more than the rest of us managed. How did you pull it off, or shouldn't I ask?'

'By holding out. I just said no.'

'Well done!'

'We were married during the Blitz. December, 1940. Me in parachute silk and Barry in full dress uniform complete with white gloves and sword. The next afternoon he was in a dogfight over the Channel. The funny thing is, I didn't mind. I thought it was the height of glamour being married to a fighter pilot. Well, it was. I adored it.'

'Weren't you afraid?'

'Of what? A telephone call? Of course, but that's something the plucky little woman had to accept in wartime, didn't she?'

Antonia put her hand to her mouth.

'He wasn't. . . ?'

'Killed in action? No. Not Barry. He came through without a scratch.'

'And you're still happily married?'

'Still married.'

Antonia inhaled on her cigarette and gave Rose a long speculative look.

'He was demobbed last February.'

'And?'

'He's in the civil service. The Stationery Office. A

distribution officer. Sounds impressive, but he's only a clerk in reality.'

'I can't picture Barry as a civil servant.'

'It is quite a transformation. You should see him go off each day with his bowler hat and briefcase.'

'He was such an outgoing chap.'

'You mean no girl was safe with him. He hasn't altered in that respect.'

'It hasn't worked out?'

'It's a mess.'

'I'm sorry, darling. Will you. . . ?'

'Divorce him? I couldn't face a divorce at the moment. It would break Daddy's heart.'

'But it's *your* life.'

'Daddy married us in his own church, heard the vows, gave us the blessing.'

Antonia pointed a finger. 'Your pa was a vicar. I remember now!'

Rose had started talking about herself to show she was friendly and now all this had gushed out. It was embarrassing. She needed to broaden the conversation. 'I sometimes wish the war had never ended, don't you?'

'We're no better off, if that's what you mean.'

Rose ran her eyes over the mink. 'Aren't we?'

Antonia dismissed that with a shrug. 'I mean the bloody shortages. What happened to domestic servants? You can't get one for love nor money.'

Rose smiled. 'I haven't tried.'

'Take rationing, then. I couldn't run my car to the end of the street on the petrol they allow you.' Antonia said all this with a straight face. She looked at the cigarette in her hand. 'And the things you have to do for a smoke.'

'You've got a *car*?'

She nodded.

'Who on earth did you marry – a duke?'

Antonia flicked off some ash. 'You wouldn't know him. Hector wasn't one of our crowd. He wasn't in the services. Reserved occupation. Do you know that air-raid shelter in Chelsea near the Five Bells? We both ducked in there when a V-1 was overhead. It exploded while we were still halfway down the steps and I grabbed him.' She grinned. 'I felt better pressed up to his wallet.'

Rose giggled. She'd always found Antonia fun and admired her nerve. She'd never listened to the jealous WAAFs who lost their men to her.

'Did it take long?'

'April. We had to wait for his wife to die.'

'Was she an invalid?'

'Maudie? No. She drowned.'

Rose caught her breath. The *non sequitur*, tossed out so casually, perplexed her. She couldn't think what to say next. It would have been in bad taste to press for more information, and Antonia didn't volunteer any.

Antonia blew out a thin shaft of smoke and coolly took up the conversation.

'So you and I end up like this.'

'Like what?'

'Two bored housewives wishing we were back in the filter room at Kettlesham Heath.'

'I don't know about that. It was no picnic. Night duty. Those beastly earphones. Bending over the map to get our plots down. I don't know which was worse, the earache or the backache.'

'Think of the compensations – the boys in the gallery.'

'Don't! I daydream far too much.'

'Listen, Rose, I've got to go in a tick. Why don't we do this again?'

'Oh, I don't know if I can.'

'But you'd like to?'

'Well, yes.'

'So we will.'

Antonia took a taxi to Knightsbridge and let herself into a first-floor flat in Basil Street, behind Harrods. A man's voice called from the end of a red-carpeted passage.

'Tea?'

'Just had some.'

'Who with?'

'Someone I happened to meet in Piccadilly.'
'Someone interesting?'
'A plotter.'
He appeared at the door, Italian in looks, but taller than most Italians.
'A what?'
'One of the WAAFs I knew in the war. We used to push metal arrows around an enormous map.'
'A *plotter*.'
Antonia tossed the mink over a satin-cushioned chair.
'Her name is Rose.'
'Nice-looking?'
'Simmer down, man. As a matter of fact she is quite pretty in a pure-bred English way. Soft brown hair in natural curls. Wonderful skin. Bright eyes with long lashes. She'd have made a very presentable deb in her day. I can see her looking out at me from the pages of the *Tatler*. Have I put you off yet?'
'Totally and utterly.'
'Good.'
'Will you see her again?'
'Next week.'
He smiled.
'What's funny?'
'Two plotters with nothing left to plot.'
'Not necessarily. What's the time now?'
'Nearly half past four. Thinking about your husband?'
'Vic darling, don't make me laugh.'
She started unbuttoning her blouse.

2

Rose stood by the kitchen table in her apron waiting for her husband to get up from his armchair. The *Evening Standard* was full of murder again and Barry was lapping up every word. He'd followed each day of the trial of Neville Heath, the man just sentenced to death for suffocating a woman in a London hotel after beating her with a riding switch. It now came out that Heath had committed a second sadistic killing. Most of Britain – the newspapers anyway – had been engrossed by the case, as if the war hadn't given them enough death and violence. Rose found it sickening, but she was in the minority. And Barry claimed an interest because Heath was an ex-pilot in the South African Air Force who had spent some months with the RAF, attached to 180 Squadron. There was, admittedly, a suggestion of reflected glory about the way he spoke of him.

'By God, he's a handsome devil.'

'Your supper's getting cold.'

'You've got to admit he's handsome. Look.' He held the paper up. Heath was pictured seated between two detectives in the back of a car.

Not my idea of handsome, Rose thought, but a sight better-looking than you, I'll grant you, with your boozer's nose and flabby cheeks and overgrown moustache. 'It'll be ruined.'

'They tried to save him from the hangman by saying he was mad. Believe me, this chappie is as sane as you and me. Any man who can pilot a Mitchell bomber must be all right in the head.'

'Barry, are you coming to the table or not?'

'I never thought the day would come when a bloody murderer wore the RAF tie at his trial. You give a chap his wings and he behaves like that. Lunatic.'

'You just contradicted yourself.'

'What I'm saying is that he wasn't fit to hold the King's Commission.'

'He wasn't the only one.'

'Cow.'

'I didn't mean you. I'll say that for you – you were a bloody good officer once.'

He hadn't listened. He was back with his newspaper. She could have added that he was the world's worst civil servant, but she didn't. He knew it.

Why antagonize him? He only passed on his frustration by humiliating her.

When Vic had a short lunch break he would meet Antonia in the Trevor Arms in Knightsbridge, ten minutes or so from Imperial College, where he lectured. He always whistled at the prices but it was the only pub in the district with carpets and soft lighting and barmaids who called you 'sir', and Antonia preferred it to anywhere else.

Today he offered her a gin and It instead of the usual shandy.

She raised her eyebrows. 'What's all this for, naughty boy? No point in getting me sloshed if you're going straight back to your boring students.'

'Is it no, then?'

'That's a little word I never use.'

She was getting some looks as usual. She was always being told she had a carrying voice. She leaned back in her chair and winked at a chinless lieutenant who was staring over his shoulder. The Trevor was the unofficial officers' mess for the Life Guards, who had their barracks next door.

Vic returned with the drinks. 'Actually I've got good news. Well, good news for me in a way.'

'Let's hear it, then.'

'I've been offered a two-year temporary lectureship at Princeton.'

Antonia put down her glass. 'Princetown? Someone's

led you up the garden path, darling. That's not a university. It's a prison in the middle of Dartmoor.'

'Princeton, New Jersey.'

She felt a prickling sensation in her scalp. 'America?'

He nodded.

'For two years?'

'It's not until next summer.'

She looked into his brown eyes. Mentally he was already over there in New Jersey. She was livid. She couldn't survive a day without him. He was *it*. She'd never known a man who excited her more. 'You bastard! You didn't tell me you applied for this.'

'I didn't think I stood an earthly. Look, Antonia, it's not the end of the world.'

How little he knew! 'Judas! Two-faced, scurvy, blood-sucking louse. I'm coming with you.'

He was back in London like a rocket. 'You can't do that. You know you can't.'

'Who says?'

'You're married.'

'I'll leave him.'

Those eyes of his opened so wide she could see white all round them. 'It's an Ivy League university. I couldn't turn up there with a married woman in tow.'

As promised, Antonia was by the bandstand at half past two, conspicuous in a lilac-coloured coat with bishop sleeves and a matching Breton sailor hat tilted back rakishly. She was getting some long looks from the nannies walking their prams.

'Let's go that way, towards the Mall.'

'It's all the same to me.'

Green Park no longer looked like a war zone. The bulldozers had flattened the barbed wire fences and the searchlight station and filled in the artificial lake in time for the Victory celebrations. Squads of Italian POWs had laid fresh turf. Today Londoners in scores were out enjoying the autumn sun.

Rose gossiped happily about old times, and Antonia

chipped in with bits of news she had picked up since. They covered just about everyone of the Kettlesham Heath crowd. Almost an hour passed before Antonia switched back to the present.

'Where do you and Barry live, then?'

Rose considered what answer she would give. She chose to keep it vague. 'Out Pimlico way.'

'A house? One of those sweet little terraced boxes covered in stucco?' Antonia should have been in intelligence in the war.

'It was all we could get and now we've got to stay until the war damage is put right.'

'So you were bombed.'

'The house across the street. A doodlebug. No one was hurt, thank God, but we lost our front door and all the windows and there are cracks you can see daylight through.'

'Bloody doodlebugs.'

'It could have been much worse. You have to look on the bright side. We can see right across the river now.' And I, Rose instantly thought, am incapable of keeping any secrets at all. I didn't want to tell her all this. She tried clumsily to cover up. 'But no one can ever find us because we haven't got a number on the new door.'

'No number?'

'No number.' Rose raised a smile. 'We don't do much entertaining.'

'You might get a visit from me one of these days.'

'Don't! I'd die of shame if you turned up.'

'Did you tell Barry you met me?'

'No. I didn't mention it.'

'Don't you two have much to say to each other?'

'The only thing he wants to talk about is that revolting murder in the papers.'

'Neville Heath. How dull.'

'Dull? I call it horrible.'

'He's a psychopath, of course.'

'Heath?'

'Well, I wasn't referring to Barry, darling.'

There was a moment before Rose spoke again.
'What's a psychopath?'
Antonia responded as if to a child. 'He has a diseased mind, my dear.'
'Obviously.'
'So what can be more dull than that? He was incapable of committing an intelligent murder. Darling, are those rain clouds, would you say?'
They took the straightest route back to Piccadilly, where Antonia insisted on tea in the Palm Court at the Ritz. In the pink and gold setting her outfit looked so exquisite that she must have known all the time she would come here. Rose, seated in front of a gilded water nymph on a rock, felt like a refugee in her green tweed coat and woollen headscarf. People at other tables glanced at her and looked away.
'I shouldn't have come in.'
'My dear, nobody's taking any notice.'
'I do have better things at home.'
'Imagine how *I* felt in the Black and White Milk Bar.'
'If only I'd known we were coming here.'
'Relax. We deserve this.'
'I'm not sure why.'
'For putting up with our ghastly husbands.'
Rose forgot what she was wearing for a moment.
'Is yours a problem too?'
'Hector?' Antonia tensed suddenly and lowered her voice. 'Don't look now, but I think a fellow over there is giving one of us the eye.'
'Oh, no. Where?'
'To your left against the window, sitting alone. Grey pinstripe. Clark Gable moustache.'
Rose stole a glance.
'For pity's sake, Antonia! He's sixty if he's a day.'
'I swear to God that's an American tie. Where would he get a tie like that in England? It *is* Clark Gable. And he's looking at you.'
'Dressed like this?'
'Americans go wild over tweeds. This is your chance,

darling. Show him some stocking and let's see if he comes over.'

Any uncertainty in Rose's mind was removed. This was a well-tried game of Antonia's, picking out the most unlikely men and casting them as heart-throbs for her friends. Amusing to everyone but the victim. She was always catching people.

'Cool down, Ack-Ack, this isn't the sergeants' mess.'

'He's panting for you.'

'Panting! He's hardly breathing. He's practically asleep. His eyes are closing. Look, he's closed his eyes.'

'*Imagining* things.'

Antonia's face was so suggestive, and the whole thing so ridiculous that Rose was forced to smile and it started Antonia off. She made sounds like a traction engine picking up steam. Rose snatched a hankie to her mouth.

'He is definitely asleep.'

'He's just pretending.'

'He's sliding down his chair. Any minute now he's going to slip under the table.'

'Don't let that fool you. He's trying to see up your skirt.'

Rose reddened and tugged the hem over her knees.

'Spoilsport.'

Before they left, a waiter handed a small white cake-box to Antonia. She thanked him and put a coin in his hand. Then she turned to Rose.

'Isn't it a bore trying to think of things to feed the cat with? I find cream quite impossible to get in the shops.'

The umbrellas were up when they came out. There wasn't a taxi in sight, so they stood under the arcade and waited for the shower to stop. Rose didn't mind. She didn't want the afternoon to end. It was like old times, only better. Antonia wasn't performing for an entire hutful of WAAFs. The entertainment was for private delectation. She couldn't tell what to believe, and she was captivated.

Antonia hadn't finished, either.

'You and I will definitely have to do something about our husbands.'

'Do what?'

'Get shot of them.'

The only way to cope with Antonia in this mood was to keep a straight face and treat everything she said with total seriousness – until you collapsed laughing.

'How do you mean – get shot of them?'

Antonia flicked her hand as if she were shaking off the rain.

Rose aped the action. 'Just like that?'

'More or less.'

'Difficult, I should think.'

'Not at all.'

'I told you I'm not getting a divorce.'

'I wasn't talking about divorce.'

'All right, cleversticks, what other way is there to get shot of a husband?'

'I can think of at least a dozen.'

'Name one, then.'

'A fatal accident.'

'Small chance of that!'

'Chance needn't come into it, darling. Quick, that taxi's pulling up.'

The Ritz commissionaire beckoned to them with his white glove. He seemed to know Antonia. He waved away some other people and held a huge brown umbrella over them as they climbed in.

At home she tuned in to the Light Programme, got *Merry-Go-Round* and started the ironing. Barry's shirts had to be ready for another week. She couldn't imagine Antonia at the ironing board these days, though she'd seen her often enough in the billet at Kettlesham Heath pressing her uniform for kit inspections and her civvies for dates with the officers. Things had moved on since then.

Antonia has, at any rate, Rose reflected. As for me, I've slipped. Those really were better times. We bleated about the food and the uniforms, but we had some point to our lives. Women had a part to play in fighting the war. We were needed. And they paid us.

I was happy. Even the first years of marriage to Barry

weren't too impossible. I still had some self-respect and so did he. And the joke of it is that we all looked forward to something called Victory Day.

Victory!

It was Friday and Barry wouldn't be in before ten. He always picked up a woman after work on Fridays. She spat on the flat-iron to see if it was hot enough. A far cry from afternoon tea at the Ritz. She picked a shirt from the heap and spread it out, dipped her fingers in a basin of water and flicked her hand over the shirt.

'*Just like that.*'

She watched the droplets darken and spread.

3

Hector was holding forth about the Britain Can Make It Exhibition as a shop window for his products, which Antonia thought was rich considering he was a Czech. She smiled at a couple at another table and said something about the weather and Hector didn't even pause for breath. She reached across the table and pulled his plate away.

It got a reaction. 'Hey, what are you doing?'

'Haven't you finished? I have.'

'That's my dinner you took away.'

'It'll walk away by itself if you carry on much longer.'

'What do you mean?'

'Never mind.' She handed back the plate.

'I forget what I said now.'

'Good. Will you give me a divorce?'

'What?'

'I want a divorce, Hec. I want to marry Vic and go to America. He's been offered a job at Princeton University.'

Hector chuckled and brought the dimples to his cheeks, which always infuriated Antonia because it made her feel like a cradle-snatcher. In reality he was twelve years her senior, yet such a shrimp that people thought of him as not much over twenty. His springy red hair was the sort that looked no different after it was combed. 'Vic is leaving? Your fancy man is leaving?'

'I'm going with him. I'm getting a divorce from you and going with him.'

'Not possible.'

A harsher note came through in her voice. 'You're going to say it's against your religion, aren't you? Listen. You don't go to Mass. You don't make confessions. You're not exactly one of the flock, sweetie.'

'Christmas I go to Mass.'

'Face it, Hector, you've lapsed.'

'Do I treat you bad?'

'We're bored with each other. Admit it. We made a mistake.'

'This is possible. Divorce is not. We will stay married till death. Understand?'

She took a gulp of wine and leaned forward in her chair. 'Have you thought of this, Hec? If you gave me grounds, I could divorce you. It's not against *my* religion.'

'Grounds? What are you talking about? I don't understand what you need grounds for if you want to leave the country.'

'Grounds – a reason, sweetie, not a piece of land. Misconduct, as they put it in the papers. You'd simply pay some woman to spend the night in a hotel with you.'

He laughed again. 'You make it sound like money for jam. How much do such women charge? Five pounds? Ten? You think I'm a complete chump? It isn't just a divorce you're planning. You want costs. And maintenance. For ever and ever. You want to carry on eating in restaurants and buying expensive clothes. I may not be a great husband, Antonia, but I'm a pretty good businessman, and that's bad business, terrible business. No deal. No divorce. Forget it.'

She said, 'Bastard. I'll just leave you.' But the words didn't carry conviction.

Already he was talking about the bloody exhibition again. The people on an adjacent stand had told him that Prestcold were planning to have domestic refrigerators back on the market within a year – far more disturbing to Hector than the prospect of his wife abandoning him.

All around them in the glitter and red plush of Reggiori's, couples were gazing dewy-eyed at each other over the wine.

'. . . I could speed up production easy, but I depend on suppliers, you see. I give you this example. Take aluminium alloy.'

'Hector.'

'Essential in manufacture.'

'Hector, I've got a question for you. A technical question.'

'You have?'

'How many volts of electricity do they use in the underground?'

'Over six hundred. Nominally six hundred and thirty DC. Why do you ask this?'

'Enough to kill someone?'

'Easy.' He grinned. 'But I never use the tube, so you'd better think of some other thing.'

Antonia smiled back serenely. 'Ah, but I might be thinking of suicide, mightn't I, little man?'

'You?' This amused him greatly. 'You've got to know which rails to jump on.'

'The live rail.'

He handed his plate to a passing waiter and removed the cruet from the centre of the table, welcoming the rare chance to impress his wife with some electrical knowhow. 'Pass me those knives.' He arranged four knives in parallel between them. 'Now, two long knives – this and this – represent running rails, understand?'

'The wheels of the train move along them.'

'Good. Small knives are conductor rails.'

'*Two* live rails?'

'Positive and negative. Positive goes between the running rails, negative outside them. In a station' – he moved his place mat alongside the knives – 'the negative conductor rail is right over there, along the opposite wall. Now, you want to electrocute yourself. For best results, you should be in contact with both conductor rails at the same time.'

Antonia frowned. 'I'd need to be an athlete or a contortionist.'

'Difficult, yes.'

'What would happen if you just hit the nearest conductor rail?'

'In theory you could still earth six hundred and thirty volts.'

'And in practice?'

Hector smiled and pressed the tablecloth with both hands to make a furrow between the knives. 'Here, below the rails in each station they have a pit. The suicide pit. Chances are that you will fall between the rails.'

'Without getting a shock? This isn't very helpful, Hec. People *do* get killed sometimes, so how does it happen?'

'Simple. They jump in front of the train, so it's not electrocution that kills them.'

She pulled a face. 'Messy.'

He laughed. 'You want to look pretty in your coffin? You'd better take phenobarbitone.'

Rose had been in bed an hour when the key turned in the front door. Barry took each stair as if it were put there to trap him, then loosed a huge belch as he passed the bedroom door on his way to the bathroom. This, she reflected, is the Battle of Britain hero, the dashing fighter pilot I promised to love and cherish.

So how will I deal with him? I'll pretend I'm asleep. I don't want a scene. Probably I won't even mention it tomorrow. The plain truth is that I'm resigned to this every Friday night. I'm resigned to being ignored when he's home every other night of the week, so why should I object when he stays out and comes home drunk?

I'm trapped in this nightmare. I haven't just slipped in my standard of living since the war. I've slipped mentally. I've practically given up.

He thrust open the door and switched on the light.

Rose closed her eyes.

She heard him lurch to the bed, then felt his hand on her shoulder. He turned her over. She opened her eyes. He stood swaying there in his braces, no collar attached to his shirt.

'Bloody trains.'

'Where are your waistcoat and jacket?'

'Bathroom.'

She got out of bed to retrieve them. If she could possibly help it, there wouldn't be a scene. Fixing her mind on the things she regarded as the duties of a wife helped to control her anger. It was a woman's job to keep her husband decently kitted for work. He owned this blue pinstripe and his demob suit and one pre-war flannel monstrosity that he refused to part with.

The waistcoat and jacket lay in a heap beside the lavatory. Mechanically she picked several long fair hairs off the sleeves and dropped them into the bowl. She shook the jacket and something rattled in a side pocket. She took out a hotel key and glanced at the disc, replaced it and took the clothes to a hanger in the wardrobe.

He was face down on the bed, still in his day things.

'Are you proposing to sleep in your trousers?'

He made a show of clawing the braces off his shoulders.

'Roll over.'

She unbuttoned him at the front and peeled off the trousers.

He tugged the bedding aside and crawled underneath.

'Had a few after work.'

She emptied his pocket and placed the loose change in the ashtray on the chest of drawers. She smoothed the trousers and lined up the creases.

'You don't have to explain.'

'What time is it?'

'Some time after midnight.'

'Quite a bit later than usual.'

'Yes.'

She clamped the trousers in the wooden press beside the tallboy. She knew why he was late. Not because he had had a few whiskys after work. The drinking was incidental to his pursuit of women. She knew all about his infidelities. She was used to being looked at by friends in a certain way and told that her husband had been sighted again in the bar of the Strand Palace Hotel. They didn't have to say any more. The entire scene was in the look.

What had delayed him then? One thing was certain: it wasn't an excess of passion. He couldn't contain himself for more than a minute even when sober. He was late because he'd gone to a different hotel, in Hammersmith. Presumably he'd failed to find a pick-up in the West End.

So he'd started again. More whiskys. More than he could handle.

He was making an effort to sound rational.

'Did you get worried about me?'

'Worried?'

'I mean, did you think I'd had an accident?'

'An accident?' Her conversation with Antonia outside the Ritz flitted into her mind and out of it. 'No.'

'Callous bitch.'

'Barry, you're in no state–'

'I could have been dead for all you care. You don't bloody care, do you?'

He was working himself up. *She* was angry, too, and entitled to be. What was picking his clothes off the floor if it wasn't caring? Rescuing his clothes that reeked of some woman and dutifully hanging them up for him. Yet she didn't want an argument. She took her dressing-gown off the hook.

'I'm going to sleep in the spare room.'

She reached to pick up her pillow and with surprising speed he grabbed her wrist and jerked her off balance. She fell across the bed.

'You're staying here and that's an order.'

'Barry, let go of my arm.'

He started wrestling with her. She was pushed face down into the eiderdown. She was shocked by the force of the attack. He had never been violent before. She twisted her head for breath and she felt her nightdress tearing at the armpit. He clapped his hand on the back of her neck.

'Don't you dare move, woman.'

'Barry, you're hurting.'

'You don't know what it is to be hurt.'

His voice had a cruel edge she had never heard from him. A horrid possibility crept into her mind. His imagination had been stoked up by the newspapers reporting those vile murders by Heath.

'Please, Barry.'

'Getting above yourself, aren't you? Bloody vicar's daughter. Need bringing down a peg or two.'

He slid his hand upwards, took a grip on her hair and twisted her head with such force that her shoulders and torso followed the movement. She was turned face up like a playing card. His leg straddled her thighs and trapped her. Whisky fumes gusted into her face.

She was rigid with fear, certain he meant to bite her. She could see the teeth bared.

'Barry, no!'

'Shut up.'

His face moved closer, rasping her cheek with his moustache. He spoke in her ear.

'You're a sanctimonious bitch. Admit it. Out with it, loud and clear.'

'Please–'

'Say it.'

'I'm a sanctimonious bitch.'

'Louder. Tell the neighbours what you are. Tell the whole bloody street.'

She shouted the words.

'Better. And you were worried sick when I was late.'

'I was worried sick.'

'Why?'

'Why what?'

'Come on. Why were you worried sick?'

He was speaking between clenched teeth. He expected an answer fast. And this time he expected her to supply it.

Her face twitched. She was too terrified to think.

'Come on!'

'I thought . . .'

'Yes?'

'I thought you must have had an accident.'

'What sort of accident?'

'What sort?'

'I want to know if you're speaking the truth. You say you thought I had an accident.'

She couldn't fathom what satisfaction this gave him and she dreaded where it was leading. She just hoped to God she could keep the right answers coming. If it spared her from physical pain she was willing to supply whatever he wanted to hear.

She blurted out the first thing she could think of. 'Er – an accident on some stairs. You fell down some stairs and broke your leg.'

'Where?'

'I don't know – the office.'

'They'd have let you know. Someone would have let you know by seven, easily. Better think again.'

'You fell off a bus. You hit your head on the road and got concussion. Nobody knew who you were.'

'So what did my poor distracted wife do about it?'

'Phoned the police. And all the hospitals.'

'How touching. And all this is true, isn't it, Rose, darling, because you were brought up to believe that lying is a sin before God?' He pressed his forefinger under her chin and pushed upwards. 'Have I caught you out?'

'I'm confused. I don't know what you want me to say.'

'Say you were lying through your teeth.'

'All right, I was.'

'And I caught you at it.'

'You caught me at it.'

This appeared to satisfy him, because he gave a grunt and withdrew the leg that was pinning her down. He rolled right away from her and sat up.

'I'm going for a piss. Don't move a muscle.'

Rose's nerves gave way to the stress. She shivered uncontrollably. Too fearful to run out, she dreaded his return. She listened to him pass water, then flush the cistern. It was all she could do to stop from whimpering when he came back. Yet she still had sufficient detachment to despise herself. That made it harder to endure, knowing what a spineless creature she had become.

He turned out the light as he came in. Then he dropped on to the bed like a felled tree, on his own side, close to Rose, without touching. She prayed that he might sleep now, but he still wanted to taunt her.

'What a flaming liar! I said what a flaming liar! Lord bloody Haw-Haw isn't in it. Let's face it, you wouldn't lose any sleep if I ended up in hospital. You were nicely tucked up in bed when I finally got in, weren't you? Weren't you?'

'Is that what upset you? I didn't realize.'

She felt slightly easier in her mind for finding a reason for his behaviour. She hadn't pictured it from his point of view. He wasn't home by midnight so she had gone to bed. Evidently he regarded this as a betrayal. It was the silliest nonsense considering how he had spent the evening, but that was the way his mind worked. He felt rejected. God, what she was reduced to!

'Shall I make you some coffee?'

'Coffee be buggered.'

'Just as you wish.'

'I'm accident-proof, if you want to know. I got through the war without a prang, didn't I? Over seven hundred flying hours. After that I'm not going to fall down the moving staircase at Victoria, am I? Or walk into a lamp post.' He made a smug chuckling sound. 'The only accident I ever had was with a certain WAAF sergeant at Hornchurch.'

She tensed again. 'What do you mean?'

He could hardly speak for laughing now. The words came out in a wheeze.

'You know what I mean. An accident. One that got away. A bun in the oven.'

'You got her pregnant?'

'That was the upshot, so to speak.'

Rose's hands crept up to her neck.

'She had a child?'

'A bouncing baby boy.'

'At Hornchurch? After we were married.' She sat up in bed in the dark. 'You had a child after we were married? You're lying.'

'Who are you calling a liar? There's only one liar in this house, and it isn't me.'

4

Antonia was emphatic. 'Darling, he made the whole thing up.'

'Don't you believe it?'

'It's absolute rubbish.'

'Listen, he told me the woman's name – Stella Paxton. She was in the MT section at Hornchurch, driving the officers about.'

'Does that prove anything?'

'But Barry's quite open about his affairs. Why would he lie about this?'

'Men have fragile egos, my flower. He came in late expecting a scene and you put him to bed like your tame teddy bear. He was insulted.'

'You think he wanted a scene?'

'A fight, more like.'

'That's rich. Here am I wondering where I went wrong and you tell me I didn't pick a fight. We've never had fights.'

'And look at the result.'

In spite of her distress, Rose smiled. She'd phoned because she needed to speak to someone. It wasn't the sort of problem you could take to your mother and father. She knew she could rely on Antonia for a heart-to-heart and some cogent advice.

'Would you have given him a telling-off?'

'A telling-off! A punch in the kisser. He wanted a reaction.'

'He's got one now – I'm devastated.'

'Of course you are, poor lamb. You've taken it all to heart.'

'He hurt me. Physically held me down and hurt me. I was terrified and he knew it.'

'It's just a game to them. They don't know their own strength.'

'Not Barry. He isn't like that. I thought he was going to strike me.'

'But he didn't?'

'Well no.'

'All right, he scared you a bit. Didn't the boys at school ever chase you with a spider or something? It's horrid, but it's not without excitement.'

'You don't understand. There was nothing playful about this. It was vile, as if. . . . Oh, I don't know. Perhaps it's my imagination. That beastly murder in the newspapers is giving me ideas.'

'Heath?'

'I told you. Barry's fascinated by it.'

'Sounds as if *he* was the one who got ideas.'

'Antonia, I don't believe he made it up about Stella Paxton and the baby.'

'If that's what worries you, you'd better find out for sure.'

'Yes, but how?'

'Go through his things, for heaven's sake.'

'I can't do that.'

'Don't be naïve, flower. If he has another woman and child and he's thinking of ditching you . . .'

'Oh, I didn't say that.'

'. . . don't you think you have a right to know? Does he keep letters, photographs, anything like that?'

'He keeps the bills in the writing desk. I've no idea what else is in there.'

'Better get busy then. Is it locked?'

'The lock isn't very good.'

'Well, then. Put down the phone and do it now. Barry isn't there, is he?'

'Of course not, but I've always respected his privacy.'

'Did he respect you when he got Stella Paxton pregnant?'

Rose closed her eyes tightly. 'Now you're telling me it's true. I don't know what to believe. Antonia, what do you really think?'

'Never mind me, sweetie. It's obvious you've got to find out for yourself.'

*

She still hesitated when it came to forcing open the desk. Her throat went dry and her hand on the kitchen knife trembled.

She hesitated because the act of breaking into Barry's desk was underhanded. She had been deceived; now she was trading deceit for deceit.

'Did he respect you. . . ?'

She tightened her grip, slid the knife in and pressed on it, supporting the flap with her left hand as it came open. Everything was stacked in front of her in the slots and shelves – bills, chequebooks, bank statements, payslips, his demob papers, photos, marriage certificate and bundles of business letters. There were fountain pens, bottles of ink, a glass paperweight and the case containing his DFC.

Ashamed of herself, she snapped the desk shut again.

She returned to the kitchen, put the knife back in the drawer and took out the small bottle of brandy that she kept in the larder. It was supposed to be for Christmas puddings, but she usually forgot to use it. It had come in useful when her mother stayed with her during the bombing. She poured some into a medicine glass.

The phone rang. She knew it would be Antonia again.

'What did you find, darling?'

'Nothing at all.'

'Really? You did get into the desk, I hope?'

'Yes.'

'I'm surprised, then. Did you find his address book?'

'Address book? No.'

'Diaries, letters?'

'Nothing of a personal nature.'

'He keeps them somewhere else, then. Can you think of any other place?'

'Not at the moment. Look, I'm going to give it some thought before I do anything else.'

'We'll work something out between us.'

'Thanks awfully, Antonia, but I ought to think this out carefully before I do anything at all.'

'Don't be so daft, darling. What are friends for? We'll sort it out tomorrow.'

'Tomorrow?'

'Elevenses in the Corner House.'

'Would you mind terribly if we didn't? I'm still rather shaky. I don't feel up to going out.'

'You poor wee thing – of course. How about Thursday?'

'I'd rather leave it for the present if you don't mind. Perhaps in a week or two.'

She wasn't too proud of herself for putting Antonia off so soon after turning to her for support, but she didn't want to be hustled into doing things against her conscience. It hadn't been right to force open the writing desk. She would find out the truth by some less underhanded means. The most obvious way was to ask Barry straight out, but she couldn't face that. It would be laying herself open to more hurt. She wanted to know, but not in the heat of argument.

5

Antonia didn't hang up the phone directly. She rang for a taxi. There was just time to change into a blue double-breasted suit and pink frilly blouse and to touch up her lips before the cab pulled up at the door.

'The tobacconist's in Sloane Square.'

There, she winked at the solemn old Scot who supplied her with ciggies.

'Have they come in yet?' She could always rely on him for a packet of some brand or other, even with the shortages. Today it was ten Escudos, passed over the counter in a brown paper bag.

'They're one and threepence, I'm afraid.'

'That's all right. How are your Hearts, Mr MacDade?'

'Disappointing, madam. They lost four nil at home last week.'

'Just what they needed, darling. Football players are like carpets – they need the occasional beating. They'll score a hatful on Saturday.'

'Is that a fact?'

She got back into the taxi.

'Pimlico, please.'

'What address, lady?'

'Perhaps you can tell me. A street where a flying bomb fell.'

'I'm a cabbie, love, not the ARP.'

'It can't be so difficult to find. The house I want is in a terrace opposite the bomb site. And it faces the river.'

They drove to Pimlico and looked for someone to ask. Every street was a porticoed terrace. A woman with a pram knew of two bomb sites. An entire terrace had been flattened in Sutherland Street and twenty people had been killed, but that was in the Blitz. Her second suggestion turned out to have been the result of high-explosive bombs in 1943. A milkman suggested Oldfield Gardens. He thought it was a doodlebug that had flattened the end house there.

Oldfield Gardens had a down-at-heel look. Some of the shabbiness was the result of war damage; much more could be put down to neglect. The houses had once looked smart with their casement windows, solid front doors and iron railings around the basement steps. Cheap replacement doors had spoilt the effect and the once-white fronts were chipped and stained.

She asked the driver to wait by the corner shop at the end of the street farthest from the bomb site. The smell of cats crept into her nostrils.

A wolf-whistle greeted her as she approached the bomb site. Some workmen were fixing posts into what had once been a front garden. She gave them a wave and crossed the road.

The last house was unusual for not having an array of doorbells. The doorstep was polished to inspection standard. She pressed the bell.

She flung out her hands and embraced Rose the moment she opened the door.

'My poor flower – I couldn't abandon you at a time like this. I've brought you some ciggies.'

Rose muttered some words of thanks as Antonia broke off the embrace and headed for the scullery.

'What a sweet house, and so tastefully furnished. Is it all yours? I love it.'

'I've got rather a headache.'

'I'll make you some tea. No, I insist. You sit down and I'll do everything. Have you got any aspirin? I can bring it upstairs if you'd like to lie down.'

She filled the kettle and lit the gas and then wandered out to look at the other rooms, calling out her observations as she went.

'Oh, a piano. Do you play, darling? I can't believe Barry likes Sigmund Romberg. He said a beautiful thing – Romberg, not Barry – "A love song is just a caress set to music." Isn't that romantic? And this must be the writing desk you mentioned.'

'Please don't touch the writing desk.'

'I wouldn't dream of it.'

'I don't mean to be rude.'

'Be as rude as you like, my pet. That's what I keep telling you – you're too polite for your own good.'

The phone rang in the front room where Antonia was.

'Leave it to me, darling.' She picked up the receiver and put it to her ear.

A man's voice, cautious and well-spoken.

'Good morning, is that Wing Commander Bell?'

'I'm afraid not. Can I help?'

'Roberts here. Manager of the Westminster Bank.'

'Yes?'

'I really wished to speak to him personally on a confidential matter. Am I speaking to Mrs Bell, by any chance?'

Antonia decided that a white lie was not only excusable, but opportune.

'Well, yes.'

'I wonder . . . is your husband away from home?'

'Away? No. He's at work.'

'Only I've sent a number of letters over the last month asking him to come and see me, and received no reply.'

'I'm sure there's a reason.'

'Undoubtedly.'

'I'll ask him to get in touch.'

'Would you? These things are better discussed man to man, so to speak. I'm sure we'll reach an amicable arrangement.'

'I hope so.'

'Thank you. Goodbye, Mrs Bell.'

She heard the click and the purring note before she replaced the receiver, thinking about the amicable arrangement that Barry was expected to reach with his bank manager. She returned to the kitchen as the kettle was boiling.

'That was Mr Roberts, the manager of the Westminster Bank.'

'Really? What did he want?'

'A word with Barry. I told him he wasn't here.'

'Stupid man. What does he expect if he rings up in the middle of the morning?'

'He's written several letters.'

'To Barry? Yes, he has. One arrived this morning.'

'He's been asking Barry to come and see him. Barry hasn't replied.'

'I can't understand that. He's awfully efficient. I wonder what this is about.'

Antonia handed her a cup of tea. 'It's staring you in the face, sweetie. He's overdrawn at the bank.'

'That's impossible. We live quite frugally. I haven't had a new dress since the war and he's still wearing the same suit. We don't even use our clothing coupons.'

'What about his nights out?'

'Oh, he doesn't believe in spending much on his women. Never more than a couple of drinks and the price of a cheap hotel room for an hour. It's a matter of pride with Barry.'

'In that case, I apologize.'

'What for?'

'For misleading you. Obviously I was wrong.'

'About what?'

'For pity's sake, darling – the child. There *is* a child. Barry's in the red because he's keeping up two households. You can't do that on the money a civil service clerk takes home.'

Rose put down her cup. The colour drained from her face. It was a long time before she spoke and then her voice came as a whisper.

'It's not true.'

Antonia took an unopened letter from behind the clock on the mantelpiece, glanced at the typed address and then propped it against Rose's teacup. Rose shook her head.

'I couldn't. He'd know.'

Antonia took out her lighter and put the flame to the gas

ring. Steam gushed from the kettle again. She picked up the letter and held the back of it to the spout.

'He won't find out.'

When it was quite moist, she placed the letter in Rose's hand, at the same time squeezing her arm.

Rose started peeling back the flap.

'From the bottom, darling. You don't want to tear it.'

She took out the letter, read it and threw it down.

'He's overdrawn six hundred and ninety pounds, the swine. The rotten, beastly swine. I could cheerfully kill him.'

Antonia returned the letter to its envelope and pressed the flap to the seal.

'This might want just a smear of glue.'

The letter was lying on Barry's plate when he got in. Rose had ripped it open at the top.

She eyed him accusingly. 'I suppose she lives in style while I count every blessed penny.'

'Not at all. I send her something to help with the child, that's all.'

'*The* child? You talk about him as if you had nothing to do with it.'

'Rosie, I'm trying to spare your feelings.'

'Thanks! It's a bit late for that.'

'All right, I should have told you. I've been sending twenty pounds on the first of each month. Michael will be starting school soon.'

'I don't want to hear about him.'

'As you wish.'

He took her at her word. She was glad of a minute or two's respite. She busied herself with the herrings she was grilling and tried to look unconcerned. She didn't speak again until she put the plate in front of him.

She said, 'What are you going to do about the bank?'

'I'll speak to Roberts. Have to go and see him, I suppose. How did he sound on the phone?'

'I've no idea. I mean I was too shocked to notice.'

'I've got a bit in National Savings. And I might be able to raise something on the insurance.'

'Where does that leave me if you drop dead?'
'What else do you suggest?'
'Why don't you pawn my wedding ring? It doesn't mean a thing to me any more.'
'This isn't like you, Rose.'
'Oh, dry up, will you?'
'Do you want a divorce?'
'So that you can clear off and marry your tart and settle all your problems? Smart thinking, Barry. I've got to hand it to you – you're no fool, whatever else you are. No, I don't want a divorce. It would just about kill my parents, and you know it. Better think again.'
They finished the meal in silence.

Barry drew aside the bedroom curtains in the morning about 6.30 as he always did. There was heavy condensation on the glass so he used the sleeve of his pyjamas to wipe one of the panes clear.
'Bloody hell!'
Rose stirred under the bedclothes.
'What is it now?'
'Come and see.'
'It's too cold.'
His voice took on an odd, shrill note. 'I won't stand for this. It's enough to turn your stomach. I'll get on to the council. See if I don't. Bloody liberty. As if we haven't got enough to put up with.'
When Barry had gone out to the bathroom, Rose slipped out of bed and went to the window. She, too, was profoundly disturbed by what she saw. She had heard some workmen hammering the day before and she had assumed they were fencing off the bomb site to keep the children from playing there.
They had erected a vast hoarding filled with the white face of a woman, a face unmistakably stricken with grief. Her pallor was set against the black hat with drapes and veil and the black high-necked dress that she wore. The lips were bloodless and the grey eyes stared upwards,

focusing on nothing. The slogan under the face was 'KEEP DEATH OFF THE ROAD'. Under it, in smaller lettering, 'Carelessness Kills'.

6

The next Friday afternoon about half past five Rose opened the door to a man with a bicycle pump tucked under his arm like a swagger stick. He raised his hat. The horrid poster behind him was gleaming in the lamplight, throwing him into silhouette.

'Mrs Bell?'

'Yes.'

'Smart.' As if no more was needed to be said he stooped to remove his cycle clips.

Rose held on to the door. The metal plate on their doorpost to discourage hawkers and circulars had gone in the bombing, and she was wary of being pestered. It was a nuisance having a front door that opened directly on to the street.

He stood up straight and stepped closer. 'Arnold Smart. Don't you remember?'

Faintly she did. There was something about the nasal twang in the voice.

'I call once a month to collect the premium. Your husband usually comes to the door.'

'Oh, insurance.'

'Obviously I've come at an awkward moment, but as your husband mentioned some urgency in the matter . . .'

'Is that so?'

'. . . I thought I'd drop the form in now. Isn't he at home?'

'He's always late on Fridays. I'll give him the form if you like. What is it exactly?'

He fingered his necktie. 'Might I step inside and wait? I don't wish to be a nuisance but I'd like to offer him some professional advice if I may.'

'I don't expect him until ten at the earliest.'

'Ten? That *is* rather late. I'd better come back another day. I do think a word in confidence might be advisable.'

She lost her patience. 'For heaven's sake, what's all the mystery for? I'm his wife. He doesn't do anything without consulting me.'

'You've discussed this with him?'

'Frequently.'

'Forgive me, then. I wasn't aware of that. It's entirely up to Wing Commander Bell, of course, but I'd weigh the advantages very carefully before surrendering a policy as valuable as his.'

Alarm bells sounded in her head, but she managed to give the impression she'd heard nothing new. 'You mean cashing it in? What's wrong with that?'

'It's a lot to sacrifice for a short-term gain. You'd get only a fraction of the five thousand you would realize on maturity – or if anything should happen to him. Far be it from me to frighten you, but I'm constantly hearing of good men struck down in their prime. None of us knows what fate has in store for us.'

'I'll mention it. Perhaps we ought to think again.'

'I strongly recommend that you do. If it's a temporary difficulty you have, we could talk about a loan of equivalent value.'

'Yes, why don't you come back and talk to my husband another evening?'

'The earliest I could manage is next Thursday.'

'That would be much more convenient. Why don't you keep the surrender form until then?'

He lifted his hat again and returned to his bicycle, propped against the kerb. He fastened the pump in place, put on the clips and pedalled away, past the great, pale face of the widow.

Rose returned to the kitchen, pulled a chair from the table and said aloud, 'You bastard, Barry. You stinking rotten bastard.'

He'd meant what he said. He was about to sell off her security. If he dropped dead and she was uninsured, she would be left with nothing but his debts.

Their marriage had become a mockery long before Barry had disclosed the existence of his second family.

He'd said a number of times that Rose could have a divorce, knowing, of course, that it would break the hearts of the two dear people she had left in the world to love. For her parents' sake she'd resolved to endure a loveless marriage to a faithless man. She'd made that decision when Barry had finally admitted to picking up women for sex. She'd lived with that humiliation long enough.

Now he had discovered that he couldn't keep two homes, two women and a child on his pathetic income. He proposed to surrender the insurance to pay off the overdraft. Deluded idiot. What would that achieve? The demands would only increase. The boy was growing up, starting school soon. Obviously it suited Stella Paxton to pester Barry relentlessly, destroy the marriage and take him as her husband.

Rose wanted to say, take the swine, you're welcome to him, yet there remained the sticking point. Because she would not consider a divorce whilst her parents were alive, she faced not only humiliation and hurt, but insolvency.

Since the war ended she'd suffered a steep drop in her standard of living to satisfy Barry's pride that he could support a wife. She'd made do with shapeless Utility clothes. Hadn't been to a hairdresser's. Hadn't been taken to the pictures or a dance. Her sacrifices had helped to pay the premiums on that insurance. She would have enjoyed going out to work if he hadn't made such an issue about it shaming a man. Too late now. Any money she made would go the same way as the rest.

Realistically, nothing short of Barry being killed could make any difference. Antonia had the solution – if she was serious.

An accident.

Rose admitted no inconsistency in her thinking. She had been brought up by loving parents who lived by the Ten Commandments. Any breach of Holy Law that she had committed as a child had so manifestly upset them that she had taken it to be a sin against her parents, rather than against God. She had found it very easy to forget about the God who was in Heaven. The only way to survive as a vicar's daughter was to treat your father as God. You could do anything at all so long as you kept him in blissful ignorance.

Barry had forced her hand. She had until Thursday evening if she was to get a penny of the insurance.

She was studying the calendar when she heard the key turn in the front door. She looked at the clock. It wasn't even eight yet.

Barry thrust open the kitchen door.

'Surprised you?'

'Well, yes.'

'What's up? You look peeved.'

'My eyes are sore, that's all.'

'See if these help.'

He handed her a bunch of red roses.

'Believe it or not, he expected the works.'

Antonia's eyes widened unusually. She hardly ever registered surprise. She had a way of treating everything as if she were hearing it for the second time. 'And did you let him?'

'Of course not. As if one bunch of flowers cancelled out all the women he's had.'

'The red roses must have cost him a packet.'

'I'm not one of his Friday night tarts and I told him so. I told him to take a cold bath.'

Antonia almost purred in approval. 'Nice work! Did he get nasty?'

'He went down to the pub until closing time. When he came in he made a clumsy effort to paw me so I bit his ear.'

'Darling, after what happened last time, you've got some pluck.'

'I was so angry I didn't think. He let me alone after that.'

Rose glared at a fat woman on an adjacent table who had stopped eating her blackberry flan the better to overhear what was said. They were in the marbled setting of the Strand Corner House. Any afternoon between the hours of three and four many a lapse of conduct was discussed over the silver-plated teapots. A string quartet was playing 'My dreams are getting better all the time'. Antonia was in yet another new outfit that looked as if it came from Harrods, a white pillbox hat and an emerald green two-piece with white polka dots.

'I wonder what he hoped to achieve.'

From the long look Antonia gave as she spoke it was clear that she suspected Barry of plotting something. Rose knew better. 'He's like that. He thinks all his faults are forgiven in bed. Sometimes they have been, I don't mind admitting. Well, forgotten, if not forgiven. I can't live like a nun. It's against nature. Good, she's leaving.'

The fat woman ostentatiously pushed aside her teacup and marched out.

Rose hardly paused. She was coming out with things that she wouldn't have discussed with a living soul until a few days ago. She heard herself analysing Barry's behaviour with such steely detachment that it might have been Antonia speaking. 'I suppose he could have been trying to sweeten me in case I raised Cain about the insurance, but I doubt it. Barry isn't a schemer. He lives for the moment, and that's what landed us in our present mess.'

Antonia, evidently sensing where this was leading, attempted to head Rose off with some homespun philosophy. 'Men like him won the war for us, but they can't cope in peacetime.'

'So?'

'Have some more tea.'

'Damn the tea.'

She felt entitled to some straight talking. It was obvious Antonia knew what was in her mind and was shying away from it with her platitudes about the war and her fussing with the teapot.

'What I'm telling you is that I'd be better off if Barry was dead.'

'Well, yes.' Antonia smiled and seemed to want to make light of it. 'Five thousand pounds better off.'

'Not if he signs that surrender form on Thursday.'

The point still appeared to elude Antonia. 'So you've got four days to change his mind.'

'Unless.'
'Unless what, darling?'
'Unless something happens to him.'
There was an interval when nothing was said. A syrupy Viennese waltz filled the silence. Antonia pushed some hair back from her forehead and looked far across the restaurant.
'Well, Rose, my dear, you'd better say exactly what's in your mind.'
'I want him to have an accident, like you said the other day.'
There was a glint of amusement in the green eyes. 'Did I?'
'Don't tease. You know you did. Outside the Ritz.'
'And you believed me, darling?'
'For Christ's sake, Antonia, if you weren't serious, you'd better tell me, because I am.'
'An accident? Well, it's not impossible. I'd have to think about it.' She traced her fingertip around the rim of her cup. 'I suppose Barry had to give up the flying when he was demobbed?'
'He hasn't seen an airfield since the war.'
'Does he drive?'
Rose shook her head. 'We can't afford a car on his income.'
'This is difficult. Is he a swimmer?'
'I'm afraid not. That is to say, I believe he *can* swim, but he doesn't ever go near water. He's not the athletic type.'
'Is he the handyman type? Could he be persuaded to replace those missing tiles on your roof?'
Desperate as she felt, Rose couldn't suppress a smile. 'Good idea, but definitely not. He absolutely refuses.'
'We're not getting very far, are we? Suppose we go about this another way. You tell me everything he does from the moment he gets up in the morning.'
'In detail?'
'The more the better.'
'I'll try.' Rose closed her eyes and concentrated. 'Wakes up at 6.30 when the alarm goes. Groans. Heaves himself

out and reaches for his slippers. Shuffles into the bathroom and uses the toilet. You asked for everything.'

'I meant it. Don't stop now.'

'Goes to the washbasin and runs the hot tap. Swears when it comes out almost cold. Swishes some over his face. Makes a lather for a shave.'

'What sort of razor?'

'Safety, I'm afraid. Brushes his teeth.'

'Toothpowder?'

'Paste. Returns to the bedroom and dresses. Woollen underwear. Blue pinstripe. White shirt and collar. Any one of three striped ties. Meanwhile, I've slipped downstairs in my dressing-gown and cooked some porridge and made toast. He comes down and opens the Ideal boiler and empties the ashcan. This is frightfully boring.'

'I'm hanging on every word.'

So Rose picked her way patiently through the daily routine until she had got Barry into bed again and switched out the light. 'Well?'

'His journey home. Go through it again.'

'But I've told you it's as safe as houses. The Stationery Office depot is just behind Harvey Nichols, so he walks around the corner to Knightsbridge tube station and gets a Piccadilly Line train to South Ken. He changes to the District Line and comes back to Victoria and walks it from there, straight down St George's Drive. He's home by a quarter past six, except for Fridays. He switches on the wireless and hears the last part of the news.'

'What time does he leave work?'

'Half past five.'

'Carrying his briefcase and umbrella?'

Rose gripped the edge of the table and leaned forward. 'Have you thought of something?'

Some seconds passed before Antonia spoke. 'Let's get one thing straight, my flower. Did you mean every word you said about Barry? You really want him to have an accident?'

7

On Wednesday afternoons the Imperial College timetable was marked 'Sport'. Some of the staff unselfishly turned out to referee football matches or cycle along the towpath shouting through megaphones. Vic went to bed with Antonia.

If it counted as sport it was of championship quality, brilliantly performed. He managed to be tender and passionate just as desired, alert to every signal she gave. She cried out repeatedly and gritted her teeth and promised herself she would never be parted from him. It was impossible to imagine it with anyone else.

The climax left every sport for dead. It should have been set to music and played at the last night of the Proms. Then they lay still.

Presently he pressed his hands into the pillow and eased himself upwards to get a better sight of her. 'These are pretty terrific, too.'

'I'll settle for pretty.'

'Just pretty, then.' He continued to look.

'Cover me up for the love of Mike. There's a wicked draught coming in.'

He removed his weight and Antonia gripped the bedclothes and pulled them up to her neck. Vic found enough space to lie on his side, resting his hand on the flat of her stomach. She let it remain there.

'I didn't know you were cold.'

'I was coming out in goosepimples.'

'Is that what they were?'

'Ha bloody ha.'

'Want a fag?'

'All right.'

They lit up. She waited a while before asking what she was dying to know.

'Have you heard any more from America?'
'No.'
'Is it still on?'
'I'm afraid so. Can't we talk about something else?'
'If you wish. What would you say to getting married next spring?'
He twisted around to face her and almost fell out of bed in the process. He grabbed her arm. 'What?'
'You heard, lover.'
'You're not free to marry anyone.'
'I might be if I get a good offer.'
'How come? What about Hector? I thought divorce was out of the question.'
'Vic, just answer my question, will you? Would you marry me if I was free?'
'Christ, I never thought of it as a possibility.'
'We love each other, don't we?'
'Well, yes. But I don't see how–'
She put a finger against his lips. 'Yes, or no?'
The puzzled look remained.
'Vic, I want an answer.'
'Yes, then.'
'Good. I don't consider this a proposal, by the way. You can save that up for the appropriate time.'
'When's that likely to be?'
'Not long.'

By Thursday Antonia had twice travelled the tube with Barry. She had waited for the evening exodus of bowler-hatted civil servants from the Stationery Office depot at 5.30. She'd taken the precaution of concealing her hair in a headscarf knotted at the front, factory-girl style, and she wasn't wearing lipstick. She had kept her distance when Barry crossed Sloane Street and made a beeline for the tube station, but she needn't actually have bothered because he hadn't been looking about him. He'd had that faraway expression that you see on the face of regular travellers. Anyway, it was six years or more since she'd been to bed with him.

Those six years had taken their toll of Barry. The laughlines were deep creases now and his neck had thickened and was chafed by a collar that he'd obviously outgrown. He'd kept the handlebar moustache and, if anything, it was bushier than before, only it simply didn't go with the bowler hat; he should have shaved it off on the day he was demobbed. Perhaps it wasn't fair to draw conclusions from someone's appearance after a day at the office, yet it seemed to Antonia that Barry had looked more jaded than he had in the old days after many nights of flying. She had no difficulty picturing him among the middle-aged men in hotel bars on Friday evenings who leered optimistically at anything in skirts.

Still, an ex-pilot's reactions ought to be sharper than the average man's. Better not underestimate him.

She had watched him buy his evening paper from the man at the underground entrance. He'd studied the front page all the way down the escalator, so she had been able to get really close to him. It was worth the risk because she could easily have lost him in the rush for the platform when the rumble of a train was heard.

Barry had evidently worked out the most convenient point at which to board the train. It suited him best to be at the rear, which meant walking the length of the platform to the Brompton Road end, behind the people waiting three and four deep. Each of the two evenings she had observed him he had allowed one train to draw in and leave, making no attempt to get on board. This way he guaranteed himself a front position at the edge of the platform. And a seat on the next train.

The position he took up was some twenty yards from the tunnel. The trains came in so fast that they couldn't possibly halt until they were more than halfway along the platform.

It wouldn't be a lingering death.

And now it was Friday and she was already on the platform, standing by a chocolate machine. She'd decided there was no need to follow him all the way down the escalator. She could wait here in confidence that he'd shortly be along. This time she had put on a plain blue and white headscarf knotted under the neck like most of the shopgirls and typists standing around her. She had a light brown coat with a belt and she was wearing gloves and flat shoes. She had an empty handbag looped over her arm.

She glanced at the clock overhead. Time enough. He should appear in two or three minutes. Two Uxbridge-bound trains had already come in, filled and gone. The platform didn't empty between trains, so she wasn't conspicuous among the numbers still waiting. Some people stood back anyway, wanting Hounslow trains.

Presently came the drone of another, building steadily in volume. The power of the tube thrilled Antonia when she had first experienced it at four years old. She'd found it vastly more exciting than the West End pantomime she was being taken to see. Even as an adult she preferred it to the buses.

Sparks lit the interior of the tunnel. She mentally rehearsed while the front of the train filled the void and thundered towards her. She saw the driver, picked out by the station lights, pale, staring ahead, his hands on the controls. The push would have to be perfectly timed and forceful.

One good shove.

A mass of red crossed her vision. The train came to a screeching stop and the doors opened. Suppose, after all, he sees a space and gets on at the other end, she thought, then told herself it wasn't possible. Barry had his routine. She just had to keep her nerve.

The sliding doors stuttered and closed and that train moved out.

The forward move to claim front positions along the platform edge had begun again. Barry still hadn't arrived. Antonia looked up at the clock and stared towards the far end.

She watched the train depart until the last spark in the tunnel, then shifted her gaze to the oncoming passengers, mentally sorting bowler hats from trilbies and checking for large moustaches.

She spotted him.

He was walking towards her in his black raincoat and carrying his scuffed leather briefcase in one hand and his newspaper in the other, with the umbrella hanging over his arm. He stared blankly ahead.

Antonia put her hand to her face as if to yawn and turned towards the map of the underground behind her. She could still watch Barry's approach. He stopped barely five yards from her.

The faint hum of the next train increased in resonance to a braying note. People stood four or five deep the length of the platform. Barry turned his paper over to look at the sport. He would let this one go.

In it rushed. The ranks broke and converged on the doors. An announcer appealed to people to stand back and let the passengers off first. Barry folded his paper and tucked it away in his briefcase.

The doors parted, people stepped out and others surged forward to take their places. The voice on the loudspeaker system sounded shocked at the mayhem.

'There'll be another one along in a minute.'

Barry was becoming restless, looking about him to see who else was in contention for a seat on the next train. Antonia put her hand to her face again.

'Stand back, please.'

The doors closed. Barry and scores of others stepped forward and formed the front rank before the train moved off. Antonia coolly advanced a couple of steps. She didn't join the line yet. She would go closer when the moment was right.

Her concentration was total. The ability to blot out what she called distractions had always been one of her strengths. During the Battle of Britain air raids she had surprised everyone who took her to be skittish and unstable by her utter reliability plotting the movement of aircraft. At this minute Barry was as impersonal to her as the metal arrows she had prodded across the map.

More passengers kept streaming in from both ends of the platform. The next train was signalled. She heard it faintly. The congestion at the platform edge increased. She moved decisively and stood behind Barry, so close that she couldn't any longer see the advertisements on the opposite wall. She had a view instead of a small section of the track, glimpsed between Barry's leg and the next man's. She could see the four rails Hector had painstakingly described for her. And the pit below the rails.

She was conscious of people closing up behind her, someone tall. She didn't turn round to look. She had a middle-aged woman on her right and a soldier on her left.

This would all be in the timing. She listened acutely to the drone coming from the tunnel, heard the swishing sound made by the sparks. She had to judge everything on the sound.

Any second.

Barry's back was beautifully straight, his legs very slightly apart.

Her eardrums throbbed to the train's roar.

Now.

She took a half step backwards and leaned into the man behind her. The moment she felt her back in contact with him she turned her head and said loudly, 'Stop pushing, will you?'

At the same time she thrust both hands hard into the small of Barry's back.

He tipped over the edge like a skittle just as the train rushed from the tunnel.

Antonia's scream merged with the screech of the brakes. Just as she'd estimated, the train travelled most of the way along the platform before it stopped. This time the doors didn't open. Other women were screaming now.

She said, 'Oh, God, we've got to get help!' and pushed her way past the woman beside her, through the crowd and out of the exit tunnel.

In a moment she glanced behind. Nobody had followed her. She took off her headscarf and walked to the escalator.

8

Rose snatched up the receiver the moment it rang.

Antonia sounded like a telephone operator, friendly and businesslike at the same time.

'Darling, are you alone?'

'Yes.'

'Been at home all morning?'

'Yes, of course. Did you. . . ?'

'Try and look surprised when they break the news to you. I'll call you in a few days.'

The phone clicked and purred.

Rose hung up. She reached for her handbag. Smelling-salts. Couldn't faint now. Unscrewed the stopper and held it to her nose. This must be a dream. Everything up to now is a dream.

They took her to the mortuary in a police car and showed her Barry's body. More precisely, they showed her his face. She braced herself for a harrowing sight, yet he was not at all disfigured. Even the moustache was intact and reasonably tidy. He was so different from her expectation, so unmarked, that she had a horrid feeling he would open his eyes when she identified him. She nodded her head and turned away. It was no longer a dream.

They assured her that he must have been electrocuted before the train hit him. Six hundred volts had stopped his heart immediately so he hadn't known much about it. On what authority they had reached this conclusion they didn't specify. Anything was justifiable to comfort the bereaved, she supposed. They said nothing about the state of his injuries under the green canvas covering. All that they kept repeating was that he hadn't suffered. She heard herself say thank you, as if *they* had arranged it humanely. The sergeant put his hands on her shoulders and steered her outside. She wept in the car as they drove her back to Oldfield Gardens. She was weeping for herself and her fear of what would happen. The sergeant said a cry would do her good.

She stood in her doorway and watched the police car drive away. Before she closed the door she glanced across at the poster of the widow. Someone had drawn a large tear under one of the eyes and scrawled 'sperlash!' underneath.

Alone in the house, she started to shiver. She opened the boiler to let it draw, knowing really that cold wasn't the cause. The anthracite Barry had tipped in after breakfast was still burning.

They had told her there would have to be a post mortem and an inquest. She wouldn't be required to say much, if anything.

She felt numb. She thought of what she had said to Antonia. '*I want him to have an accident.*' A death sentence.

I condemned my own husband to death and asked someone else to be the executioner. Was that really what I intended? Wasn't it just a cry of despair that Antonia misunderstood?

No, I can't duck the truth. I meant what I said. I wanted him removed and she was willing to do it. We called it an accident and it sounded excusable. We didn't describe it as a killing. Or murder.

It was an accident. I've got to think of it as an accident, or how will I convince everyone else?

She got up and tried to occupy herself by taking the carpet sweeper into the front room and using it until her arms ached. On the table was the vase containing the roses Barry had brought home for her the previous Friday. They had darkened and drooped. After she'd carried them to the boiler she noticed blood on her fingers. She'd gripped the stems so tightly that she hadn't felt the thorn pierce her skin. And she'd left a trail of red petals across the floor. She reached for the carpet sweeper again.

She needed distraction and nothing she did would

supply it. Several times she considered ringing her mother, then couldn't brace herself to tell the lies that would be necessary. Later, perhaps.

Increasingly she grew fearful of the truth coming out. There was going to be an inquest. The coroner would try to discover what actually had happened in the underground. There would be witnesses.

It troubled Rose that she had practically no knowledge of what had happened on Knightsbridge Station. Antonia had given her no clue. She might have bungled it terribly. There might be witnesses who would swear they had seen a woman push Barry off the platform. They could provide descriptions. Someone could have followed Antonia after Barry fell. At this very minute she might be making a statement to the police.

Rose was in no doubt that if Antonia was caught and accused, she'd name her accomplice.

She opened the larder and reached for the brandy and just at that moment the doorbell rang. The brandy bottle slipped from her grasp and smashed on the floor. She was petrified.

By now it was past eight. All the lights were on. She couldn't pretend she was out.

It rang again, longer, more insistently.

She sighed heavily, stepped over the mess the broken bottle had made and went with mechanical steps through the passage to see who was at the door.

The light wasn't helpful. That wretched poster threw everything in front of it into shadow. Momentarily she believed she saw a policeman with drawn truncheon standing on the doorstep. Then she realized it was a bicycle pump he was holding.

Mr Smart, the insurance agent. He'd arranged to come back with the surrender form. He gave a professional smile.

'Sorry to be calling so late, Mrs Bell. I tried earlier, but you were both out, so I came back. Is your husband at home?'

'He's dead.'

The smile vanished. 'Dead?'

'This afternoon.'

'You're serious? Quite, quite, quite. I can see you are. Oh, my word. How appalling.'

'Yes.'

'Dreadful. Might I enquire. . . ?'

'An accident.'

'On the road?'

'In the tube.'

'The tube? He didn't . . .'

'. . . take his own life? Apparently not. They told me it was an accident. He fell off the platform.'

'Poor fellow. Poor you, Mrs Bell. Tripped and fell. Pardon me for asking, but approximately what time did the tragedy occur?'

'Between 5.30 and six, I suppose. I didn't ask.'

'And at which station, Mrs Bell? The reason I enquire is that in certain cases, very occasionally I hasten to say, the company appoints investigators. Most unlikely in this case, I should think.'

'It was Knightsbridge.'

'Ah. The District Line?'

'The Piccadilly.'

'Yes, of course. Impossibly overcrowded at that time. I say, are you alone? Isn't there anyone with you?'

'I'd rather be left to myself, thank you.'

'You're quite sure there's nothing I can do? Rest assured that the company will fulfil its obligations to the letter. To the letter, Mrs Bell. I presume there will have to be an inquest. We are obliged to wait until after that, you understand. Forgive me for saying so, but how providential that your husband didn't surrender his policy when I called last week. God moves in mysterious ways, doesn't He? Then if you're absolutely certain I can't be of any practical help . . .'

He backed away as if he couldn't wait to escape, for all his professions of concern. In seconds he was pedalling his bike so fast up the street that his dynamo lamp put out a beam like a searchlight.

*

Several more times in the next few days Rose's nerves were tested by unexpected callers. Each time she expected to be arrested. The vicar called on Friday and recommended talking to God as a remedy for grief. On Saturday morning two men in raincoats looked so like detectives that she actually did send up a prayer. They turned out to be colleagues of Barry's from the Stationery Office, calling to express their condolences. She made some coffee and they all said that Barry was a fine man struck down in his prime. The same morning one of the neighbours called and asked her to sign a petition to have the hoarding across the street removed. When she saw the sheet of paper in his hand she thought it was a summons.

By degrees she started to believe that her arrest was not, after all, imminent. She busied herself writing to everyone who needed to know about Barry's passing. He hadn't made a will, so she asked the bank for legal advice and they offered the services of their legal department. She phoned her parents after Evensong on Sunday. They wanted her to leave everything and come to the Rectory, but she said she preferred to stay busy, and there was plenty to occupy her in Pimlico.

Daddy asked if she had some friend she could rely on to help her through this ordeal. She answered yes and thought of Antonia. She couldn't have faced it without.

Hector was listening to the *Brains Trust*. He habitually tuned in on Sunday afternoons at four. He didn't listen much to the wireless, except for the news, preferring to spend his evenings working upstairs in his office. He found comedy programmes like *ITMA*, which always had Antonia shrieking with laughter, impossible to follow. But Professor Joad and the others talked good sense at a speed he could understand.

To his surprise, Antonia had joined him in the drawing room beside the set. She'd arrived midway through with tea on a tray, which he was afraid would bring his listening to a premature end, but she sat in silence until he switched off at the end.

She asked, 'Was it as riveting as usual?'

'Better than last week. Better questions.'

'Let's have a *Brains Trust* of our own. I've got a question for you.'

'Yes?'

'What would you do if I was dead?'

He sniffed. 'Funny question.'

'On the contrary, my swain, it's serious. I can hardly wait to hear your answer. Suppose I hopped the twig. Would you be able to manage without me?'

He gave her a pained stare. 'Why do you ask me such a ghastly thing?'

'Be honest, Hec. You'd be a free man again. No one to tear strips off you when you came in late. No enormous bills from Harrods and Fortnums at the end of each month. You could live the life of Riley.'

Hector's logical mind hadn't got past her first proposition. 'You are not ill?'

'God, no.'

'You wouldn't kill yourself? That time we talked about the tube, it was a joke?'

She felt the colour rise to her face. 'The tube? A joke, yes – forget about that. Dismiss it from your mind. I already have.'

'Then I don't understand the question.'

'It's hypothetical.'

'Sometimes, Antonia, I find you impossible to understand.'

9

Rose's thoughts couldn't stretch beyond the inquest. She dreaded having to appear in public, trying to seem convincing as the devoted widow in front of all those experts and professionals. The letter arrived on Monday, a stiffly worded notice from the coroner's office asking her to attend the court on Thursday at 11 a.m. It terrified her. On Wednesday night she had the worst nightmares of her life.

Mr Burden, one of the senior people from the depot where Barry had worked, decently arranged to collect her in a taxi and accompany her to the court. He was an overbearing man who talked nonstop about Barry and what marvellous company he'd been with his saucy stories and witty remarks. Rose looked out of the window.

It turned out to be unlike anything she had expected. Barry's was only one of a series of deaths that were up for consideration. The case wasn't called until nearly noon. Inside there were no wigs or robes to be seen and the coroner looked and sounded like a variety turn. He could easily have passed for one of the Western brothers, such was his air of suave, world-weary irony.

Rose was more alarmed than reassured. When the main witness, Albert Abbot, a street vendor, was called there was a question about the goods he sold. Abbot insisted on using the term 'haberdashery' and the coroner said he presumed the witness meant nylons on the black market. The comment was mean considering that there were police witnesses present. Abbot was obviously used to looking after himself and he wouldn't be drawn, but Rose knew that when her turn came she was most unlikely to get away with any evasions.

Abbot's evidence was crucial. He had been on Knightsbridge Station standing close to Barry on the evening he was killed.

'I was taking the tube to Earls Court like I always do round about that time.'

'What time, Mr Abbot – or is that something else you wish to conceal?'

'Quarter to six, and I've got nothing to conceal. I seen him regular down there. Handlebars out to here. Couldn't miss him, could I? Always got himself a seat in the end carriage. When the train come in he was through them doors like a jackrabbit.'

'But not on the evening in question.'

'That's obvious, isn't it?'

'I am endeavouring to establish what you saw on that occasion, Mr Abbot.'

'Right. When I come along, he was in his usual spot, nicely placed for the doors. He'd worked out the right place to stand, right opposite the Sandeman poster. As a matter of fact, I always made a point of getting as close to him as I could.'

'Because you assumed he was likely to be one of the first aboard the train?'

'Didn't I say that? I like to get into the train quick, so I can stand my suitcase containing my haberdashery just inside the doors where people won't fall over it. It's a fair size, that case. All right, your honour, I'm coming to it. Upon the evening in question, to use your words, I wasn't quick enough to get right behind him. Some doll steps in first.'

Rose twisted two fingers in the strap of her handbag and tightened them. She was beside Mr Burden, three rows from the front. She'd borrowed a black coat for the inquest and found a small matching hat to which she had sewn stiffened net to veil the upper part of her face. It made her conspicuous, but she couldn't risk giving the impression that she was anything but griefstricken.

'If this is the young lady who featured in the fatal incident, you will need to furnish a better description than "some doll", Mr Abbot.'

'Right you are, your honour. She was quite tall, dark coat, brown, I think, with a belt. She was wearing a scarf on her head, so I don't know what colour hair she had. I didn't see much of her face either, but you can take it from me she was twenty-five or thereabouts. Nine times out of ten you can tell from the back.'

There was some subdued amusement at this.

'What I or anyone else can tell from the back is of no consequence, Mr Abbot. It is your assessment that matters, and if you tell us that the young lady was twenty-five, so be it. At this point I should inform the members of the jury that despite extensive enquiries by the police, they have been unable as yet to trace the person just described.'

Rose swallowed and looked straight ahead.

'Kindly continue, Mr Abbot.'

'Well, like I said, she was standing behind the bloke with the handlebars, and I was right behind her. To be honest, it's always a bit of a scrum when the train starts coming. She sort of took a step back when I was about to move forward. I got an elbow in my ribs and she half turned round and yelled at me to stop pushing.'

'And were you?'

'Strewth, no. I say that on my word of honour.'

'I hope everything you have told us is on your word of honour, Mr Abbot. It had better not be otherwise. What happened after she complained?'

'She seemed to lose her balance. She put out her hands and gave the poor beggar a shove in the back. He was taken by surprise and what with his briefcase and umbrella he couldn't do nothing to save himself. The train was just coming in and he fell straight in front of it. He must have been killed outright. He didn't suffer.'

'Thank you for your reassurance on that point. However, we'll hear the opinion of our medical witness before reaching a conclusion.'

'Just as you like. I was there.'

'That is not in dispute. And did you notice the young woman's reaction to the incident?'

'She had her back to me, like I said. She screamed. She

said something about getting some help. Then she pushed past the woman next to her and I didn't see where she went after that. There was women screaming and some people running away and others wanting to have a look.'

'You are quite certain that she said she was going for help? There is no evidence that she stopped to report the incident to anyone.'

'She must have panicked and run off.'

The coroner was letting nothing get by. 'You're not here to give an opinion, Mr Abbot. Do you remember precisely what she said after she stopped screaming?'

'Not every word, no. I was trying to see what happened to the poor bloke under the train, wasn't I?'

'However, the gist of what she said was that she intended to go for assistance?'

'For help, yes.'

'I think there is no purpose in persisting with this. Unless the jury have any questions they wish to put to the witness, he may stand down. Thank you, Mr Abbot.'

A second witness, a soldier, gave evidence next and added nothing to Abbot's version of events. He was questioned closely about what he had observed of the fatal push. He had seen the woman in the headscarf sway back and forward and he was satisfied that she had reached out because she had lost her balance.

A London Transport official described the procedure for getting the public safely aboard trains in the rush-hour. It was agreed that Knightsbridge was one of the busiest stations, with passengers streaming in from either end of the platform. However this was the first time such an incident had occurred there. The edge of the platform was paved with ribbed stones to prevent people slipping and most people stood back a yard or so until the train stopped.

The coroner asked whether it was reasonable for someone to take a step backwards when the train came in.

'Somebody standing close to the tunnel might. You get a gust of air as well as the sound of the train.'

'But most people stand their ground?'

'Experienced travellers, yes.'

A pathologist from St George's Hospital took the stand and reported on the post mortem examination. In spite of what had been suggested, he said that death was not caused by electrocution. The impact of the train was the primary cause. The deceased had suffered multiple injuries, including a fracture to the cervical region of the vertebral column. Death had been almost instantaneous.

The coroner glanced up at the clock. 'In view of the evidence already given, I don't think it will be necessary to call Mrs Bell, the widow of the deceased, to give evidence. This might have been pertinent if there had been any possibility that the deceased took his own life, but it is evident that we can rule out suicide entirely. For the same reason I shall not be calling his employer or his doctor. I thank them for attending the court.'

Rose closed her eyes and felt the tension drain from her muscles. The relief was profound. It was a reprieve. In the state she was in she'd have given herself away, she was certain.

'Ladies and gentlemen of the jury, I shall presently ask you to reach a decision as to the probable cause of this man's unfortunate death. The sequence of events leading up to the fatal incident is not in dispute. He took up a position at the edge of the platform close to the tunnel from which the train arrived. There was some movement behind him precisely as the train was about to enter the station. The young woman immediately to his rear appeared to lose her balance and press her hands against the back of the deceased, who plunged off the platform. The train struck him and killed him. It is a matter of regret that the police have been unable to trace the lady concerned. It would have been helpful to have heard her account of the incident.'

He paused and looked around the court.

Rose sat still and looked back at him. Her veil was trembling like a web in the wind.

The coroner resumed. 'One might postulate a number of explanations, one of which I am bound to invite you to consider, however remote it may appear. If the young woman felt some malice towards the deceased, it is not impossible that she could have followed him to the station with the intention of causing his death.

'Should you feel that this hypothesis has any relevance whatsoever, I must advise you to bring in an open verdict, there being insufficient evidence to reach any stronger conclusion. I would then instruct the police to redouble their efforts to trace the woman. If, on the other hand, you take the view that there was no malice involved, then there can be no other verdict than accidental death.'

Rose looked across at the jury. They didn't even retire to consider the verdict. The foreman conferred with them and stood up.

'We believe it was an accident, sir.'

10

A sleek white Bentley Mark VI drew in smoothly to the kerb in front of St James-The-Less Church in Moreton Street where Rose had been waiting almost twenty minutes. Antonia was at the wheel.

'Hop in, darling. We're about to go slumming across the river. A pint and a pork pie in the Prince Regent. Do you know it?'

Rose didn't know it. Nor did she know the man sitting beside Antonia. His presence threw her into angry confusion. Her first impulse was to turn and march away, and ten days ago she wouldn't have hesitated. Having it brought home to her that she was now incapable of such a simple act of independence incensed her even more as she got into the back seat. The man turned and grinned at her in a way that was meant to be friendly. He got a cold stare in return. She was in no frame of mind to be sociable. Antonia was the bloody limit. This wasn't meant to be a pub-crawl with some fancy man in tow. It was her first chance to talk to Antonia after the hellish week she'd been through.

Talk? Rose didn't trust herself to speak.

The car had turned and started across Vauxhall Bridge before she could bring herself to take another look at the man, and then her thoughts weren't charitable. Probably about her own age, he had the sort of fine black hair that would start receding before he was thirty. The deep-set brown eyes and tanned skin made her think of Italian prisoners of war in work-parties she had seen from the windows of trains. She'd always ignored their waving and whistling.

Meanwhile Antonia carried on as if it was a party. 'Say hello to Vic, darling. He's the dishiest man in London, as you can see, and I've been dying for you two to meet.'

He turned and offered his hand. It was broad, with

strong-looking fingers and a crop of dark hair. Rose put hers out mechanically and had it gripped.

'Poor Rosie lost her hubby last week. A frightful accident in the tube. She's had a basinful of sympathy, so you needn't say a word.'

In Rose's estimation Vic didn't look as if comforting words were on the tip of his tongue.

She said, 'I don't want to go into a pub.'

'Nonsense, darling. A drink will do you the world of good.'

The lunch-hour was noisily in session in the Prince Regent. People stood face to face bellowing at each other. They were three-deep at the bar and there was so much smoke you could have taken it for the gun deck of a man-of-war. Why Antonia had suggested this as a place to talk was beyond Rose's comprehension.

Vic took their orders and joined the throng at the bar.

'He'll be ages. How are you coping?'

'Can't we go somewhere more private?'

'Nobody's listening. Now it's all over you've got to return to the world of the living.'

'Barry isn't buried yet.'

'I know that, love. You've got to pick up the death certificate, correct? We'll do it this afternoon.'

'Both of us?'

'You want some moral support, don't you?'

'Is it wise?'

'Calm down, Rose. It's perfectly normal for someone else to tag along, a friend to hold your hand, so to speak. When's the funeral?'

'The day after tomorrow.'

'We'll have a couple of drinks with Vic and I'll drive you over to the registry office. Have you filled in the insurance claim yet?'

'The bank are looking after that for me.'

'You bet they are, the sharks. Remember that's *your* money. Don't let them do you for a single penny.'

Antonia was wagging her forefinger like a schoolmistress. She finished by tapping the back of Rose's hand. Then she grasped her wrist and squeezed it.

'We pulled it off, my flower!'

Vic had cleverly succeeded in getting served at once and was edging through with a tray of drinks and slices of pie. Antonia waved her white kid gloves.

'He's divine, isn't he?'

'Who is he exactly?'

'Ask him. He isn't dumb. God, and we haven't even found a table yet.'

They had to make do with a windowsill. Vic noticed that someone had dropped cigarette ash on Rose's sleeve. He insisted on flicking it off with his handkerchief. In other circumstances she would probably have accepted him as a pleasant addition to the company. There was nothing she could object to in his behaviour. It wasn't his fault that he happened to be unwelcome. Antonia, the real culprit, bulldozed on regardless.

'Victor, my love, Rosie wants to know who the bloody hell you are.'

He gave Rose a tolerant smile. 'Don't let her bother you. She does it to me all the time. She's probably told you already, but if it's of any interest I lecture in chemistry at Imperial College.'

This wasn't enough for Antonia. 'Come on, you do research as well. You've got your own lab filled with the most fearful-looking chemicals.' She swung back to Rose. 'He could poison the whole of London if he wanted to.'

Vic rolled his eyes. 'Now why should I want to do that?'

'Tell Rose about your swimming, then. This is really bizarre, darling.'

He sighed. 'Do I have to? I'm one of that eccentric band of health fanatics who swim in the Serpentine every day. I might as well tell you the rest, or she'll make me sound like a monster. I have a liking for French films, traditional jazz and, against my better judgement, one deplorably outspoken blonde lady.'

Antonia punched him playfully in the ribs. 'You mean sophisticated, ducky.'

'I mean exactly what I said.'

His manner towards her suggested a close relationship. Rose wondered how much Antonia's husband knew about it.

Antonia gave her a nudge. 'Now it's your turn, darling.'

Rose shook her head. 'Anyone can see what I am: totally out of place in this atmosphere.'

'Rubbish. Victor, you beast, I'm going to tell you something quite remarkable about my friend Rosie: she's never comfortable with what she's wearing. For God's sake tell her she looks wonderfully elegant in black or she won't let us stay for another drink.'

Rose sighed and turned up her eyes in exasperation. 'I don't mind waiting outside.'

However she stayed and was persuaded to try some vodka in her tomato juice. Vic secured a table for them and handed round Balkan Sobranie cigarettes. Rose hadn't tried the brand before and found it strong. To mask the taste she finished her drink in a couple of gulps and Vic fetched her another. To her immense relief the focus of conversation shifted away from her. Antonia brought it round to female film stars and held forth about passive, wishy-washy heroines who deserved to be knocked about by sadists like James Mason in *The Man in Grey*. She said any intelligent woman would have stood up and applauded the scene in *The Seventh Veil* when Mason crushed Ann Todd's delicate hands under the piano lid.

Rose said she hadn't seen the films and anyway violent men had no appeal for her.

'Sorry, my poppet. Shouldn't have brought it up.'

Vic looked at his watch and remembered he had a lecture to give at two. They drove back across the river and put him off at Victoria, where he could get the tube.

Antonia blew him a kiss before he disappeared. 'Isn't he bliss to be with? I knew you'd get on famously with him.'

'That isn't the point. We had things to discuss.'

'Rosie, my precious lamb, you'd better get one thing clear in your head. Post mortems don't appeal to me in the least. I did what you asked me to do and now it's up to you to make the best of it.'

'Well, yes. Don't think I'm ungrateful, but–'

'It's beginning to sound like it.'

Rose gave up protesting. She'd allowed her emotions to dictate to her. She had craved some human contact after the ordeal of the inquest. And the one person in the world she could share her experience with had put up the shutters. Well, perhaps it was sensible. After all, there was nothing of practical importance to be discussed with Antonia. And aside from their reminiscing about the war and their bouts of giggling they hadn't truly found much in common. Antonia's brashness was a strong disincentive.

Besides, she would never be able to think of Antonia in the same way, knowing what she had done down there in the tube. Rose told herself that she personally was just as culpable – if not more so – for suggesting it. Yet she would have been incapable of pushing Barry under the train. She was convinced of that. The fact that Antonia had done it in cold blood set her apart. She was uncomfortable to be with now.

Rose said, 'You're absolutely right. I must be more self-reliant. You don't need to come with me this afternoon. Just drop me outside the registry office.'

'Darling, I'll do no such thing.'

'I mean it.'

'Shut up and listen to me. I won't be coming in just to hold your hand. You're going to help *me* this afternoon.'

'Help you? How?'

'You don't object, do you?'

Rose hesitated. 'What am I supposed to do?'

'Because it wouldn't show much gratitude, would it, little sister, after I put my precious life at risk to get you out of your particular pickle?'

'Antonia, I've said how grateful I am.'

'And now you have an opportunity to show it.'

'Tell me what you want me to do.'

Antonia drove on for some time without answering.

Rose said, 'So long as it isn't against the law.'

Antonia laughed. 'Sweetie, asking to visit the ladies isn't illegal.'

The fire in the waiting room had gone out, probably days ago. The windows were still painted over for the blackout and last summer's flypapers hung from the lights. Torn pages from *John Bull* and *Everybody's* littered the threadbare lino. About twenty people sat and stood in silence broken only by a crying child and regular coughing.

Between them, Rose and Antonia got through a packet of ten Senior Service before their turn came. They'd been told that Deaths were upstairs.

'Next.'

'You know what to say?' said Antonia before they went in. 'You're looking awfully pale.'

'Isn't that the idea?'

The Assistant Registrar (Deaths) Knock Before Entering had a purple twinset that tended to emphasize the papery appearance of her skin. Her coke stove was alight and the clock on the wall was ticking. She was writing the date on the top sheet of her pad of death certificates.

'Yes?'

Antonia steered Rose forward by the arm, as if she were blind. 'This is Mrs Bell, whose husband was unfortunately taken from her in an accident last week. I'm her friend.'

'Is she the informant, or are you?'

'She is.'

'Can't she speak for herself?'

'She's rather distressed.'

Rose smiled wanly at Antonia. 'I'll try.'

'The name of the deceased, then?'

'Bell. Barry Desborough Bell, DFC. Wing Commander.'

'So his occupation was RAF Officer?'

'No. Civil Servant. Clerical Officer.'

'So you mean Wing Commander retired. You should have said so. I could have spoilt the certificate, couldn't I? What was the date of death?'

'October 10th.'

'As long ago as that?'

'There was an inquest.'

'I see. I can't do anything without a report from the coroner, you know.'

'His office said it would be here this morning.'

'They promise all sorts of things. Fill in this form, please. This is not the death certificate, but one we require for our records.'

The registrar snatched up a sheaf of papers from her in-tray and thumbed rapidly through them. Rose dipped the pen in the ink and started to write, prompted once or twice by Antonia.

'*Your* name.'

'Oh, yes.'

Suddenly Rose put down the pen and turned to Antonia. 'I think I'm going to be sick.'

The registrar scraped back her chair. For a moment it seemed that she meant to escort Rose to the toilet. Apparently she thought better of it.

'Downstairs and to the right at the foot of the staircase. Second door.'

Antonia got up and opened the door. 'Do you want me to come?' She mouthed the words, 'Say you can't find it.'

'I can manage. It may be just a drink of water I need.'

Rose went out. The registrar started again on her sheaf of papers, watched by Antonia. The tick of the clock was like a time-bomb.

The door opened again and Rose looked in. 'I'm fearfully sorry.'

The registrar stared at her. 'What's happened? Didn't you reach it in time?'

'I couldn't find it. Could I trouble you to show me?'

With a sigh like a burner in a balloon, the registrar rose, yanked her cardigan across her chest and stumped to the door. 'It's perfectly easy to find.' Halfway downstairs she turned and asked Rose if she was pregnant.

Somehow, Rose held herself in check. She was sorely tempted to ask the same question back. However, she'd agreed to go through with this, so she shook her head and followed meekly down the rest of the stairs to the appropriate room.

At least the woman had the grace to tell her to take her time, although possibly her office floor was paramount in her thoughts.

Rose whiled away some minutes studying the walls. She'd never understood what drove people to publicize their love and hate in such places. Then she washed and dried her hands and returned upstairs. Antonia sprang up and grasped her hand and asked if she felt any better. It seemed like over-acting, though the registrar ignored the performance. She announced that she had located the letter from the coroner's office. The paperwork was completed in a short time. Rose paid the fee for extra copies of the death certificate and put the documents in her handbag.

Outside in the Bentley, Antonia leaned across and planted a loud kiss on Rose's cheek.

'You were brilliant, darling. Brilliant! It was quite a blow when she didn't go out with you the first time. What an old dragon!'

'Are you going to tell me what it was all about?'

'Haven't you guessed by now? Look.'

Antonia opened her handbag and took out a folded piece of paper. She spread it across her knees and then passed it to Rose.

'A death certificate?'

'A *blank* death certificate – with the duplicate they keep for their records.'

'You took it from her desk? But it's got a number on it. She'll know it's missing.'

'She won't. I'm not soft in the head, Rosie, my love. I nicked it from the bottom of the pad. Careful – we don't want it looking dogeared, do we?'

Rose frowned and handed the certificate back. Antonia replaced it in her handbag and started the car.

'Aren't you going to say I'm a genius?'

Rose didn't answer.

'I mean, it couldn't be easier from now on. We've cut out all the snags. We won't need a doctor's certificate. We fill in whatever we like and take it to the undertaker.'

'*What* couldn't be easier?'

Antonia smiled and swung the car into the traffic of Kensington High Street.

'Antonia, what couldn't be easier?'

'How would you like to meet my husband?'

11

Antonia was talking like a tour guide as she drove the Bentley up Portland Place and into Park Crescent. The route they were taking, she informed Rose, had been built by John Nash as a triumphal drive for that randy old swank the Prince Regent, all the way from St James's Park through Regent Street and Portland Place to what was planned to be a royal pleasure pavilion in Regent's Park. The Crescent had been conceived as a circus, but the funds ran out, so it was cut off halfway, and of course the pleasure pavilion was given the axe as well. Most of Nash's beautiful terraced houses had now been taken over by embassies, clubs and businesses. Antonia's was one of the few still in use as a private home.

All this was lost on Rose. Her thinking had stopped at two death certificates, one with Barry's name on it, the other blank.

She'd been so preoccupied with what had happened in the past ten days that she'd failed entirely to see where it might lead. Barry's 'accident' had been a brilliant remedy for her troubles. Antonia had made it seem simple, doing what was necessary as if it were a common courtesy, like sharing an umbrella. Now, with the same serene indifference, Antonia was planning something else, and Rose was expected to join in. You can't share an umbrella without walking together.

The car door slammed. Antonia was already out and making an exaggerated gesture to Rose to follow.

'Come on. You need some strong coffee. You're looking more and more like that God-forsaken woman on the poster.'

'Well, the inquest was no picnic.'

Rose followed her between the twin columns at the entrance and up white steps into what could have passed as a set for one of those frothy films about the high life made to distract audiences from post-war austerity. She didn't believe real people lived in such opulence. You could have held a dance in the hall. The corniced ceiling was high enough to house two crystal chandeliers. There was a crimson carpet. Satin-striped wallpaper. An oval mahogany table with a silver tray for visiting cards.

Antonia tossed her fur coat over a chair. 'Hector insisted we furnish it in Regency. He's so hidebound. When we've got rid of him I'm going to strip it bare and start again. I want white walls and huge abstract paintings. Do you like Ben Nicholson?'

Rose missed the question. The skin at the back of her neck felt as if something had crawled across it.

'The painter, darling.'

Her legs started to shake. If she wasn't to make a complete idiot of herself she had to stay upright and mouth some words that would keep Antonia talking about the house. 'Who did you say?'

'Ben Nicholson.'

'He's a painter, is he? I can't say I've heard of him.'

Antonia reached around Rose's shoulder and gently helped her off with her coat. 'Sweetie, you should never admit such ignorance. What you should say is, Nicholson's all right, but I prefer Stanley Spencer or Paul Nash or – who *do* you prefer?'

Rose's thoughts were still in turmoil. Name an artist. Any artist. She couldn't. 'I don't know anything about modern art.'

'Christ Almighty. Then you should definitely meet Hector. He thinks Picasso is something Italians eat. Make yourself at home in the sitting room – second door – and I'll see if he's in yet. He was supposed to be having lunch with a French professor. Ten to one he's sleeping it off.'

'Antonia, don't disturb him on my account. I'm sure there'll be another opportunity.'

There was a pause.

'The opportunity is now, my flower. It's got to be faced.'

She grasped Antonia's arm. 'Just a moment. I'd like to

get this clear if you don't mind. What exactly has got to be faced?'

Antonia made light of it. 'Did I make him sound like an ogre? Don't worry – he's the one who should look out.'

Rose didn't pursue the question. Mentally she was reeling. She stepped into the room Antonia had indicated. It was as large as her own kitchen, sitting room and passage knocked into one. The dominant colours were blue and white. A tall clock startled her by chiming the quarter-hour. The date 1765 was painted on it in gold. Sets of china and silver were ranged about the walls in display cabinets. Waist-high Chinese vases that she took to be Ming stood on either side of the fireplace, where a white Persian cat was staring at the flames. It raised itself, arched, yawned and came to rub its head against her legs.

She stooped to run her fingers through the fur, wanting urgently to find some way of calming her nerves. She tried marshalling the few facts she'd learned about Hector: the meeting with Antonia on the steps of the air-raid shelter; his civilian status in the war; the death by drowning of his wife, whose name Rose had forgotten. To which could be added his ignorance of modern art and his lunch today with a French professor. And the evidence all around Rose that she had never been so close to real wealth.

Antonia pushed open the door. 'Just as I thought. He says he wants black coffee. How about you?'

'Coffee would be nice. Can I help?'

'No, I want to show off. We had a couple of servants until two weeks ago, a married couple, Irish. They took exception to something I said and walked out in a huff. Getting replacements is the very devil. However, I've learned how to make coffee, so I don't miss a chance to impress visitors. You can come and see the kitchen if you like.'

Rose stopped in the kitchen doorway and put her hands to her face. 'Oh, Antonia!'

'What's that? My fridge?'

It stood on stilts, a humming white cabinet of monumental size with a door like the front of a bank vault that

Antonia needed two hands to unfasten and swing open. Rose gasped in awe at the intricate arrangement of shelves and trays inside, the Perspex storage boxes, the ice compartment and the place for bottles. For the moment her terrors were suspended.

'You like?'

She gave a start. Her nerves were in no state for surprises. Possibly the small man at her shoulder – who could be no one else but Hector – hadn't meant to startle her. He was so short that he'd slipped under her protective radar. She looked into a fleshy, smiling face framed in unruly reddish hair. Alert, brown intelligent eyes. Small, even teeth. A quite low-pitched voice with a strange intonation.

'You can order one from me. In production next year.'

Antonia slammed the fridge door. 'For Christ's sake, Hector, she lives in a matchbox. Rosie, this impetuous little man is my husband.'

Hector was unperturbed. Whether or not he understood, he treated her remark as a recommendation. 'Yes, I take orders now. Quality vacuum cleaners and fridges. Take the work out of housework. The only thing you hear from GEC, Prestcold, any of those companies is, fridges are on the way, worth waiting for, coming soon. Me, I take orders. How often do you wash your clothes? Soon I have a washing machine on the market better than anything in America. How do you do?'

They shook hands. He must have been ten years Antonia's senior, possibly more. Redheaded people carry their age well.

Rose was trying hard to place the accent. She hadn't expected a foreigner.

'I've never seen such an amazing fridge.'

'You like to see my high power vacuum cleaner?'

Antonia put a restraining hand on Hector's shoulder. In her heels she was cruelly taller than he. 'Hec, my cherub, you're boring my friend already. Why don't you take her into the sitting room and talk about something unmechanical while I brew up my delicious coffee?'

Out of earshot in the sitting room Rose confided to Hector that after all she would be interested to hear about his work.

'Are you sure?'

'Certain.'

'I thought so.' He pulled two chairs together and gestured to her to be seated. 'Antonia has heard it many times before. It's not news to her no more. You know, Rosie, engineering is in my blood. My father he had the first motor car in Prague. When I was still in short trousers he showed me how to strip. You understand?'

'Take the engine to pieces?'

'And assemble again. Clever boy, oily fingers, I went to technical school. Worked in a motor car factory seven years, made enough ackers to kiss my father goodbye, go to America. Detroit. Bloody hard work. Making automobiles by day, aeroplane parts by night. I worked six to midnight for a small guy starting up. Four, maybe five hours sleep, but no matter. This was one hell of a good time to be in aero-engineering. I had a brilliant idea for a carburettor nobody thought of. So my friend says, Hec, why don't you give up making automobiles and be my partner? Half-share in the business. We shake hands and sign a paper. In two years, big profit. Big expansion. I expanded, too. Don't smile. I mean I got married. Maudie, a sweet girl from Detroit who wanted only one thing – to get the hell out of there. So I told my partner the problem. He bought me out and we sailed to England. 1931. *Mauretania*.'

'Romantic.'

Hector winked. 'Good business, too, Rosie. Plenty of customers for aero parts. I made the best carburettors Britain ever saw. I started a small factory in Surbiton, handy for Vickers. In seven years I had customers all over. I built factories in Birmingham, Southampton, Oxford. Many orders. Then the war came along. Aircraft production went crazy. Lord Beaverbrook cried out for carburettors. Everyone wanted carburettors. A. V. Roe, Vickers Supermarine, Handley Page, Fairey.'

Hector was warming to his story. The cat made a run for the door as Antonia came in with the coffee.

'Has he bored you stiff with his carburettors, darling? He talks about them the way other people talk about their operations.'

'I find it fascinating.'

'Liar. You don't have to stand on ceremony with us. Hec, do something useful and hand round the biscuits. I bet he hasn't said a word about your unhappy experience. You're all dressed up in black and he hasn't even asked why. You'd have to arrive in a hearse for him to take any interest and then he'd have the bonnet up to look at the carburettor. Hector, my friend Rose lost her husband last week, and when I say lost I mean he fell off the platform in the tube.'

'The tube. Oh, Jesus. Six hundred and thirty volts.'

'See the way his mind works?'

'It doesn't offend me.'

Rose smiled at Hector. To be fair, he'd looked distinctly concerned when he spoke of all those volts. If there was offence to be taken, it was at being invited to discuss his shortcomings in front of him as if he were deaf or stupid. He may have been socially out of step, but he had energy and honesty. She liked the disarming way he'd told his story, without the pretended modesty that most Englishmen seemed to feel was necessary when speaking about their achievements. He'd earned his fortune through hard work and enterprise and wasn't ashamed to say so.

Now for some curious reason he was looking at Rose with awe.

He refused to be intimidated by Antonia. He found a way of excluding her just as blatantly as she'd talked over him. 'I feel close to you, Rosie. You and I, we both had the same experience.'

Antonia thrust a cup of coffee towards Rose. 'He means his wife had an accident, too. Careful how you drink this stuff. It's out of a bottle. I won't blame you if you spit it out.'

She took a sip. 'It's not at all bad.'

Hector held out the biscuits. 'These help to disguise the taste. She drowned, my Maudie.'

'How dreadful.' In common decency she felt obliged to react as if she hadn't heard the information before. She just hoped Antonia wouldn't take her up on it.

'It was in a swimming pool. In the war I had this country house in Hampshire for weekends. Nice grounds. Nice pool. Long way from Portsmouth and Southampton. Pretty safe from bombing. Our friends came sometimes. Maudie liked to give parties.' He glanced across at Antonia, which was a mistake because she slickly took over the story.

'She'd had a skinful, and that's no exaggeration, darling. She'd been on rum and peppermint, of all things. She couldn't have swum a stroke if she'd tried.'

'Did anyone see what happened?'

'Most of us were on the terrace dancing to the gramophone. One of the staff spotted her lying on the bottom soon after midnight. Six feet down.'

'Six feet six.'

'There speaks the engineer again. Hector, dear, you shouldn't say things like that. It gives an appalling impression, as if you didn't care. Of course we both know that couldn't be further from the truth. It wasn't his fault she was so depressed.'

Hector gave a nod. 'Time to change the subject, eh? Rosie, do you like to cook?'

'Well, when I could get eggs and things, yes.'

'We can get plenty. Butter. Sugar.'

Antonia sighed. 'There you go again.'

'What's wrong now?'

'Rosie's going to think we're on the black market, that's what's wrong. The fact is, Rose, that I'm the world's worst cook, so we generally go to restaurants. I never get through my ration books.'

Hector grinned. 'Biggest fridge in London. Bugger all in it.'

He got a glare from Antonia.

Rose laughed. Why take offence? She and Antonia had

heard plenty worse in the old days. She was suddenly aware how much those few minutes with Hector had relaxed her. She'd been terribly strung-up before.

She smiled happily. 'I don't blame you. I'd bloody well eat out as well if I could afford it.'

'Why don't you come out with us, then?' Antonia suggested.

'Oh, I didn't mean that.'

'Don't be so coy. We'd like your company, wouldn't we, Hec?'

'But of course! Tomorrow?' His sharp eyes shone at the prospect.

She was ambushed by their solidarity. 'I couldn't possibly before the funeral. Perhaps later in the week?'

'Saturday.'

Soon after this was agreed, Hector had to answer the phone. Antonia got up.

'You look all in, darling. I'll drive you back to Pimlico.'

In the Bentley, Rose tried to launch a bland, undemanding conversation.

'I love your house.'

'Who wouldn't?' Antonia didn't pause. She came straight out with it. 'What do you think of my husband?'

The tension clamped Rose again like pincers. What was she expected to say? 'I didn't realize you'd married a foreigner. He's so different from most Englishmen.'

'God, I hope so!'

'He made me welcome.'

'He would, so long as you listen to his tedious life story and coo at intervals. I'm sick of it. It drives me up the wall. That and his vacuum cleaners.'

'Do you think he knows?'

'Of course he does. He's so full of himself that he doesn't give a shit.'

'I'm sorry.'

'Sweetie, I'm not fishing for sympathy. I didn't waste any on you, did I?'

Rose looked away, not wanting to go into what Antonia

had done in lieu of sympathy. 'Doesn't it get dark early now? It's not even five o'clock.'

'I want an end to it.'

'A divorce?'

'No chance of that. It's against his religion. He's a Catholic. Doesn't go to church or eat fish on Fridays, but when it comes to divorce, he's unshakeable. It's against God's law. That's how he was brought up.'

'Have you asked him? If it doesn't mean so much to him now, perhaps he'd see his way to giving you a divorce.'

'What use is that to me? I'd lose everything and have to pay the costs.'

'Why?'

'I'd be the guilty party, wouldn't I?'

'You mean. . . ?'

'You know what I mean. Let's face it, Rose. I've got a lover. To put it in legal claptrap I've committed adultery on a number of occasions. No prizes for guessing the name of the fascinating man.'

'Does Hector know?'

'He turns a blind eye. The only way it would come to his attention is if he found us at it in his precious fridge, or doing something naughty with the vacuum cleaner.'

'There may be other grounds. Has he ever been cruel to you?'

'Hector?' She found this amusing.

Now Rose had started, she felt obliged to continue. 'Is there any chance that he's been with someone else? There must be plenty of designing women who'd fancy a man with his money.' She wished immediately that she'd kept her mouth shut.

'Like I did, you mean?' Antonia let the question hang in the air just long enough to give Rose a wrench of embarrassment, then dismissed it. 'No, darling, no vultures circling overhead. I'd know.'

Mercifully the conversation stopped for the traffic at Piccadilly Circus. When they'd crossed to the Haymarket, Rose changed to a different tack.

'I'd be glad if you'd put me down in Victoria Street. I'd like to get these documents to the undertaker.'

'Whatever you want, my dear.'

'Thanks.'

Antonia added, 'By the way, I shan't be coming to Barry's funeral.'

'That's all right. I didn't expect you.'

'It doesn't mean I've lost interest.'

'I know.'

'And no disrespect meant to Barry.' She slowed for a traffic light. 'It's a burial, I take it?'

'Yes. Just a few people.'

'Brompton Cemetery?'

'Yes.'

'Poor old Barry. Grounded at last.' The light changed to green. 'I'm going to have Hector cremated.'

12

On the night before the funeral Rose was surprised to get a phone call from Rex Ballard, one of the Kettlesham Heath pilots, a Squadron Leader who it turned out was still serving there. He had heard about Barry's death from his sister who worked in the coroner's office. He remembered Rose, of course. He said he would be driving up from Suffolk in the morning with three old chums from Battle of Britain days. Rose tried explaining that it was to be a quiet family funeral. Rex was not to be put off. In that case, he said, there would be room at the graveside for a few old friends who wanted to pay their respects, wouldn't there?

The 'old friends' had grown to fourteen by the time they gathered around the grave in Brompton Cemetery. Three civil service people from the Stationery Office who Rose had never seen before stood rigidly at one end with their furled umbrellas in front of them like reversed rifles. The Irish couple who lived two doors away in Oldfield Gardens and never missed a thing had turned up, thoughtfully with only two of their six children. Also, wearing black armbands, one of the barmen and two regulars from The Orange, where Barry used to drink. Then the quartet from the RAF, stouter and redder in the face than they'd looked in 1940 and now without a moustache between them.

The family group consisted of Barry's stepsister Daphne and her obnoxious husband Ronald, Rose's parents and Aunt Joan. And Rose herself.

Her father had offered to read the service. She'd said at the risk of hurting him that she would find the whole thing too distressing. She preferred to have the words spoken by a priest she didn't know. Daddy nodded and said he understood. Rose hoped to God that he didn't and never would.

Even then it was an ordeal going through the motions of

lament with them beside her and everyone watching for evidence of grief from the wretched widow. She kept her head bowed and bit her lip and dabbed her face with a hankie. They were genuine tears. The ritual hardly touched her, but she wept for all the lies she would be forced to tell before the afternoon was out.

They all said afterwards how splendidly brave she had been.

Her mother and aunt had helped her prepare some food at the house for after the funeral. Spam sandwiches mostly, plates of digestive biscuits and slabs of trench cake. The cake was her mother's contribution, from a First World War recipe that the Ministry of Food had disinterred for the Second. It was made without eggs and Mother rashly announced that the original trench cakes had kept for three months on the Western Front. No one enquired why they hadn't been eaten in all that time, but when she offered to pass the recipe on there was an embarrassing silence. Only the Irish children tried any.

Much against her desire, Rose remained the centre of attention. Offers of support were showered on her.

'I want you to know, my dear, that we at the Stationery Office wouldn't want you to get into difficulties. If there's anything that needs attention, my name is Gascoigne and this is McGill and our young colleague here is Tremlett. Remember, won't you? Anything under the sun.'

She had an engaging picture of Gascoigne, McGill and Tremlett under the sun, bare-chested on the roof replacing the war-damaged tiles.

'So kind.'

'Not at all. Barry was held in the highest esteem at the depot. We shall not look upon his like again, as the Bard expressed it. Now that we know each other. . . .'

The bonhomie was excessive, like Victory Day all over again. Why am I so cynical? Rose asked the kettle as she filled it.

As for the RAF mourners, they had their own way of combating depression. They took turns going out to the car to top up with something from a bottle. Out of respect for the cloth, as they put it (meaning Daddy, who could see very well what was going on, and wouldn't have been averse to a nip), they used teacups and let it be known that they were drinking Russian tea.

'Never would have guessed your Pop was a parson, Rose. You should have told us, you know.'

'Why?'

'Freddie here would have moderated his language.'

'Did he say something? I didn't hear him.'

'Lord, no. He's been the soul of discretion today. I'm talking about the war. In the ops room. The things you heard must have made your toes curl.'

Rose shook her head. 'Let's make no bones about it, we were all living on our nerves. I said a few strong words myself when I was pressed.'

'My dear, I never heard them pass your lips. But you're right about the pressures. Say what you like about our flying skills, we needed the luck of Old Nick to survive. Dear old Barry, rest his soul, was in the thick of it and came through triumphant every blessed time. Even when he got in trouble he limped back somehow, hours late, with that beautiful fatuous grin on his face. He was indestructible.'

'So were you, as it turned out.'

'Yes, but we could all name plenty of good lads who didn't make it home. If there's any sense in it all, we're bound to ask why we were spared.'

'Rex, I'd better get round with the tea before it gets cold.'

'Just a moment, dear. I'm shockingly hamfisted with words, I know. Always was. What I'm getting at is this. Somehow we *knew* Barry would always come back. He gave you that sense of living a charmed life. So when I was told he'd fallen off a railway platform, I couldn't believe my ears. The Piccadilly Line? Dear old Barry? That's not like him, I said, not like him at all.'

'Accidents happen all the time.'

'Not to the likes of Barry. To tell the truth, I still haven't taken it in properly. Standing there in the cemetery this afternoon I kept thinking, this isn't right. Any minute I'm going to feel a tap on my shoulder and I'll turn round and it'll be old Barry in his flying kit having a bloody good laugh at us.'

One of the others, Peter Bliss, had been getting restless. 'Put a sock in it, Rex.'

'What's up?'

'You're talking baloney.'

'Pardon me, old son, but it's a fact. Barry always came back. Always.'

'This is hardly the time and place to go on about it.'

Rose gave Bliss a nod of thanks and moved off to fill the teapot again. She found her mother in the kitchen washing plates with Aunt Joan. An opportunity, Mummy had decided, for a heart-to-heart.

'Now that it's over, we want you to come home with us for at least a few weeks, my pet. You look so dreadful, I can hardly believe it's my own daughter.'

'Mummy, I appreciate the thought.'

'It's more than a thought, dear. I absolutely insist, and so does your father.'

'I know you mean well, but it's out of the question. There's too much to be done here.'

'Nothing that can't wait. I couldn't possibly go away tonight and leave you alone in this dreadful . . . I mean, in this house with . . . with so many memories.'

Aunt Joan came tactfully to her sister's aid. 'It was that face on the hoarding across the road that upset us. So depressing for you to look out on all the time.'

'The widow? I've got used to her now. She doesn't bother me in the least. Really.'

'As if we haven't all seen enough horrors since the war ended.'

'I'll manage perfectly well by myself, Mummy.'

'It isn't as if you have friends you can turn to. I don't mind telling you I don't take to those Irish people.'

'They're neighbours. I'm not without friends, believe me.'

'Friends? Up here in London? Who, for instance?'

'Um, people you wouldn't know. Ex-service.'

She was too late to bite back the last words. Her mother gave her a sharp look. God, how much longer would the kettle take? She tried turning the gas up. It was already fully on.

The cross-questioning began in earnest. 'Air Force people then?'

'Yes.'

'Ex-service, you said. You don't mean the men in the other room?'

'No.'

'WAAFs?'

'You wouldn't know them, Mummy.'

'I didn't see any WAAFs here today.'

'They couldn't manage it. Would you be a dear and put out some more biscuits? We're about to run out in the other room.'

'There's plenty of cake left. They've hardly touched it. Do you really want to use up all the biscuits? All right, if that's what you want. We'll talk about this again, dear. I'm far from satisfied.'

Rose filled the teapot and went in search of the civil servants. They'd managed to corner her father and were telling him about the inner workings of the Stationery Office. He was reacting with every muscle of his face, as if no subject interested him more passionately. By the nature of his occupation he was a splendid listener. She'd watched him earlier doing his stuff with the Air Force. Dear, generous-hearted Daddy.

It would be folly to go home with her parents, sweet as they were. Between Mummy's sharp questions and Daddy's spirituality she'd be confessing everything before the train left Waterloo.

What a shock they'd get! She had never so much as hinted that the marriage was unhappy. The few Saturday afternoons she'd taken Barry back to the Rectory he'd played the part of the loving husband and she'd been grateful for the effort he put into it. The fact that he'd spent the previous evening in the arms of a tart in some hotel room seemed as unthinkable as Daddy dropping an 'h' or Mummy a stitch.

How, then, could they even begin to comprehend the truth about Barry's death and her part in it?

Gascoigne the civil servant appeared beside her. 'My colleagues and I will be leaving in a few minutes, Mrs Bell.'

'Thank you for coming.'

'It was a pleasure.' He coughed. 'That is to say, thank you for your hospitality. One small matter I wished to mention. Mr Bell left a few personal items in his desk including a photograph that may be of some sentimental value, a fountain pen and, I think, some tickets for a dance. I placed them in an envelope for safe keeping.'

'I don't suppose they're important.'

'Ah, but I wouldn't want to dispose of them without your seeing them.'

'Could you put them in the post?'

'I'm concerned about the possibility of the pen leaking over the other things. Would you like me to arrange for someone from the depot to bring them here? It didn't seem appropriate today.'

'That's all right. I'll come to the depot and see if they're worth keeping.'

'Really? I don't want to put you to any trouble.'

'I'll let you know when I'm coming.'

After repeating his offer to do anything of practical help that Rose could think of, Gascoigne gathered McGill and Tremlett and left. For a moment it appeared as if the Kettlesham Heath crowd were lining up to say goodbye as well. Not so. Rex Ballard still had something on his mind.

'I suppose you haven't run into any of the girls lately?'

'The girls?'

'WAAFs, my dear. Your fellow-plotters.'

Rose's pulse beat faster. Rex was one of those people who put you at ease and then poleaxed you with something he'd discovered. He'd found out about the funeral. What else did he know?

'I think we all went our own ways. One met so many people in the war.'

'True.' He looked wistful. 'They're a very insipid bunch on the station now. No sense of fun. I wouldn't mind having a get-together one weekend with some of the wartime crowd. A sort of reunion. Do you think it's a good idea?'

Was that all he meant? The relief!

'I'd need to think about it.'

'We'd have to find out where they are now, of course. You've lost touch with everyone, have you?'

With uncanny timing, her mother pushed a plate of trench cake between them. 'Far from it, Squadron Leader. Rose was telling me just now that her ex-service friends are all she's got in London, weren't you, dear?'

Rose sidestepped. 'Mummy, we're talking about Kettlesham Heath now, not Hornchurch. I met Rex at Kettlesham Heath.'

'Oh, I'm out of order as usual, am I? Have some cake anyway.'

'It looks delicious. Unfortunately I'm not the cake-eating type, Mrs Mason, but I say, if there's another spam sandwich . . .'

While her mother went off to cut more bread, Rose let it be understood that a squadron reunion wasn't to her liking. She told Rex candidly that she'd regard it as an ordeal rather than a pleasure. He said he sympathized. However, in case she changed her mind later, he'd let her know if the idea came to anything. Soon after, the RAF party set off for Suffolk in their Standard 12.

When her parents finally left with Aunt Joan they all but dragged her off the doorstep and into their small car. She escaped by undertaking to visit them at the earliest opportunity. They also extracted promises that she would say her prayers each night and finish every crumb of the trench cake. She thought, I'll need more than prayers if I do.

13

Alone in the sitting room Rose threw off her shoes and collapsed on the settee. Her legs ached, her head was ringing from being the focus of so much conversation, but the sensation of relief was like champagne. Barry was buried and the funeral was over.

She was beginning to think that she'd reward herself with a sherry before facing the washing-up when she heard a sound from upstairs. Someone was in her bedroom. What she'd heard was the loose floorboard in front of the wardrobe.

It frightened her. She'd quite convinced herself she was alone in the house. She sat up, reached for her shoes and put them on, at the same time checking mentally which of the guests had definitely left. She glanced out of the window. No cars were left in the street.

Another creak from the floorboard.

She couldn't fathom who it could be, or why they should be where they were. The noise definitely hadn't come from the bathroom. Whoever was up there was creeping about, not wanting to be discovered.

That stupid remark of Rex Ballard's crept into her mind, about Barry always coming back. Stupid and irresponsible. This time Barry couldn't possibly come back.

Yet she'd heard that board creak a thousand times before and it had always been Barry upstairs.

She stood with her hand on the banister rail, listening. She ought to have called out and asked who was there. Her throat wouldn't function. She was going to have to go upstairs and look inside that bedroom. If she didn't face it now, she'd never be able to sleep in the house again.

The landing light was on, but that meant nothing. It had got dark in the last hour. People would have needed the light to use the bathroom.

She told herself this had to be done. Without pausing, she mounted the stairs, crossed the landing and opened the bedroom door.

The light wasn't on in there. The light from the landing picked out the figure of a man in front of the wardrobe dressed in Barry's demob jacket.

Rose caught her breath and took a step back.

'What are you doing?'

He turned. 'Hello, Rose.'

It wasn't Barry, of course. It was Barry's oafish brother-in-law, Ronald. And Daphne, his harpy of a wife, stepped out of the shadows and took her place beside him. They'd been in there in the dark, communicating in whispers.

'Has everyone gone, then?'

'I supposed they had.'

'Didn't you know we were still here?'

'Hope we didn't frighten you, Rose.'

'What the hell are you doing in my bedroom?'

Ronald was a master of the art of bluffing his way out of embarrassing situations. He had plenty of practice, for his manners had always been abysmal. 'Merely trying on one or two of Barry's jackets, my dear. Seeing that you'll have no further use for them, I thought I'd offer to make some room in the wardrobe. It's not a bad fit really, is it?'

'Take it off.'

'There's no need to take offence, Rose.'

'Isn't there? Who invited you up here? I didn't.'

Daphne, long resentful of Rose annexing her brother, bared her claws. 'We didn't expect you would. Barry wouldn't have thought twice about it. He was sweet-natured.'

'Get out of my house, both of you.'

'*Your* house now, is it? That tripped off the tongue very easily. How do you know it's yours? Have you seen the will?'

'There isn't a will.'

'No will? I find that hard to believe.'

'Frankly, Daphne, I don't care what you believe.'

'I suppose you think you'll inherit everything. Well,

you've made a serious mistake. As his only blood relative, I shall instruct my solicitor to begin proceedings. I'm entitled to my share and I intend to claim it.'

'Your share of what – his debts?'

Daphne gave a cry like a seagull. 'My brother wasn't in debt.'

'He was overdrawn several hundred pounds. If I were you I should think twice before you go to the expense of a solicitor.'

Ronald peeled off Barry's jacket, held it at arm's length as if it were flearidden and let it drop in a heap on the bed. He picked up his own and took Daphne by the arm. 'Better leave it for the present, old girl.'

Daphne ignored the advice. 'Barry couldn't possibly be in debt. He was an ex-officer, for God's sake. A civil servant. None of this rings true, Ronald. She's lying. He must have left a will. All those pilots who risked their lives in the war left wills. I believe she's destroyed it, that's what she's done.'

'Steady, Daph.'

'I'm going to get to the bottom of this.'

Rose was unmoved. 'At this minute, Daphne, you're going to get to the bottom of the stairs and straight out of my house.'

'With the utmost pleasure. I don't wish to remain in it a minute longer.'

Watching from the front room window as they retreated up Oldfield Gardens to catch a bus, Rose doubted if she would hear from either of them again. She returned to the kitchen and took out the sherry. On second thoughts, she put it back. She'd already given herself the boost she needed.

Sleep was slow in coming. Fragments of conversation flitted in and out of her brain. At about two in the morning she got up and made some tea. She carried it into the front room and got out the writing pad. She was in no way depressed. She felt strong. She'd been firm with her parents. And in giving Daphne and Ronald their marching orders she'd discovered something new in her personality. Now she was ready to take up the pen.

27 Oldfield Gardens,
Pimlico,
London SW1.

Dear Miss Paxton,

Although we haven't met, Barry told me about you and your child. I am his lawful wife – or was. I am sorry to inform you that Barry was killed in an accident in the underground on Thursday, 16th October. The funeral took place yesterday at Brompton Cemetery. I understand what a shock this must be for you.

Barry made no will. Even if he had, the state of his bank account would have rendered it meaningless, for he was overdrawn seven hundred pounds.

Believe me when I say I am in no position to assist you or the boy. I can only repeat in sincerity that I am sorry.

Yours truly,

Rose Bell

It didn't take long to write. When she had finished, she soon fell asleep on the settee.

14

Shortly before 7.30 on Tuesday morning a taxi entered Hyde Park by the Cumberland Gate, drove around the Ring and halted just across the bridge over the Serpentine. Antonia, who was the passenger, sensibly remained inside wrapped in her mink, for there was a thick frost. Her breath was making ice on the window. She rubbed at it.

'A little closer, driver.'

'You wouldn't be thinking of joining them, miss?'

'No fear.'

The all-weather bathers were taking their dip. A dozen at least, including women, were in the water paddling joylessly about.

The driver stopped at the point closest to the water. 'Like ruddy lobsters, except that this lot go in red and come out blue.'

Some minutes passed. It seemed to be a case of first out's a cissy. Then two of the women waded to the bank and started the exodus.

Antonia sighed. 'They get no credit for this unless they break the ice to go in. Then they get their picture in the papers.'

'I can think of easier ways, miss.'

One of the last to emerge was Vic, wearing trunks and chatting to two middle-aged men in oldfashioned costumes with shoulder straps. Although Antonia inclined to the view that people who did this must be coldblooded or mad, or both, she wasn't totally disapproving. Vic's body was good to look at even in these conditions. There was a suggestion of power as he moved, and his damp body-hair darkened the flesh and picked out the muscles as he flexed them.

She wound down the window and called his name.

He stopped and stared. Then he recognized her and

gestured that he needed to dry himself. She nodded. He went into the brick bathing house to change.

The driver had watched all this with interest. 'Boyfriend, miss?'

'Sort of.'

'Funny time to meet.'

'I spent most of yesterday trying to find him.' She took out her cigarettes and offered him one. 'He'd better not be long.'

'Doing up his buttons won't be easy with frozen fingers.'

'Don't worry. He'll get a roasting from me.'

She stared across the steely sheet of water until Vic emerged from the bathing house in his overcoat and came over to the taxi and climbed in.

'Well, this is an unexpected pleasure. What are you doing here?' He leaned across to kiss her cheek.

She withdrew her face out of range. 'Making one final attempt to track you down.'

'You were looking for me?'

'For the last twenty-four hours.'

'Sorry. I was sent to Birmingham. A conference. I got back at eleven last night.'

'You could have picked up a phone'.

The voice from the front interjected, 'Where to, please?'

She clicked her tongue impatiently. 'I suppose you're ravenous for breakfast now.'

The driver switched on his engine. 'There's a place at the top of North End Road. It ain't the Savoy, but you'll never taste a better bacon and egg.'

Later, after they'd put this recommendation to the test, Antonia conceded that the driver hadn't been far wrong. Her pleasure in the meal was much assisted by a full apology from Vic.

She forgave him, and more. 'I'm coming to stay with you some time in the next week or so.'

'To *stay*?'

'Yes, won't it be divine? Our first whole night together. Then our second and our third and–'

'What's Hector going to say about this?'

'I haven't spoken to him yet. He won't be any trouble.'

Vic glanced around the small café. Some traders from the market in wide-boy overcoats with heavily padded shoulders were in for breakfast. No one seemed to be listening.

'Antonia, I'd like to know more about this. Are you up to something?'

'Of course I'm up to something. I want to marry you and go to America.'

'Yes, but I don't want some bastard with a flash-camera bursting into my flat and taking pictures of you and me in bed.'

She laughed. 'How did you get that dopey idea?'

'That's the way people arrange it these days.'

'Arrange what?'

'Divorce.'

'Sweetie, how many times do I have to tell you divorce is out of the question? Forget about men with cameras.'

He sighed. 'I don't understand it.'

She lodged her foot against his. 'Don't try. Simply enjoy it while you've got the chance.'

Mr Smart, the insurance agent, was on the doorstep again, in the act of raising his trilby as Rose opened the door. His nose and ears were pillarbox red.

'Good day, Mrs Bell. Bright but cold. Ice about.'

'You'd better come in.'

He placed his hat and bicycle pump on the hallstand and removed his clips. 'How are you settling down?'

'I'm managing the best I can. Would you care for a cup of tea?'

'That sounds agreeable.'

'If you don't mind the kitchen, it's warmer in there.'

He stood rubbing his hands by the boiler. The teacloths from yesterday's wash-up were draped from the struts attached to the flue.

Rose reached for the matches and lit the gas under the kettle. 'What have you got – more forms for me to fill in?'

'I require no more than a signature this time. The funeral was yesterday, I believe.'

'Yes.'

'I dare say you're glad it's over.'

She detected an undercurrent of disapproval in the voice.

'It kept me busy. I was grateful for that.'

'Stopped your mind from dwelling on things.'

'True.'

'Are you able to get any sleep at all?'

She gave him a long, cool look. 'While we're waiting for the kettle, Mr Smart, don't you think we should get down to business?'

'As you wish. This is what you are waiting for, I think.' He took a brown envelope from his pocket and placed it ostentatiously on the kitchen table. 'Your cheque for five thousand pounds.'

She resisted the polite impulse to say thank you. Why should she? Nor did she snatch up the envelope and rip it open. She put out cups and saucers and went to the larder for milk.

'I shall require your signature on the receipt.'

'Naturally.' She noticed her Coronation biscuit tin taking up room at the front of the larder and remembered what it contained. 'A piece of cake?'

Mr Smart unexpectedly laughed, and there wasn't any humour in the laugh. 'Tell me, is that an offer of something to eat – or self-congratulation?'

She felt the blood drain from her face. 'What exactly do you mean?'

He gave a superior smile. 'A piece of cake. One of those cheerful phrases the RAF has given the language. Is that what all this has been, Mrs Bell? A piece of cake?'

She clenched her teeth. She thought, I've been through a police interrogation, an inquest and a funeral. Am I to be tripped by this pipsqueak insurance man? He's only guessing. He can't be certain. She prised the lid off the tin and held her mother's trench cake in front of him.

He selected a slice. There was a sneer on his face, as if the act of handing over the cheque had absolved him of the need to curry favour. 'Strictly between ourselves, I've come across some queer things in the insurance business, but this is one of the queerest. The very day your husband is due to surrender his policy, he's killed in an accident. Astonishing. You can hardly blame my company for wanting to make sure of the facts. We put the case in the hands of our best investigators. They find that the only person who stands to benefit – no sugar, if that's my cup – has a watertight alibi. Sorry, I shouldn't use the word "alibi". It implies that an offence was committed and we know it wasn't, don't we? The coroner was satisfied, his jury were satisfied and our investigators were unable to prove that anything irregular had happened.'

So it was supposition. He knew nothing about Antonia.

'Then I suggest, Mr Smart, that you stop imagining things.' Rose pushed the tea towards him. She reached for her handbag and took out her fountain pen. 'Do you have that receipt?'

'In the envelope.'

He finished his tea and left without touching the cake.

Some time after midnight Hector stopped work in his office downstairs and came to bed. He undressed in the dark, padding about in his shirt-tails so as not to disturb Antonia.

He didn't disturb her because she was still awake. She lay in silence in her own bed with her eyes open, waiting. The plan of action she was shortly to outline to Hector required his total concentration. She wanted him passive, in bed, where he had no choice except to listen. He had to be made to understand that his part in the plan was not only necessary, but inescapable.

She waited two or three minutes after he'd climbed into bed.

'Hec.'

'Mm?'

'What did you think of Rose?'

'Who?'

'My pretty little friend from the WAAF.'

'Rosie Bell? Nice girl. Why ask me?'

'I've decided to kill her.'

The bedsprings screeched. 'You gone mad?'

'I knew you'd say that. Listen, will you? It's the perfect answer to our problem. We invite her here to cook for you while I'm away.'

'You're going to *kill* her?'

'Pipe down and listen. I said I'm going away for a few days.'

'Going away? Where?'

'I'll come to that. I won't really be away. Not far, anyway. I've arranged to stay somewhere near. We give Rose the key and she lets herself in to make you a pie or something. I saw the way she looked at you when you asked if she could cook. She'll do it for you. I'll be hiding in the house. I surprise her and knock her out with chloroform. Then I smother her with a cushion. No blood. No mess.'

'Antonia, this is raving mad, you know.'

'No, it isn't, and I'll tell you why. I've managed to get hold of a blank death certificate.'

'A doctor's certificate?'

'No. Get a grip on yourself, Hector, and *listen*. A death registration. The one the registry office issues. With that we can get a body buried. We fill it in ourselves. We won't even need a doctor's certificate. It's quite straight-forward.'

'You think?'

'I'm certain.'

'But it's wicked to think of killing that poor sweet girl. What has Rosie done to hurt you or me? Nothing. She trusts us.'

'Poor, sweet girl! Hector, you're a mutt. That sweet girl is bloody dangerous. She's got to be stopped.'

'Stopped? What is she doing?'

'Any day now she'll go to the police.' Antonia took a deep breath. 'My fault, I admit it. I was taken in like you. Stupidly I let something slip about Maudie's death.'

Hector groaned. 'Maudie! Oh, no! You opened your big mouth. Crazy!'

Smoothly and expertly, Antonia embroidered fiction over the facts. 'Days ago I made some remark about having to wait for Maudie to die before you and I could marry. Then of course she met you and almost the first thing you told her was that Maudie drowned. I don't blame you, Hec, but she was on to it at once. She won't let it pass. She's been pestering me about it ever since. She's that sort of person. I'm certain she knows already.'

'Would she really go to the police?'

'You've met her. She's a vicar's daughter. A model bloody citizen. She'd regard it as her moral duty. She's got to be stopped, Hec.'

His reply was muffled, as if he'd pressed his hands to his face. 'I can't do this, Antonia.'

'You don't have to. I'm doing it. It's too bloody late to discover you have a conscience.'

He was silent for a long time.

'All right, you crazy bitch. After you kill Rosie in this house, what do you say to her people? She tripped over the cat and fell downstairs? She choked on a fish bone? You think her mother and father are going to believe you? And who arranges the funeral? You can't take this certificate to the undertaker and get her buried yourself.'

'No, my sweet. That's your job.'

'*Mine*? You make a big mistake there.'

'Calm down and listen to me, little man. You've jumped to all the wrong conclusions. Give me credit for some intelligence. There will be no trouble from Rosie's people because they won't know she's dead. The name on the death certificate will be mine. It will be *my* funeral, Hector. Can you get that into your head?'

He took a huge breath and then exhaled in a series of nervous bursts.

Antonia was in no hurry to move on. She wanted the essential message to sink in first. He was not unintelligent.

When he spoke again his tone was sceptical, but he'd got the point. 'Her body, your funeral.'

'Exactly. That's why you must make the arrangements. It isn't much to do, considering what you get in return. No more worries over the Maudie business. And you'll be a single man again. A widower for the second time. We were talking about it only the other day. A life of your own, you old goat. You'll never hear from me again.'

'Oh yes? Where will you go?'

'America, with Vic.'

'They won't let you stay.'

'Don't fret over that. I'll be married to him and he's got that job at Princeton.'

'*Married*?'

'Birdbrain. Haven't you worked it out? I'll be using Rose's identity. It's simply a matter of going through her handbag after she's dead. Her identity card will be there. If by any chance it isn't, the key of her house is sure to be, and I'll collect it the same evening and become sweet little Rosie Bell. I'll marry Vic at a registry office somewhere outside London within a couple of days. New surname. New passport. New country. Isn't it neat?'

'What about her people? They will report that she's missing.'

'Hector, thousands of people are missing. Haven't you ever looked at those lists in the Sunday papers? The police can't keep up with it. What's one more missing woman?'

He gave up trying to pick fault with the plan. He turned obstinate instead. 'I won't do this, Antonia. It's a mortal sin. I should never have let you kill poor Maudie. I suffer terrible dreams for that. I can't stand by and let you repeat that wicked thing.'

'Come off it, Hector! Don't get high and mighty with me now. It doesn't wash. We're in this together.'

'Not together. Leave me out.'

'How can I? Be reasonable. I can't arrange my own funeral.'

There was another scrunch from the bedsprings as he kicked out in fury. 'You tell *me* be reasonable? Killing another innocent woman – is that reasonable?'

'She's not so innocent as you think, but that's not the

point. I'm going to insist that you help me in this, Hector. You and I are going to make it happen exactly as I told you. I shall definitely kill her. If anything goes wrong, if you fail me, I swear to God I'll see you swing for killing Maudie.'

'Maudie! *You* pushed her in the pool!'

'With your connivance. You wanted to get rid of her. You were sick of her black moods and her drinking. I told you what I was going to do. That made you an accessory before the fact of murder, Hector. That's a hanging offence.'

'I didn't know how serious you were.'

'You stood back and let me get on with it. An English court of law isn't going to waste much sympathy on a nasty little foreigner who gets his mistress to do the dirty work for him. I might get away with a life sentence, but it's the rope for you, make no mistake about that.'

She let him brood on that. When he spoke again it was with an air of resignation.

'Say what you want. Exactly.'

She went over her plan minutely. And after she'd told him the undemanding but necessary part she wanted him to play, she added that she also required twenty thousand pounds to get settled in America.

He was silent.

She said it would be a once and for all payment. He would never hear from her again.

He said she could have it. Then he called her a blood-sucking monster.

She wished him a cheery goodnight.

15

Rose's nerves had given her another bad night. On Wednesday morning she needed to do something to occupy her mind so she went to Gorringe's and blued two clothing coupons and some of her new wealth on a roll of parachute silk. She'd decided to run up a set of underclothes on the sewing machine. Her dreary Utility things would go into service as floorcloths. Walking around the shop she drew up a mental shopping list, a wardrobe for the good times ahead. After a decent interval she would get a 'long look' coat, a suit with padded hips and shoulders, a couple of day dresses in bright prints and some shiny sling-back shoes. But the silk undies came first. It would create a bad impression to break out too soon after burying Barry. She didn't want the likes of Mr Sharp spreading rumours. Yet she couldn't wait to blot out every memory of Barry, throw out all the clothes she'd worn while she was married to him and start afresh. Well, some silk undies would be a start. No one need know what she was wearing underneath. Not without an invitation, she told herself in an effort to be frivolous. People were always telling her she was too solemn. She went straight up to Haberdashery and bought five yards of lace trimming.

She snipped and machined all afternoon with the firm intention of wearing her handiwork on Saturday when Antonia and Hector took her out to dinner. Up to now she'd been intimidated by Antonia's clothes. It would be a confidence boost to wear silk under her dreary old suit.

She was going to have no nonsense from Antonia, she decided. A week's respite from that domineering presence had given her a chance to think for herself. Antonia was clearly playing some elaborate and tasteless charade. She had always enjoyed shocking others, but that remark about having Hector cremated had been the limit. And that dangerous escapade to obtain the blank death registration certificate was obviously part of the same ghoulish game.

Wasn't it?

It was horrid to talk about doing away with Hector as if he were just as expendable as Barry. The two couldn't be compared. Barry had degenerated dangerously. He'd started to get violent. There would have been no escape. But Hector offered no threat whatsoever. He'd done nothing despicable that Rose had heard of. In fact he appeared rather charming. His worst fault, it seemed, was that he talked too much about his work – hardly a capital crime. Antonia was bored with him. She wanted to be rid of him, but there was a catch. She also wanted his money, to keep on living like a countess. Not a nice reason for killing anyone.

That, in Rose's eyes, would be a very wicked murder. Of course it was nonsense. It had to be.

She had an unpleasant shock on Friday. The doorbell rang at lunchtime and when she answered it she saw two children with the lifeless body of an adult man between them. They were trying with difficulty to support him at the armpits. His head hung over his chest and his knees had buckled under him. He was dressed in a grey trilby, shirt, trousers and boots. The elder child grabbed the head and jerked it upright.

'Penny for the Guy, miss.'

The face was a crudely drawn mask. The body was stuffed.

'Bonfire Night.'

'Isn't it rather early for that? It's still October.'

They were the Irish children from two doors along. They stood staring at her.

'I'll see what I've got in my purse. Did you make him yourselves?'

'Yes, miss.'

'He doesn't look very warm, dressed like that, in just a shirt. Wait a minute. I've got an idea.'

She returned presently with Barry's demob jacket, the garment Ronald had been caught in the act of trying on. 'See if this fits.'

'That's too good for the Guy, miss.'

'I've no use for it. Look, it suits him.' She laughed. 'And here's a tie. He'll look smart in a tie.'

In Barry's jacket and RAF tie, he looked distinctly smarter.

Antonia phoned on Saturday morning and suggested they met at the restaurant at eight.

'Reggiori's, in Euston Road, practically opposite St Pancras, darling. It's my regular haunt, red plush and brass, suits me down to the ground, terribly decadent, but the food is as good as you'll get anywhere. Can you make it, or would you like me to collect you?'

'That won't be necessary.'

'Reggiori's at eight, then.'

'Antonia . . .'

'What, darling?'

'Will Hector be there?'

'God, yes. I haven't bumped him off yet.'

The fine silk stirred against her skin as she moved. She'd made French knickers and a slip and trimmed them with the lace. To complete the ensemble, she was wearing the one pair of nylons she owned. Over it all, she had the severe black suit with the false shirt front she'd worn for the inquest. And her soon-to-be-discarded tweed coat.

She left the house about twenty to eight with the intention of walking along to Vauxhall Bridge Road and finding a taxi. First, her attention was caught by the road safety poster opposite. Something else had been added to it. She crossed the street. They'd carefully coloured the widow's face, giving her lipstick, rouge and mascara. The eyes were now light blue. The falling tear had been blocked out entirely. If not a merry widow, she was certainly less bleak than before.

Rose smiled at her.

16

Reggiori's must have been a cleaner's nightmare. Ornate fittings in abundance: the original gas jets, hat pegs, doorknobs, hand rails and bar furniture. More brass than the Royal Philharmonic. Red plush settees, wall mirrors, mosaic floor, ornamental tiles, potted ferns and silver cruets.

Antonia waved from a table against the wall and Hector stood up and helped Rose into her chair. Whatever it was on his hair smelt expensive. She smiled her thanks. The guarded look he gave her in return was difficult to understand. He'd been so open the last time they had met.

After they'd ordered, Antonia asked about the funeral and Rose told her how Rex Ballard, Peter Bliss and the others had driven down from Kettlesham Heath. 'I wasn't too happy about them coming at first, but as it turned out they helped me get through the day.'

Ridges of tension showed in Antonia's cheek. 'You didn't mention my name?'

'No, I didn't.'

'Did they?'

'No.'

The lines softened and disappeared. 'I expect they were shocked about Barry.'

'Rex could hardly take it in.'

'I bet he wasn't lost for words, though.'

Rose smiled. 'No.'

The wine waiter arrived and Hector asked whether Rose cared for Italian wine. She made the mistake of asking if wine wasn't rather extravagant and got ticked off by Antonia.

'The war's over now. You've got to get out of that scrimp-and-save mentality.'

'People in your circumstances can. It's not so easy for the rest of us.'

'Oh, send me to the guillotine, darling. I don't know how the poor live.'

Hector turned from ordering the wine and showed that he had missed the point entirely. 'I think in this country they don't use the guillotine.' He made a 'V' shape between thumb and forefinger of his right hand and pressed it hard into the angle of his neck and jaw, at the same time pulling an imaginery lever with his left hand. He ended the performance by giving a doglike stare at Rose that made her feel extremely uneasy.

She took a sip of water and tried to think of some other topic, but Antonia was unaffected.

'I see that our ex-RAF colleague went to the scaffold this morning.'

'Oh?'

'Neville Heath.'

Rose tensed. Hector made a vibrating sound with his lips but it didn't discourage Antonia.

'According to the *Star*, he took leave of the world in style. They asked for his last request and he said he'd like a whisky. When it was handed to him and everyone was waiting he said, "I think I'll make that a double." Nice sense of humour.'

Rose said, 'I can't admire a man who did the things he did. Can we change the subject?'

'If you like, darling. What shall we talk about – carburettors? No, Hector, it's meant to be a joke, like the double whisky.'

Hector didn't talk about carburettors. He told them he'd spent another good day at the Victoria & Albert Museum, where his refrigerator was being demonstrated at the Britain Can Make It exhibition. Crowds had formed every day around the stand and there was tremendous interest from retailers.

'How thrilling for you! I must come and see it.'

His chestnut eyes suddenly shone again. 'You tell me when. I can get you in complimentary.'

Antonia studied her fingernails. 'Don't get carried away, Rosie. Just about everything in that tinpot exhibition is marked "For export only", including his precious fridge.'

Hector glared at her.

The minestrone made a timely arrival. Rose took a first spoonful, watched by Antonia.

'Good?'

'This wasn't out of a tin.'

'Did your parents come up for the funeral?'

'Yes. They asked me to go home with them.'

'Why? Do they need looking after?'

'They were thinking of me.'

'You're lucky. They must be fond of you. My mother's impossible. Even Hector can't stand her.'

'Not true, Antonia.'

'Oh, get away with you, Hec. You complained of a headache last time and we had to leave early.' She picked up a slice of bread and started picking it to pieces. Rose, as she listened, quickly sensed that Antonia was at it again, manipulating people, but this time Hector seemed to be the target. 'This is fearfully boring for you, Rosie, but now that the subject of Ma has come up, I've got something to ask my husband. I had a letter from home this morning, dearest. It's about Lucky.'

Hector frowned. 'Lucky?'

'The dog, you chump.' She sighed and turned to Rose. 'If ever an animal was misnamed, it's this one. Ma collected it from the dogs' home when I was still a schoolgirl, that's how old it is. It was blind in one eye and she felt sorry for it. A cross between a bull terrier and a Bedlington, if you can imagine that. Pink eyes and white woolly hair. It's been run over twice and has a metal splint in one leg. One of its ears was torn off in a fight and it went deaf in the air raids. Lucky!'

Hector nodded. 'First time I met this Lucky, he make water on my new shoes.'

'Thank you, dear heart. The dog has an unreliable bladder to add to its miseries and Ma's, but I wasn't going to speak of it over dinner. The latest bulletin is that it's developed a chronic case of mange. The woolly coat is dropping like snow all over the house. Ma says she must face the inevitable.'

'He must go?'

'Poor old thing, yes. What's that song of Gracie Fields? –"Wish Me Luck as You Wave Me Goodbye". – The thing is, she can't bear the thought of taking the old dog to the vet, so she wants me to go up there and do the necessary.'

Hector's eyebrows pricked up. 'Kill it?'

'Pass it over to the vet. She's in a frightful state about it.'

He lifted his shoulders and spread his hands. 'You'd better go, then.'

'But it's bound to mean two or three days away. Apart from all that travelling, I'm going to have a distraught mother to deal with.' She hesitated before asking Hector in a voice pitched on a tragic note, 'I suppose you won't come with me?'

Rose sipped her soup and looked into the mid-distance. She wished Antonia had saved this conversation for later.

Hector shook his head. 'Britain Can Make It.'

'So Hector obviously can't. No, I don't mean to be rude. I shall just have to go on my own. You *do* understand that the doggie has to be dealt with, Hec, my pet?'

Antonia's concern for her husband was as warming as it was unexpected. A pity she called him her 'pet' in the circumstances, but he seemed not to take it badly.

He leaned towards Rose. 'My wife, she is highly suitable for such a sad duty. No nerves. No panics.'

'I can believe it.'

The matter still wasn't settled to Antonia's satisfaction, even though Hector had given his blessing. There was the problem of his eating arrangements. 'How can I go up to Manchester knowing you won't eat a thing? It's no good looking at me like that, Hector. You're too proud to eat in a restaurant alone.'

He shook his head. 'Not too proud. I don't enjoy it, that's all.'

'It comes down to the same thing.' She swung round and

addressed Rose. 'You see how difficult he makes it? The silly man won't have a hot dinner for as long as I'm gone.'

'How does he manage for lunch?'

'Never eats it. This is the only substantial meal he gets. He's going to collapse if he doesn't eat something.'

The thought crossed Rose's mind that if all Hector was lacking was a dining companion, she could easily volunteer. This thought was overtaken by another: this concern for Hector's eating arrangements didn't square with Antonia's plans for him. No, she thought. Something lies behind this.

She slipped in a suggestion. 'Couldn't you cook something like a stew before you go and leave it in the oven for Hector to warm up?'

As if Hector hadn't heard of anything so humble as stew, Antonia provided a rough translation. 'Goulash.'

He gave a shrug.

'Darling, he'd like nothing better, but there are two little snags. First, I couldn't make a stew to save my life, and second, Hector would blow up the house trying to light the gas.'

'Could I do it?'

'Light the gas?'

'Prepare the evening meal.' The suggestion came from Rose spontaneously, and immediately after making it she cursed herself for being so impetuous. Then she thought about the prospect more calmly and decided that if Antonia were away in Manchester there couldn't be any harm in it. She'd do as much for any friend. It was a practical and agreeable way of dispensing at least a little of the obligation she had to Antonia. 'I can easily cook up a stew, but I don't know about goulash.'

'It's just extra seasoning, like curry. That's a thought!' Antonia smiled knowingly at Hector and he nodded back.

Rose looked towards each of them in turn. 'What's that?'

'Could you make a curry for him? He'd adore that.'

She liked the suggestion. It would be much more

tempting to serve up to Hector than plain old stew. 'Well, yes. I make quite a passable lamb curry.'

'Darling, that's awfully good of you. Let me buy the ingredients. The meat. Everything. It'll keep in the fridge. We'll give you a key and you can let yourself in whenever you want and do the cooking. Hector gets home about six from the exhibition. He won't be a minute late if there's a curry waiting. You're an angel.'

Hector raised his glass to her. 'The lady who is about to save my life.'

She felt herself go pink.

At the door of Reggiori's, Antonia was handed a box not unlike the cake-box she'd picked up at the Ritz. Rose asked what the cat was getting for supper and learned that it was salmon.

They drove her back to Pimlico in the Bentley. She thanked them profusely for the meal and for bringing her home.

While Hector was turning the car she stood waving from her front door.

'Like some little girl who went to a birthday party.'

'What?' Antonia was staring out of the other window at the road safety poster.

'Rosie. Such nice manners. I believe you're wrong about her. She wouldn't make trouble for us with the police. Didn't you see how she really wants to cook dinner for me? She jumped at it. How can you think of this wicked thing?'

'Don't start up now, little man. I'm pooped.'

'Pooped from telling so many lies.'

Hector wasn't used to getting the last word, so it was no surprise when Antonia pitched in as they were motoring up Park Lane. 'She really took you in, didn't she? You're a sucker for the little-girl-lost look. The timid smile and watery blue eyes.'

'No wonder her eyes are sad when her husband just died. Don't you have no pity?'

Antonia shook with amusement, taking gusts of air

through her nostrils. 'You prize idiot! She isn't suffering. Barry was no loss. She killed him.'

He drew the car in to the kerb and switched off the engine. 'Antonia, I do not believe this.'

'He was a washout as a husband so she shoved him on to the Piccadilly Line and picked up five thousand in insurance. Don't waste any sympathy on Rose Bell, my innocent. She's a killer. You can ask her.'

'How can I ask such a thing?'

'Ask her if she really misses him. You'll see the guilt in her face.'

17

Rose used a key Antonia had given her to enter the house in Park Crescent early on Tuesday afternoon. Antonia had phoned that morning to say she was catching the 11.25 from Euston, adding that she'd stocked up at Fortnum's and a little place she knew that didn't bother with ration books and she'd left heaps of things in the fridge and Rose was to use whatever she wanted and to hell with austerity.

Until the moment the latch clicked behind her, Rose hadn't foreseen the unease she would feel letting herself into someone else's house. All five doors leading off from the hall were closed. She wished she'd been more observant of the layout when Antonia had brought her here before, instead of goggling at it all like a GI in Piccadilly Circus. She did remember that the blue and white sitting room looked on to the street, so presumably that was the first door, but which was the kitchen? Somewhere ahead. She stepped forward, grasped a handle, turned it and found herself staring into darkness. Judging by the musty smell, it was the route to the cellar.

She closed that door and tried another. Second time lucky. Hector's enormous fridge gave a welcoming throb. She slipped off her coat and hung it on a hook behind the door.

There was a folded note on the kitchen table with her name on it. Antonia's writing was huge. It ran to several sheets.

> Rose Darling,
>
> You're one in a million.
>
> Meat in the fridge. Also butter and as many fresh veggies as I could carry home. Onions on the windowsill. Raisins and sultanas in the canisters on the dresser (second shelf) next to all the spices. Be generous with the curry powder – Hec doesn't believe

it's the real thing unless he breathes fire after it. Oh, and if you want to go to the trouble of rice, there's a packet beside the breadbin. Hope I haven't forgotten anything essential. Found the ingredients in the New World cookery book, which I'm sure you won't need to use – I've never used it either!

Hec says he will be in about six each night and for once he definitely means it.

Raffles will finish any trimmings from the meat. Did I mention that he's the cat?

I'm counting on being back by Saturday. Let's all have another meal at Reggiori's. By God, you deserve it!

Love,

Antonia

It was a good thing that Raffles was mentioned, because before Rose had finished reading the note she felt a movement against her leg. A second or two earlier and neither she nor the cat would have got much pleasure from the contact. She picked him up and faced the scrutiny of his large orange eyes.

'So you're Raffles, are you? Shall we see if we can crack this safe together? Oh, my word, look at this!'

A family could have fed from that fridge for a month. She put Raffles down and collected butter and lard by the armful just to find a way through to the milk.

Having filled the cat's saucer she went back to the fridge. Presently she located the meat – beautiful boned lamb and heaps more than she needed for a single curry, whatever the capacity of Hector's appetite. She picked a large piece that must have weighed two pounds or so, then looked round for a knife and chopping board. She was going to need extra time for working in a strange kitchen.

Everything she required was somewhere nearby, only had to be found first. It took the best part of an hour to collect all the ingredients, chop the meat and onion and take it through the frying stage, but she got engrossed in the cooking and didn't fret about the time.

She hadn't felt so pleased to be preparing food for

months. Cooking lost its appeal when your husband told you frankly that he regarded eating as 'stoking up'. Barry would have cheerfully stoked up every day with baked beans if they were put in front of him. It wasn't as if Rose hadn't tried to educate his taste. Time and again, notwithstanding rationing and shortages, she'd put some special dish on the table after queuing and cooking most of the day only to see him bolt it without looking up from the evening paper.

She stirred in two tablespoonfuls of curry powder, enough, she decided, to produce the strong curry Hector expected without altogether masking the other spices, for she'd found ginger, garlic and paprika lined up on the dresser. Raisins, sliced celery and chopped apple and tomato went into the pot to simmer with the meat until it was tender. Reggiori's had better watch out!

By then it was getting on for half past four. She washed up and thought about setting the table. It ought to be ready for when he came in. Where was the dining room, she wondered. She didn't want her famous curry to be eaten off the kitchen table.

She dried her hands and went to explore. She felt she'd earned the right to try those doors in the hall.

As she switched on a light she gave a cry, half admiring, half envious. A spacious, beautifully proportioned room, cream and pale green, with an oval table that could have seated a dozen easily and still didn't dominate. A fire had been laid in the grate, so she put a match to it and watched it take. Then she went to the windows and drew the curtains. They were ivory-coloured velvet and they skimmed the floor.

She found silver cutlery, placemats and napkins in the top drawer of a mahogany sideboard opposite the fireplace. Like the cooking implements, they'd not been given much use.

It was while she was setting the place for Hector that she had a paralysing thought: why was she putting out a dessert spoon? There was nothing to follow. She'd been so absorbed in preparing the curry that she hadn't given a thought to the rest of the meal.

There *had* to be some form of dessert, but what? There wasn't much time. What would be acceptable after a piping hot curry? Something moist. Fruit? After all the trouble she'd taken with the first course it would be a dreadful letdown just to open a tin of peaches.

A fresh fruit salad would be better. Coming out of Regent's Park tube station on the way to Antonia's she'd passed a stall selling apples and pears and there had been hardly any queue to speak of.

She looked at the time, shovelled some more coal on the fire and collected her coat.

On the way she thought of something better. There was a story her mother delighted in telling about the evening Daddy had thrown his annual dinner party at the rectory for the church wardens and their wives. It had always been a staid affair. That year Mummy had found a recipe for pears poached in red wine which proved to be such a success that two or three of the guests had become merry after second helpings. When they'd all tottered out at the end of the evening, Daddy had asked what the recipe was called. Mummy had given an innocent smile and said, 'Wardens in Wine'. A warden, she'd discovered, was an old English name for a pear used in cooking.

She'd noticed several bottles of Burgundy lying on their sides on the floor of the larder. If there were any pears left on the greengrocer's stall, her problem would be solved.

Although it was almost dark, the man was still there, working under an electric light bulb. Rose bought three large Comice pears. Twenty-five past five. Ten minutes' preparation and twenty for the poaching. She could just get everything done in time.

The simmering curry was giving off a rich aroma when Rose got back to the house. She checked that the fire was burning well in the dining room and then set to work in the kitchen. While she was peeling and coring the pears, her thoughts returned to Antonia. How odd that any woman equipped with this dream of a kitchen could take no interest in cooking. Terribly sad, really, that Hector devoted his working life to manufacturing labour-saving machines for women and was married to someone who didn't appreciate them in the slightest. Perhaps Antonia should have employed a cook. Well, she has, in a way, Rose thought, smiling. I'm in service here. I'm not doing it from altruism. I'm under an obligation to her; she killed my husband, so I cook for hers when she goes away. Not a bad division of responsibility from my point of view.

In fact, I'm enjoying it. It must be years since I had such a satisfying afternoon.

It was too bad that oranges were still blue books only. A few thin strips of peel would have completed the dish. At least there was spice. She added sugar and a few cloves. Then she brought it all to the boil and let it simmer.

Time to heat some water for the rice.

I wonder if Antonia has any idea what a treat this is for me. Or, come to that, what a treat is in store for Hector. To be fair, she provided all the ingredients. That meat is superb. It smells delicious.

She's so inconsistent, talking to me about wanting to do away with Hector, and then going to no end of trouble to see that he's properly fed.

Unless . . .

Unless I've totally misunderstood what's going on.

Please God, no!

She's capable of it.

She knows I'd refuse point blank if she asked me to administer poison to her husband. But what if I'm unaware of what I'm doing?

'*Be generous with the curry powder.*'

Curry will mask the taste of arsenic or strychnine or whatever she managed to obtain from her boyfriend Vic, the chemistry lecturer. The plan is horribly clear. She went to her mother to give herself an alibi. In my ignorance I'm about to serve up a poisoned curry for Hector and kill him. When she comes back from Manchester she'll fill in the blank death certificate and have him cremated.

Or am I imagining this?

He'll be here any minute.

18

Hector opened the kitchen door and looked in. His eyes lit up when he saw her and he gave a huge sigh of relief, almost as if he'd expected somebody else to be there.

'Smells nice.'

'Please ignore the smell.'

'Why?'

'I'm sorry. There won't be any curry after all.'

He gave a gurgle of amusement. He was going out of his way to be pleasant. 'It's done. I can smell it. Where is it?'

'It's gone.'

'Gone? Gone where?'

'Down the toilet.'

'Is this a joke, Rosie? You wouldn't make fun of me?'

'It was a bad curry. You couldn't possibly have eaten it. I'm going to try and do something else instead. It won't take long, I promise. Do you like omelettes?'

'Please – my curry – what went wrong?'

He put it to her with good-natured concern, as if enquiring after the health of a friend. Rose felt compelled to give him an answer. What she told him, however, was a lie. If he was convinced that his wife had set a trap to poison him, he'd go straight to the police. Even if he was unconvinced, he would want an explanation. As sure as God made little apples, the truth about Barry would come out.

She did her best to make it plausible. 'I suppose I was nervous. Something went wrong in the cooking.'

'You burnt it?'

'Not exactly.'

'I can't smell burning.'

'No. It was what went into it. The ingredients. They weren't right. I'd like to try again tomorrow, if you'll allow me. I'll get it right next time. Now will you please let me cook you an omelette or a fried egg or something?'

His eyes had a sceptical glint. He crossed the room to the sink and ran his forefinger around the inner side of the saucepan Rose had half-filled with water.

She moved fast. She reached out to him and grasped his sleeve. 'Don't!'

'You don't let me taste? Not even taste?'

She snatched up a teacloth and wiped his finger clean. 'Not even taste.'

He laughed and took a grip on her hand through the towel and squeezed it. She had her back to the draining board so she couldn't easily move.

'You know what I think you are, Rosie – apart from Antonia's best friend?'

Her neck and shoulders tensed. She was suddenly convinced that he'd misinterpreted her actions and was about to make a pass. She was in no state to deal with it. She swayed back and took a shallow, rasping breath.

His hand darted to her face and lightly pinched the point of her chin. 'A fusspot. A proper little fusspot.'

It was embarrassing on both sides. Faced with her jittery reaction he'd fallen back on a fatuous gesture and the sort of silly, doting thing said by middle-aged men to their simpering wives. He must have felt it as acutely as she, because he backed off at once.

Rose turned to the sink and made a performance of wiping the saucepan clean as her mind raced. Perhaps she'd been mistaken. Perhaps he'd only meant to make light of the problem over the curry. He'd responded to her state of nerves by touching her. It was innocent, a spontaneous gesture.

When Hector's voice came again it was from a safe distance. 'I'll make a bargain with you, Rosie. You cook me curry tomorrow. Tonight I will take you to Reggiori's.'

She looked across the table at him. He was still wearing his camelhair overcoat and he'd picked up his porkpie hat. 'I couldn't possibly.'

'One little mistake in the cooking and you lose your confidence? This is not good, Rosie.'

'I'll make the curry. I said I would. What I mean is that I couldn't under any circumstances go out to dinner with you.' She turned to face him across the table. 'It's not the right way to behave, you see. I can't be seen having dinner with someone else's husband.'

'You did the other night.'

'Antonia was with us.'

'So the people in Reggiori's know it's all right. Rosie is Antonia's friend, not Hector's lover.'

She felt the colour spread across her face. Mortifying. 'Please allow me to cook you something else.'

'Not possible.' He was adamant, like a chess-player who knew he had mate in three. 'I had no lunch today.'

'No lunch. But why?'

'Antonia told you. I never eat lunch. Only this meal. Now I need – how do you say? – a square meal. Not omelette.'

'Anything else would take hours to prepare.'

'Not at Reggiori's.'

She *couldn't*. What sort of woman would dine in public with a married man the week after she'd buried her husband? It would be deplorable. Yet she felt piercingly guilty for depriving Hector of the meal he'd looked forward to eating. The possibility had to be faced that she'd been mistaken about the poison and thrown away a perfectly good meal. And she knew Hector objected to going to restaurants alone; it wasn't some stratagem he'd just thought up. It was her whole justification for being here.

He lifted her coat off the hook on the back of the door. 'All right, Rosie. Please forget what I said. I will take you home now.'

She was caught off guard. 'Where will you eat?'

He gave a shrug. 'I don't know. I don't intend to starve. I will come home, look in the fridge, make myself a sandwich.'

From the fridge. 'No.'

He arched his eyebrows.

She had a picture of him opening the fridge and finding the rest of the meat, or something else that Antonia had laced with poison. 'I've changed my mind.'

He thoughtfully suggested they sat at a table for four rather than one of the more intimate doubles. To anyone interested it must have seemed that they expected to be joined by the rest of their party later.

'You look nervous, Rosie.'

'I am, a little.'

'You want some wine?'

'No, thank you.'

'Not many people are here so early as you and me.'

'No.'

'That's good?'

'Yes.'

He made a noble effort to be entertaining, talking of the gadgets he'd seen at the exhibition and the way women's lives would soon be transformed. For a man, he had some revolutionary ideas. Most women would have thought of them as mutinous. He talked about the drudgery of housework and rejected the idea that it was a proof of virtue. 'All that scrubbing of doorsteps. What for? So that all the neighbours will say she's a good woman like us, scrubs her step every day. Rosie, very soon all those good women will get red hands and lumpy knees. Don't be like that.'

She smiled faintly. 'What should I do, then – buy one of your machines? Do you supply a doorstep-scrubbing machine?'

'No. There is no market for such a machine. Simply forget about your doorstep.'

'And have all my neighbours think I'm a slut?'

'The women maybe. Men think something else. What nice legs this lady has.'

She looked primly down at her plate. Being foreign, he may not have appreciated how personal some of his remarks appeared.

'It's true. You have legs like Betty Grable's. Better.'

'I'm sure you mean it kindly, but I wish you'd talk about something else.'

'Not your legs?'

'Not my legs.'

'Your chest?'

Her arm jerked and she spilled some soup. She picked her napkin off her lap and rearranged it, trying frantically to think of something to divert him from this tack. 'I wonder if Antonia will telephone you tonight.'

'Excuse me, Rosie. My English. I don't think you understand. I said "chest". Is it more suitable to say "chests"?'

'It's unsuitable however you say it. Perhaps she telephoned you earlier? I dare say she would want you to know she'd arrived safely.'

'I am so sorry. I think I embarrass you with my bad grammar.'

'It's not the grammar.'

'You don't think so?'

'It's the personal things you mention.'

'I understand. I think I mean bust. Can I say you have a pretty fine bust?'

Through iron persistence she succeeded at length in directing his thoughts to Antonia. It appeared that he didn't expect a phone call. They didn't phone each other unless it was necessary. They had nothing to say to each other. 'Antonia, she doesn't understand me.'

'Oh, yes?' Rose kept her response as bland as possible. Of all the come-ons men resorted to, that was the corniest.

He tried to do better. 'She has a friend. A man friend. You know?'

'It's none of my business.'

'This friend is off to America soon. Nice new job. Princeton University. Antonia wants to go with him.'

'Mm?'

'Yes. It's true. You can ask her.'

'I wouldn't dream of asking her a thing like that.'

'Antonia and me, we sleep single.'

Opportunely the arrival of the main course foreclosed discussion of the sleeping arrangements. Hector had ordered Dover sole in breadcrumbs, which he explained wouldn't spoil his appetite for the curry Rose had promised for the next evening. She didn't want to be reminded about tomorrow. Getting through the present evening without misunderstanding was as much as she could cope with.

He gave her the cue for a more congenial line of conversation. 'So you were one of the WAAFs, like Antonia?'

'Yes. At Kettlesham Heath. I expect she's told you about it many times.'

'But I would like to hear from you. What did you do?'

'I was a plotter, like Antonia. In an underground control room. Very hush-hush. We had to sign a paper promising not to say anything about our work.'

He seemed to find this amusing. 'Ladies talk so much they can't keep no secret.'

'You're mistaken. We're much more discreet than the average man.'

'Yes?' He gave her a silly grin and she almost lost patience with him. His own life was threatened and he was so complacent that he hadn't a hope of finding out.

'Take Antonia. She's much more guarded than you appreciate. If she has a reason to keep something to herself, nothing will drag it from her.'

'You think?'

'I'm certain.'

His expression changed. 'Rosie, you are right about Antonia. She is a plotter still.'

She hesitated. He was an eager listener and she was on the brink of saying too much. 'Most of us women have our secret hopes and plans, if that's what you mean. Anyway, I was telling you about Kettlesham Heath. It was demanding work – sheer hell sometimes – and we couldn't afford to make mistakes. Actually Antonia was the most reliable of all the girls on watch. She didn't get tense. She could talk and joke and keep everyone smiling and never lose her concentration.'

'She was popular?'

'Certainly.'

'Plenty of officers went out with her. It's all right, she told me this.'

'Well, yes.'

'And you, Rosie? Did you have plenty?'

She allowed herself to smile. 'I wouldn't describe it in quite those terms. I wasn't so popular as Antonia. If I'd been asked I'd have gone out with almost any officer with wings. Any of us would. It was a question of prestige. Good looks and age came a long way after rank. They had to have stripes on their sleeves and the more the better. Funny, isn't it? There were some good-looking fellows among the sergeant pilots, but to go out with them was slumming. It was the service mentality, I suppose. Silly. I married a wing commander.' She stopped and lowered her eyes. She hadn't wanted to mention Barry.

Anyone with a modicum of tact would have moved to another subject. Hector sat up in his seat and leaned on his elbows and gave her a penetrating stare as if nothing interested him so much. 'Tell me, Rosie, do you miss your husband?'

She frowned. His dark eyes locked with hers and it was almost like being interrogated. She wondered for a petrifying moment if he suspected something. Then with a sense of relief she realized what this was about. How typical of a man, she thought. He thinks I'm on the lookout for someone. How can I possibly convey to him that those stories about freshly widowed women falling for the next man who passes the time of day with them arc untrue, quite monstrously untrue?

'I should never have got married.'

'You don't miss him, then?'

'I'd rather talk about something else.'

'Won't you try again?'

'It's most unlikely.'

'You will get lonely.'

'I don't suppose I will.'

'You are very pretty. Some fellow will ask to marry you soon.'

It was a long time since anyone had paid her any kind of compliment. In her situation it was inopportune, but better than an insult. Or an interrogation.

'Shall we look at the menu again?'

He looked mystified. 'I spoke something wrong?'

It might have been uncharitable, but she had a suspicion that Hector was overplaying the part of the foreigner baffled by English. He'd lived in America and England for fifteen years or so and must have used the language pretty effectively to earn the money he had.

They decided to have coffee instead of desserts. He offered her a liqueur. She thanked him and said no, adding that she didn't want to stop him from having one. She smoked a cigarette while he had a brandy. She needed the smoke. She'd staunched the flow of personal remarks, but she felt uneasy. His eyes never left hers. She didn't know if it was her imagination or if he was planning something.

As they were collecting their coats, he suggested she waited inside the restaurant while he fetched the car, which he'd parked in a side street.

'That isn't necessary. I'll take the tube from here. The meal was delicious. Thank you.' She thrust her arms into the coat and made a decisive move towards the door. 'I'll see you tomorrow.'

'Rosie!' He caught up with her outside and clutched her arm to restrain her. 'I said I will drive you.'

'No, thank you.'

'Excuse me, but why not?'

She was flustered, so the words that came out sounded more ungrateful than she intended. 'You wanted a meal and I came with you out of politeness. Now would you please let go of my arm?'

He walked beside her as she set off smartly along Euston Road. 'Please, did I say something wrong tonight?'

'You're making this very difficult.'

'I cannot allow this, Rosie.'

'Hector, I'm not your property.'

This had a startling effect. He flung up his arms as if in surrender. 'Forgive me. I should never have said such things. You are Antonia's friend. You come specially to my house to cook a nice meal for me. What disgusting manners I have!'

They'd reached a street corner and had to stop for the traffic. Some people standing there had picked up Hector's last remark and turned round. He must have seemed comical making an exhibition of himself in his expensive overcoat and porkpie hat. Rose didn't find it amusing.

She made a sideward step and tried to give the impression she was unaccompanied. Hector didn't move. He simply raised his voice. 'Please forgive me. Allow me to be a gentleman and drive you safe home.'

She looked to right and left, hoping to God that the underground sign was somewhere about. An elderly couple had joined the group at the curb. The woman was trying to prompt Rose by nodding and smiling.

Hector was oblivious of his audience. 'Don't go down the tube, Rosie.'

It was like an echo of the old tear-jerking ballad 'Don't go down the mine, Daddy'. Ludicrous. This could only get more embarrassing. He wouldn't give up. And she didn't want it to end in a blazing row.

She spun around. 'All right. Which way is the car?'

After all, she'd made her point. He could be in no doubt now that she wanted him to remain at arm's length.

During the drive to Oldfield Gardens Hector behaved impeccably. He was charming and witty. He talked glowingly of the curry she had promised him the next day and how in order to put his mind at rest he planned to lock the toilet door and hide the key. She took it in good part and said she could think of dozens of ways of disposing of a curry and some of them were very messy indeed, so he'd better leave the toilet open and trust his luck and hers.

'This your street, Rosie?'

'Yes, don't you remember? The house at the end, opposite the hoarding.'

He drew in and braked.

She turned and leaned back slightly in the same movement to keep her face out of range. 'Thank you. It was a splendid meal.'

'Only second best.'

'Perhaps.'

'We'll find out tomorrow, eh?'

'If you're still willing to risk it. Hector. . . ?'

'Yes?'

'There is still some meat in the fridge. You won't use any, will you?'

'You think I want to cook a midnight feast? Without anyone to share?'

'I just wanted to mention it.'

He laughed softly. 'Rosie, believe me, I don't touch nothing.'

She opened the car door, profoundly relieved at getting home without incident. On an impulse she reached out and put her hand over his, squeezing his fingers slightly. 'Tomorrow, then.'

19

That night Rose had an inspiration. A stunning solution to all the problems. She was certain it would work.

To tell it right, the idea didn't come in a blinding flash. She came to it through a process that started the moment she left Hector.

Her first thought after watching the Bentley turn in the road and sweep out of Oldfield Gardens was that she'd made a perfect fool of herself. She should never have squeezed his hand like some schoolgirl on a blind date.

She closed her front door and leaned against it with her hands clasped against the back of her neck and her eyes pressed shut and played the scene in her mind again, trying to see it from Hector's point of view. He could have taken the gesture as what it was, a clumsy attempt to show she had his welfare at heart in spite of the hard time she'd given him. Or, more alarmingly, as a promise of passion. How she wished she hadn't added that, 'Tomorrow, then.'

Maybe he'd already dismissed the whole thing from his mind.

She considered this a moment and discovered that it wasn't the comfort it should have been. Deep down, she hoped he hadn't treated the incident as unimportant. For all Hector's hair-raising remarks, he was a stimulating companion. And he gave you his total attention.

How Antonia could contemplate killing him was beyond belief. There was no question that she meant to do it. She'd got the death certificate ready. She'd talked about having him cremated. He was doomed. He might have been dying in agony at this minute if he'd eaten that curry.

Rose started to shake. She went through to the kitchen and opened the larder and saw the space on the shelf where the brandy had been. She gave a moan as she remembered smashing the bottle.

A cigarette, then. She found the packet and her lighter and sat at the kitchen table taking quick, shallow puffs, unable any longer to shut out the horror of what was happening.

No wonder she was in a state. She was poleaxed by the conviction that she had come so close to poisoning Hector. And angry at her own stupidity and Antonia's deceit. Above all, she was frightened.

If Hector had died and his murder had been discovered, Antonia, up in Manchester, would have had a convincing alibi. The prime suspect would have been Rose herself.

She winced, as if the pain were physical. As a schemer Antonia was in a class of her own. She had planned from the beginning to use her. There was a price to be paid for Barry's death. It was naïve in the extreme to suppose the favour could be repaid by cooking a few meals for Hector. He was down to be murdered.

'Not by me,' she said aloud. 'There was never any suggestion of that. *Never*.'

Antonia seemed to think nothing of killing people. She'd pushed Barry under the train without turning a hair. She'd contrived to have Hector poisoned while she went to visit her mother. And – Rose shuddered as she remembered – she'd talked of waiting for Hector's first wife to die – by drowning. At the time it had seemed incomprehensible. Not now.

Pull yourself together and be positive, Rose told herself. How stupid of Antonia to think that the answer to every problem is murder. Hector's only offence is that he won't give her a divorce. Surely they can end their unhappy marriage in some other way?

She drew more deeply on the cigarette.

Then the inspiration dawned.

If Hector won't give Antonia a divorce because he's a Roman Catholic, why shouldn't *she* divorce him? If he's the guilty party Antonia can take her case to court and win. She can have a share of his fortune, which she's after, and she'll be free to marry Vic.

Above all, Hector's life will be saved.

Her mouth went dry as she pursued the idea. On what grounds could Antonia divorce him? Cruelty? That won't wash. Desertion? Definitely not. Insanity? No. Failure to consummate? Unlikely.

That left adultery. Antonia had brushed aside the possibility of other women. '*No vultures circling overhead. I'd know.*'

In that case Hector has to be persuaded to take a lover.

Rose plunged a hand into her hair and gripped it hard at the roots.

It has to be me.

I can't, she thought. Jesus Christ, it's only three weeks since my husband died. I'm a widow. I don't love Hector. I've met him on three occasions. I've never been so embarrassed as when he made that pass at me in the kitchen and ended up calling me a fusspot. I don't find him attractive.

Do I?

No use questioning my motives. Suddenly to be taken out for a meal after five years of being ignored is quite head-turning, but that doesn't come into it. I wouldn't dream of going to bed with Hector. Not unless everything altered and made it possible, anyway. And then not for many months. . . .

I must get this clear in my mind. I won't be doing it for any other reason than necessity, to save him from being murdered, and myself from worse trouble than I'm in already.

She felt groggy. That brandy would have been a lifesaver at this minute. There was some ginger wine somewhere in the front room. She collected it and poured herself a large glass.

I'll be the 'other woman' in a divorce case. Horrible. It's sure to be in the newspapers. Mummy and Daddy will get to hear of it. They don't read the gutter press, but plenty of people in the parish do. A divorce scandal is the very thing I was so desperate to avoid. I had Barry killed because I wouldn't divorce him.

Oh, God, what's the alternative? Hector will be killed.

He's a decent man, utterly different from Barry. He takes a pride in his work. He treats me as if I'm a member of the same species, not some lower order. He made a terrible mistake when he fell under Antonia's charm, but I can understand exactly how it happened. Knowing the force of Antonia's personality, I can't believe Hector had any part in his first wife's death. He obviously misses her. He must have been rushed into marrying Antonia when he was most vulnerable.

Killing him would be wicked. Indefensible. Yet Antonia will find some way of doing it, with my help or without. She wants him dead. And if she's arrested, one thing is certain. She'll name me as her accomplice.

What it comes down to is the lesser of two evils. What would you rather have your daughter be, Daddy – an adulteress or a murderess?

She lit another cigarette.

If only there were more time. To be any use at all, the thing had to be accomplished before Antonia returned from Manchester. She would come back expecting to find Hector dead. Instead, she would be handed the alternative – an admission of his adultery.

She reached for the bottle again.

How soon, then?

Tomorrow.

With an effort to suppress her fears she gave some thought to the practicality of getting Hector into bed. Or getting into bed with Hector. She didn't think of it as seducing him. If she'd read the signals right, he wouldn't need much prompting. She hadn't forgotten how he'd squeezed her hand in the kitchen at Park Crescent, or how he'd made her blush with his personal remarks in Reggiori's. He was a foreigner, yes, and they got into muddles sometimes, but to say she had legs as good as Betty Grable's and a 'pretty fine bust' couldn't be put down to faulty syntax.

She could cook a tempting meal, anyway. She'd cook that curry to perfection and serve it with a bottle of

Burgundy. Then a spectacular dessert was wanted: why not peach melba?

With the menu decided, she let her thoughts creep ahead. I have set a place for Hector at the oval table in the dining room. Before he eats he invites me to join him, but I insist with a demure smile that I have come there only to cook. I serve the meal and leave him to savour every delicious mouthful, telling him I have things to attend to in the kitchen. I wash the dishes and the pans and leave everything in immaculate condition.

Then I offer him coffee.

I ask how he likes it, and he doggedly says he would like it best if I will drink it with him. I weigh the suggestion solemnly and say instead that if he is kind enough to drive me back to Pimlico I'll make coffee for both of us there.

So I show him into the front room at Oldfield Gardens, where the fire glows warmly. I go to the kitchen to make the coffee. Presently I call out casually that if he looks in the sideboard he'll find a bottle of champagne and two glasses waiting.

The train of thought stopped abruptly. She flinched at the prospect of sex with Hector. She hadn't even kissed him up to now. True, she wasn't without experience, but compared with Antonia. . . .

She shivered.

She would see how she felt in the morning.

20

Frost-patterns had formed on the inside of the bedroom windows. She scraped away a section to see if it was foggy outside and saw the words 'Carelessness Kills'.

A superfluous warning. She had already decided to buy fresh ingredients for the curry, regardless that the lamb alone would use up all her meat ration for that week. She couldn't believe it was possible for Antonia to have introduced poison into the vegetables, but just to be certain she would buy them fresh. Plus curry powder, which certainly couldn't be left to chance.

She was first in the queue for the butcher's when he opened at 8.30.

'Yes, for you, as it happens, I do have some prime lamb, Mrs Bell. People coming to stay?'

'Not to stay. Just a meal for a . . . for some friends. People have been very kind to me.'

'Glad to hear it. Does you no harm to have company. Takes your mind off things.'

'I hope so.'

'That's the spirit, my love. Never say die.'

After the grocer's and the greengrocer's she took a bus to Regent's Park and let herself into the house in Park Crescent. It wasn't ten o'clock yet.

She took her shopping into the kitchen and unloaded it on the table. She'd managed to get a brick of Wall's ice cream for the peach melba, so she stacked that with the ice trays in the fridge. The meat also went into the fridge. She took out what was left of the lamb Antonia had supplied, wrapped it in newspaper and stowed it in her shopping basket. The suspect curry powder joined it.

Her reason for coming so early wasn't to do with cooking.

She'd woken about six in a changed mood from the

near-panic of the night before. She'd reached a decision. She would search for evidence that Antonia had poisoned Hector's food.

She needed to be certain. Sex with Hector was an alarming prospect but she was prepared to face it if she could find proof that his life was under imminent threat.

She would look for evidence of poison. A good detective would have known what to do. He would have had the food analysed by a toxicologist.

She had to search for the poison itself, or the container it came in.

And (because she really ought to keep an open mind) she would also look for that letter from Antonia's mother. The letter that supposedly summoned Antonia to Manchester to put Lucky the luckless dog out of his misery. She would be surprised if the letter existed. She was pretty certain that these few days of absence had more to do with putting Hector down than Lucky. But she was here to find out the truth.

Might as well start with the obvious and the most unpleasant, she thought. The dustbin. After sifting through muck and rubbish for twenty minutes everything else will be like picking daisies. She opened the back door.

Two dustbins, one empty and the other only half full, thanks to Antonia's dislike of cooking. The smell wasn't as suffocating as it might have been because the contents were mostly dry. She moved them piece by piece into the empty dustbin. The wrapped vegetable parings she had placed in there herself the day before, a pile of newspapers and magazines, a cornflakes carton, a couple of tea packets, several salmon tins (for that pampered cat?), a whisky bottle, a wine bottle, a laddered stocking, cigarette butts and packets, a matchbox, some razor blades, combings of blonde hair, a lipstick holder and some packets of ash and cinders that she unwrapped and sifted with a stick.

She defied the freezing air long enough to check everything again and stack it in the original dustbin.

She came in and ran the hot tap for a wash, glad that

the dirtiest job was over and untroubled that it had yielded nothing.

Next on her list was Antonia's dressing room. In a house this size it was inconceivable that Antonia didn't have a room of her own.

The act of going upstairs didn't need to be charged with tension just because it was unexplored territory. She'd made up her mind to treat it casually. On the wall up the staircase there was a collection of framed photographs of allied fighter planes, so she paused to brush up on her aircraft recognition. Nobody likes being alone in a strange house, she told herself, unless like me they're making a search for something.

One of the stairs creaked under her weight and there was an immediate thump from the floor above. She wasn't alarmed for long. The cat came down to meet her at the turn before the next flight. She scratched the top of its head.

'Later. I wouldn't forget you, would I, Raffles?'

She reached the first floor and started opening doors. A study, evidently Hector's, with design drawings on the walls, a rolltop desk and leather furniture. Next to it a library stuffed to the ceiling with technical books in several languages. Then, stale from disuse, a spare room that Antonia would probably have called the glory-hole. Anyone wanting to hide something had unlimited scope in this house. The dressing room was still the likeliest place. She went up to the next floor.

The nearest door was open and she glimpsed two brass bedsteads with a polar bear rug between them, so she went in. The walls were papered in a startling geometric design of overlapping pink arcs and blue triangles, neither restful nor romantic – which summed up Antonia, Rose thought. Hector's pyjamas lay across the black eiderdown on the bed to the right. They were conspicuous, to put it mildly – bright red with white spots that played tricks on the eyes and moved about like the lights in Piccadilly Circus. She refused to believe they were Hector's choice. She put the blame on Antonia again until it occurred to her that they must have come from America, where Hector had lived some years. On second thoughts she decided polka dot pyjamas were like modern paintings. You might very well grow to like them as they became more familiar.

Through the door on the opposite side and into Antonia's dressing room. She got a shock as she met her own reflection in a wall mirror.

White wardrobes with glass handles were built along two walls. She opened a door and gave a long low murmur of envy. She was no authority on furs, but she recognized mink, ocelot, silver fox and chinchilla and plenty she couldn't name but would have gone through fire to wear. A lustrous black coat with raised shoulders and no collar that must have been straight from Paris, it was so fashionable; three or four sensational capes for evening wear; and a heap of tempting hats and collars and things on the shelf above.

She couldn't resist running her fingers through the chinchilla. If I had just one of these I'd be in my seventh heaven, she mused, but *all* of them. Small wonder Antonia refuses to be parted from them.

She wrenched herself away and crossed the room to the walnut dressing table, a long, low arrangement of drawers in a curve with three tall mirrors embellished with Art Deco rosebuds and ribbons. Resisting the temptation to try the spray scents on top, she opened and closed each of the drawers quickly to get an impression of the contents, lingering a moment at the one containing jewellery.

You're here to look for poison, she told herself.

Any time she had reason to hide an article – usually nothing more sinister than a birthday present for Barry – she tucked it among the smalls at the back of her underwear drawer where nobody but herself had any business to look. Here in Antonia's bedroom it seemed as sensible a place as any to begin the search.

She ran her hand through the layers of satin and crêpe de Chine and felt sick with envy as she thought of her day running up her parachute-silk undies.

No bottles, phials or pill-boxes. Antonia kept plenty in

there to make a man's heart race, but nothing to make it stop.

The second drawer was deeper and had something more promising pushed to the back behind a nightdress – an antique rosewood box with mother-of-pearl inlay. Rose lifted it out. By the size and weight it probably contained letters or photographs. Frustratingly it was locked and there was no sign of a key. She cleared a space for it on top of the dressing table, opened the next drawer and almost at once found a tin containing curlers, safety-pins and other odds and ends including hairgrips. The lock on the box looked a simple fastening, so she tried poking the end of a hairgrip upwards through the keyhole. After a few attempts something clicked inside.

She opened the box.

On top was a photo of Vic, the lover, in cap and gown at some university ceremony. There were several old letters postmarked in the war years. A picture of an air-crew beside a Blenheim bomber. Printed dance invitations, pressed flowers, some twenty-first birthday cards. The sort of collection most women keep somewhere. No phials of poison. No letter from Manchester. She clicked her tongue impatiently. She was about to close the box when she noticed that the padded underside of the lid was hinged and had a small hook and hasp where it could unfasten. She eased it open. Out fell a folded document.

She'd seen it before. It was the death certificate Antonia had stolen from the Registry Office. The certificate intended for Hector. Nothing had yet been written on it. She held it a moment. The paper was shaking in her hand. Her impulse was to rip it to pieces, yet she hesitated.

Tear it up, the inner voice prompted her. And another immediately countered: don't – unless you want Antonia to know that you came up here and went through her things.

She folded the certificate and replaced it where she had found it and fiddled with the lock until it clicked back into place. She replaced the box in the drawer and told herself she was there to look for other things.

Where else?

She decided to try the top shelf in each of the wardrobes. They were too high for a proper inspection, so she carried across the stool from the dressing table and stood on it. She reached in among a collection of belts and hats.

And froze.

A sound had come from downstairs. She was certain it was the front door being opened.

She held her breath and listened.

The front door clicked shut, beyond any question. She strained to hear. It was doubtful whether someone's tread on the hall carpet would carry up to her. A pulse was beating so loudly in her head that she could easily have taken it for footsteps.

Seconds passed. She let out a tremulous breath, like a swimmer just out of the water, and drew in more air.

A board gave a sharp creak. Then another. Whoever had entered the house was coming upstairs.

It can only be Hector, Rose told herself to stave off panic. Who else could have let themselves in? He must have come back from work to fetch something. He's going to that room on the first floor that he uses as his office. He won't have any reason to come up here.

The steps were perfectly audible now. They reached the turn after the first flight and continued upwards to the first floor. They didn't after all enter Hector's office. They continued up the next flight.

He was coming up to the bedroom.

She had to overcome the paralysis she felt in her limbs. She couldn't be found delving into Antonia's wardrobe. She twisted her head to right and left, looking for somewhere to hide. Common sense told her she'd make a noise disturbing the hangers if she tried climbing in with the clothes. Better, surely, to accept that she'd be found in the room and think up some plausible reason for being there. But she didn't want to be caught standing on a stool with her arms in the wardrobe. She gripped the front of the shelf with both hands and made a stronger effort to use her legs. She staggered off the stool.

The footsteps reached the top stair and crossed the landing at the moment she pulled the stool away and closed the wardrobe. She backed against the wall, mentally rehearsing. 'Hello, Hector. I thought I heard you coming up. I happened to be passing so I brought a few groceries in and then I heard this noise upstairs so I came up to investigate. I'd quite forgotten about the cat being in the house. Am I very brave or very silly? Can I get you a cup of tea or anything?'

She heard him enter the bedroom and cross the room. He appeared to go towards one of the beds because there was a chink as if he'd picked up a piece of china or something on the bedside table and put it back. There followed the softer sound of the sheet on the bed being drawn back. Why was he touching the bedclothes? Surely he wasn't going to bed! Perhaps he had come home feeling ill. In that case, she'd have to wait for him to fall asleep. There was no way out except through the bedroom.

He didn't climb into the bed. He moved around the side of it and approached the open door of the dressing room.

Rose waited, flat to the wall, biting her underlip. He'd need to come right in to see her.

She saw the reflection first. It appeared in one of the side mirrors of the dressing table. And it wasn't Hector she saw.

21

It was Vic, Antonia's lover.

Immediately after Rose glimpsed him he turned away without appearing to notice her reflection, deciding, it seemed, that he had no reason to enter the dressing room. She didn't argue with that. She didn't move or breathe.

He prowled about the bedroom for a few seconds more. Then she heard him move out and start downstairs as if he was in no sort of hurry.

Her thoughts darted ahead of him. She'd hung her hat and coat on the hook behind the kitchen door. He would know for certain she was somewhere in the house if he looked in there. Never mind the coat; her handbag was on the kitchen table with some of the shopping.

She counted the flights of stairs, waiting for that loose board to shift under his weight and tell her that he was within a few steps of the ground floor. Half a lifetime seemed to pass before the rasp of wood travelled up to her.

She crept out to the corridor to listen over the stairwell. A door was opened down there. She clenched her right hand and put it to her mouth, for he had started talking to someone. The resonance of the voice reached her, but not the words. She strained to listen, and by degrees she decided that it was only one voice. He must have gone into the front drawing room and picked up the telephone, because when the talking stopped she heard the ping of the receiver being replaced.

She backed away from the banisters. She couldn't stand this much longer. If he came upstairs again she was certain she would scream.

Then she heard the front door being opened and shut.

When she was absolutely certain she was listening to the clatter of his steps in the street she ran back into the dressing room and moved as close to the window as she dared. The figure fast disappearing around the curve of the Crescent was unmistakably Vic.

Rose shook. She'd come all through the war without giving way to nerves. She'd always said in the air raids that it was up to each individual to control herself and stay calm. What a sanctimonious prig she'd been! She'd once watched a woman – a WAAF – run screaming from a shelter before the all-clear. Others had immediately started to cry hysterically. Pandemonium had broken out. The incident had infuriated Rose. She had felt that the woman deserved to be charged with cowardice or indiscipline or whatever King's Regulations called it. Now she herself knew what fear felt like. The urge to quit the house was overwhelming.

She should have taken a grip on herself and resumed the search she'd started. Instead she went downstairs and collected her things and left.

She walked fast down Portland Place towards Oxford Circus, wanting to shake off the physical and mental tensions. Keep moving, she told herself, and try to make sense of what happened. What was Vic doing there? He must have been in possession of a key to let himself in. His own key? Fat chance! The lover with a latchkey was an arrangement as likely to appeal to Antonia as darning socks.

No, Rose thought, Vic had been given the key for a different purpose – to check what had happened in the house in Antonia's absence. He had been sent to see if Hector's corpse was lying there. And he had phoned Antonia to report that it was not.

How foolhardy, how idiotic – to turn to Vic for help and put everything at risk!

Don't get angry, she told herself. Stay in control. How will Antonia react? She might convince herself that the poison was slow to take effect. She might think it was diluted in the curry and that a second helping will do the trick. She might even guess correctly that he didn't have any at all. After all the trouble she's taken over this plan she'll surely give it another night to work.

Rose carried on past Broadcasting House and All Souls into Upper Regent Street. Her step was still rapid, yet with more purpose in it than panic. She needed no proof of poisoning now, no more convincing that Hector's life was in her hands. It was almost noon and she had plenty to do.

She made her way across Oxford Circus to the top end of Regent Street. To Liberty's, to buy a nightdress. Thank God for that insurance money!

At the lingerie counter she asked to see the range. She was in luck. Some nightie and negligé sets in Swiss lawn had just come in. White, black and peach. The white looked marvellous against her skin. She pictured herself in the negligé, at home with Hector, in front of the bedroom fire, sipping champagne from the crystal glasses her glad-eyed Uncle Ben had given her as a wedding present. They'd never been used because Barry said champagne was for launching ocean liners. She would definitely find a shop that sold the stuff. And scent. The funds could run to something more alluring than the eau de Cologne she'd used for years.

'Will madam be taking the white?'

Madam took the white. And then took a taxi to Selfridges' to pick up a vintage Pommery. After that to the cosmetics counter for a bottle of *Chypre* by Coty, some Arden powder, a cherry-coloured lipstick and a bottle of Cutex Cameo nail varnish.

After that it was laughable being driven back to Pimlico to open a tin of Spam for lunch. Rose promised herself that if she handled this evening smartly she wouldn't be living in her slum of a place much longer. She made a sandwich and some tea and ate standing up, taking drags at a cigarette between bites. Then she applied herself to getting the house into a state fit for a romantic encounter. She whisked round with a duster, throwing things into drawers. Upstairs she changed the sheets and pillowcases and laid the fires. Finally she threw some bath salts in the bath and ran the water. She allowed herself twenty minutes.

22

When she left at half past three she was wearing the dreary green tweed overcoat that she meant to replace at the first opportunity, but under it the snazzy black and white dress she'd made for the Oldfield Gardens party on VE Day. And her new silk undies.

There was a worrying suggestion of fog in the afternoon air. She considered what to do if a real pea-souper came down. Hector might see it as a God-given excuse for her to stay the night in Park Crescent. If so, he was in for a disappointment. She'd feel like death in that great mausoleum of a bedroom surrounded by Antonia's things. And she wouldn't be any happier in a hotel room if he suggested it. That would be ghastly. She couldn't face it anywhere else but home.

She hailed a taxi in Vauxhall Bridge Road. The driver reckoned that in a couple of hours London would be at a standstill. Rose said she'd known fog to lift in a matter of minutes. He laughed.

'Lady, I won't argue with you, but don't ask me to come and fetch you. You're my last fare today.'

She didn't answer. She was thinking ahead. She would persuade Hector to drive her back to Pimlico, whatever the conditions.

She was sure it was no thicker by the time they pulled up outside Antonia's house. She paid the fare and took the key from her purse. She walked calmly up the steps and let herself in, resolved not to give way to the jitters. She was going to apply herself to the cooking.

She switched on the hall light.

'There you are, my flower!'

The voice hit her like a snapped violin string. Antonia was standing halfway up the stairs leaning languidly on the banisters as if she had been home all day. She was in a black sweater and slacks, manifestly relishing this moment.

Rose stared, speechless, her brain whirling.

'I see you left some shopping on the kitchen table, darling. Was that for Hector? I must settle up. I say, you look absolutely shattered. Is anything the matter?'

The words penetrated faintly to Rose's brain, as if she were buried under rubble. She wasn't listening anyway. She was thinking about her white nightie from Liberty's draped across the bed at home. And the champagne waiting in the sideboard.

She made an effort to say something intelligible. 'When did you get back?'

'Half an hour ago, no more. A little bird told me it was safe to come back, so I did.'

'Safe?'

'Hector.'

'What about Hector?'

'Darling, you did brilliantly.'

Her heart thumped. 'Did what, Antonia?'

'Rosie, dear, you don't have to put on an act for me. You know he's lying dead in the bathroom.'

She felt the blood drain from her face. She would faint any minute. She fought against it, letting her handbag drop and propping herself against the wall. 'He can't be. I don't believe you.'

Antonia was cruelly casual. 'I suppose something didn't agree with him. Could it have been your curry by any chance?'

'He didn't have any.'

'What?'

'I threw it away. We went to Reggiori's.'

Antonia stared at her for perhaps five seconds. 'For a quiet one, you're a fast worker.'

'Hector insisted on taking me.' Rose heard her voice thicken with anger. 'He ate none of that stuff you left in the fridge.'

The green eyes flashed. 'Why not, for God's sake? You really thought you had a chance, didn't you? Who the hell do you think you are, sneaking off to a restaurant with my husband? I gave you instructions. I went to the trouble of writing them down.'

'I don't believe he's dead.'

Antonia made a sound that was something between laughter and scorn. 'Come up and see, then. We've got to move him to the bedroom.'

'Then you killed him yourself.'

The voice took on a harder note, reinforced by a wagging finger. 'Watch what you say, darling. We're in this together. Sisters in crime. Remember? You'd better.'

'I've done nothing wrong.'

'Try telling that to the police.'

'You've called the police?'

'Idiot. They'll be onto us if we don't do something about the body. It's got to be carried up to the bedroom to look more natural when the undertaker comes. In case you've forgotten, I happen to possess a blank death certificate.'

Rose wetted her lips and tried to summon some inner strength. She didn't see how it was possible for Hector to be lying dead up there, but she had to find out. She stretched out her hand to the banister rail and started up the stairs. It felt like climbing out of a tar-pit.

'That's more like it, *chérie*.'

Antonia went ahead. She reached the top of the first flight and stepped to the room at the end talking like a ward sister dealing with a student nurse. 'This is no picnic, I grant you, but it could be worse. We'll manage easily between us.'

When Rose reached the bathroom, Antonia was already inside, talking. 'It must have been quick. He couldn't have suffered much.'

The link in Rose's mind with hospital was reinforced by a pungent smell she distantly remembered from years ago, when she'd had her tonsils removed. She took a step into the bathroom and looked around the door. There was no corpse in there.

She jerked towards Antonia to protest and several things happened quickly. At the edge of her vision she caught a glimpse of something white flying towards her face. Her neck was seized from behind. She flung up her arm defensively and knocked the white object upwards. It reeked of the smell she'd noticed. She was being chloroformed.

Her neck was clamped in the crook of Antonia's arm. She was forced to gasp for air just as the pad was thrust towards her face again. This time she couldn't push it away. She succeeded in deflecting it slightly and turning her face aside. It missed her mouth and nostrils and made stinging contact with her cheek. She dragged it off with both hands and fought for possession of it. She wasn't as strong as Antonia, but with her two hands she prised some of the fingers away.

Antonia removed the arm that was around Rose's neck and made a grab for the pad. She wasn't quick enough. Rose seized it from her and flung it into the bath. Momentarily Rose had the advantage. Antonia had reached out like a tennis player retrieving a serve and she only needed a push to lose her balance.

Rose supplied it.

Antonia crashed between the side of the bath and the wash basin, bringing down a glass shelf. If she was hurt it wasn't apparent. She recouped immediately.

Rose had turned to escape, but she was grabbed by the ankle and fell on her hands and knees. She was hauled in like a hooked fish. She kicked out with the free leg and caught some part of Antonia, possibly her chest.

There was a yelp of pain.

Rose's left ankle was given a vicious twist that forced her to roll on her back. At once Antonia hurled herself forward. She was unquestionably the stronger of them. Rose squirmed against the side of the bath to avoid being pinned down. They wrestled head to head. Then her hair was grabbed and her head forced against the floor. Antonia pressed down on her, tugging viciously at her hair while she manoeuvred herself into a sitting position by bringing her knees up to the level of Rose's shoulders and forcing them down. Her thighs flattened Rose's breasts.

Rose looked up into the wildcat eyes. She felt a hand at her throat, forcing the collar apart and she believed she was going to be strangled. But the pressure came on the back of her neck. Her pearl necklace bit into her flesh and snapped as Antonia jerked it from her throat, scattering beads across the room.

'Cheap imitations, ducky.'

The face came closer. The blonde hair brushed Rose's cheek.

'What's that scent you're wearing? It stinks.' Antonia slapped her hard across the face.

She stared back and bore the pain in silence. Then she was conscious of a shift in the weight. Antonia was reaching behind her into the bath, groping for the pad of chloroform. Rose sensed an opportunity. Although her head was held and her shoulders were flat to the floor, her hips were still slightly angled against the bath. She flexed, raised her knees and got enough leverage from her feet to buck forward. Some hair was torn from her scalp in the process, but she managed to tip Antonia off completely and drag herself free.

She got off her knees, stepped clear of Antonia's flailing arms, and rushed out of the bathroom and along the corridor. She'd lost her shoes, which was an advantage in taking the stairs at speed. Antonia was up and in pursuit, but Rose was quicker. She jumped the last few steps and dashed across the hall to the door and dragged it open. The inrush of foggy air gave her hope. She lurched into the street and ran blindly.

23

A policeman in braces and with his sleeves rolled up opened the door of the room where Rose had been sitting for longer than she could estimate, bent forward with her face in her hands. He stood just inside, taking stock.

'Ready to talk now?'

She raised her head. She had panicked when they had brought her in and now despair had set in. She felt too exhausted to protest. Her brain rebelled at concocting a story that would satisfy them. She was certain she would get confused and blurt out the whole devastating truth.

'What time is it?'

'Just gone six.'

'Six in the morning?'

'You *are* in a state.'

'I'm thirsty.'

He went out, leaving the door open. Although she wasn't being kept in a cell, she was resigned to being transferred to one shortly. She had been driven here in a Black Maria with barred windows. This was just a place where they questioned people, somebody's office, with a desk and several chairs and hooks on the wall for coats. She'd kept hers on. The coke stove in the corner wasn't giving off much heat.

She had got off to a bad start with the desk sergeant by refusing to answer his questions. It was the first time she'd ever been in a police station. She hadn't trusted herself to say anything that wouldn't get her into trouble. Her silence had made the sergeant hostile. She was convinced that whatever she said he would keep her in custody. Up to now they didn't know anything about her except her name and where they had found her, but they'd break her down. It wouldn't take much.

A man she hadn't seen before brought in some tea in a

chipped enamel mug. He had his jacket on, with a sergeant's stripes. He was silver-haired and his smile didn't sit well with his toothbrush moustache and drooping eyelids. He tried to pitch his voice to sound reasonable. And failed.

'So your name is Bell.'

'Yes.'

'Christian name?'

'Rose. I told the other man.'

'Mrs Rose Bell.' He'd noticed her ring, of course. 'Living with your husband?'

She didn't like the tone he used. It stung her into a response. 'He's dead.'

'The war?'

'No. Last month.'

'As recently as that?'

'It was an accident.' She stopped. She needn't have come out with this. She'd meant to say the minimum. Her nerves had betrayed her.

'Bad luck.' He didn't sound sympathetic. 'A road accident?'

No use denying it now. 'The tube. He fell off the platform.'

'Nasty. Not uncommon, though. Do you have any other family? Children?'

'No.'

'Have you got a permanent address, Mrs Bell?'

'Yes.'

He waited a moment. His voice slipped into a harder register. 'Come on, now. Let's have it. You're wasting police time.'

'In Pimlico. Oldfield Gardens.'

'Pimlico. Yet one of our patrols found you on Paddington Station in the small hours of the morning. Is that where you normally spend the night? It's a long way from Pimlico. I'd have thought Victoria Station was more convenient.'

He kept looking at her legs. The ruins of her stockings hung in ribbons.

He developed his theme. 'It all depends what you were up to, doesn't it? I'm told by certain ladies who parade there that Paddington is better for business than any other London terminus.' Seeing the outrage in her eyes, he smiled. 'But they don't take kindly to newcomers, as you appear to have discovered. What happened to your shoes?'

She was bitterly insulted. 'That's a filthy suggestion! I demand an immediate apology.'

'Do you now? What are you wearing under that coat, then? It looks pretty tarty to me.'

'Bloody hell!' Her anger galvanized her. She was damned if she'd give in to personal abuse. She'd grown up in awe of policemen. They were fatherly figures who helped you across the road and told you the time if you asked, but she would cut this bastard down to size because she didn't see a decent London bobby standing in front of her; she saw a reincarnation of Barry, a sneering, sarcastic bully, who despised and resented women. She wasn't putting up with any more of it.

'Fetch your superior, please.'

The grin vanished. 'Hold on, Mrs Bell. There's no need for that.'

'I want to make an official complaint.'

'All right. I spoke out of turn. I withdraw everything I just said.'

She glared at him. 'You were asking about my shoes. I lost them on the train.' The lie came readily to her lips. She would lie and lie to this sadist.

He asked which train.

'The tube.'

'So you took the tube?'

'Yes.'

'You bought a ticket, I hope.'

'Of course I did.'

'Where would that have been? Victoria?'

She nodded.

'Right, then.' He folded his arms aggressively. He was looking for an opening and when he found it he would be ruthless. 'Just tell me how you were able to pay for the ticket without possessing a handbag or even a purse?'

'I lost my bag on the train.'

'Along with the shoes, I suppose. London Transport Lost Property Office is having a busy night. I presume you had your Identity Card in the handbag?'

'Yes – and it might be a damned sight more useful if instead of persecuting me you got on with the job you're paid to do and found my things for me.' With that, she put her hands over her face and sobbed loudly. See how he coped with that, the swine.

He tried without much success to sound like an uncle. 'Well, my dear, I've got to get the facts to know the rights and wrongs of it, haven't I? Where were you going on the tube?'

She sniffed. 'Nowhere in particular.' She had a good thought. 'I was on the Circle Line. I was depressed. I couldn't stand it at home when I thought of what had happened to. . . .'

'Your husband?'

'Yes.' Another sob. 'So I went down the tube, meaning to – oh, I don't know what I meant to do, I was in such a state.' The lies were coming fluently. She'd needed that stinging reminder of her late husband. Barry had got no more than he deserved. But the police wouldn't see it that way. She was fighting to get out of this place.

'And you got off at Paddington?' His probing was more conciliatory.

'Great Portland Street.' Her brain was working better. From the state of her feet it was obvious that she'd done some walking. 'I got off at Great Portland Street and walked to Paddington.'

'Did you have any reason to make for Paddington?'

'No particular reason. I just kept walking in the fog.' Rose gave a little-girl-lost look. She decided to consolidate. 'Could I have some tea, please?' She put her hand to her head. 'And some aspirin?'

He ignored the plea. 'You didn't get those scratches on your neck by walking.'

She'd been aware of some discomfort, but then her entire body was aching. She found the scratches and traced them with her fingers.

'They're fresh. And what happened to your cheek? It's bright red.'

The place where the chloroform had made contact. 'I must have walked into something.'

'A right-hander, by the look of it. There's no two ways about it – you were in a fight, and you didn't come off best. Look at your coat.'

'I was attacked in the tube. They stole my bag.'

'And your shoes?'

'To stop me giving chase.'

'This is more like it. Description?'

She shook her head. 'I fainted. I don't remember.'

'Then how do you know you were in a fight?'

'You just told me.'

The sides of his mouth turned down and he marched out and slammed the door.

Presently a constable came in with a tray. When Rose saw the aspirin and the two biscuits, elation flooded into her weary body. She knew she was winning.

In about twenty minutes the sergeant returned. 'Your husband was Wing Commander Bell who was killed on Knightsbridge Underground Station on October 10th?'

'Yes.'

'I want you to give the constable a description of the things you lost, the bag and the shoes. Then we're sending you home. I suggest you see your doctor next time you feel depressed. It's better than travelling the Circle Line.'

24

She was led out to a police car and seated in the rear next to a young officer with a Welsh accent who offered her a cigarette and struck a match for her.

'Pimlico, is it, Mrs Bell?'

'Oldfield Gardens. Have they finished with me, then?'

'You can relax now.'

Relax? she thought. Jesus Christ, the chance would be a fine thing! She drew on the cigarette and saw it shake in her fingers.

I was almost murdered last night. There's no question that Antonia tried to kill me. That was no pillow fight.

And it was no spur-of-the-moment attack. Antonia lured me up there, into a trap. She had the chloroform ready in the bathroom. Where could she have got hold of chloroform?

Vic! He works in a science lab. She and Vic are in this together.

Two's company, three's a crowd.

When I met Antonia, she didn't tell me about Vic. I stupidly believed the desperate things we agreed to do were a secret between two women. A pact. Now I know Antonia has a stronger loyalty.

Antonia and Vic have decided to eliminate me. They think I doublecrossed them because I failed to poison Hector.

If they killed me, how would they hope to get away with it? It's ghastly to think about, but how would they dispose of my body? They need the blank death certificate for Hector. Presumably they'd bury me in some deserted place.

'Oldfield Gardens, is it, Mrs Bell?'

'What?'

'Where you live.'

'Oh, yes.'
'Feeling shaken up, are you?'
'Just a little. I lost my key. How am I going to get in?'
'We'll force the lock, unless you keep a spare under the mat.'
'No.'
'Pity. Sensible, though.'
They turned into her street.
'It's the last one on the left.'
She stepped out of the car forgetting that she was still without shoes and gasped as her feet touched the pavement. The driver supported her arm and helped her through the gate.
'Don't worry, Mrs Bell. We'll have you indoors in no time. PC Owen has a rare knack of getting through locked doors, haven't you, Taff?'
Constable Owen rounded the front of the car. 'We won't need to. There's someone inside.'
Rose had started to say that such a thing was impossible when the front door swung open and Antonia looked out.
The devil.
'Rose, darling, what on earth has happened to you? Was there an accident?'
Rose went rigid.
The constable responded by bringing his hand more firmly around her arm. 'Right, Mrs Bell. Got to get you inside.'
Antonia, her features creased in concern, stepped forward and came along the path. 'She's been missing all night. She doesn't know what she's doing or saying half the time. It's the shock. Has she told you? The poor little soul lost her husband last month. Come on, my flower, you'll freeze out here. I've got a lovely fire going in the front room.' She reached out to take Rose's other arm.
'No!'
'It's tragic, officer. I don't know what she's been telling you, but I've known her for years. Isn't that right, Rose? I won't say how much I've done to help her these last weeks. That's the way friends should be. We stick together like

sisters.' She looked into Rose's eyes. 'I mean it goes without saying, doesn't it?'

Rose knew with numbing certainty what she meant. Never mind what went without saying. She'd said it. They stuck together. Sisters in crime.

She turned to the constable. 'I want to get back in the car.'

Antonia smiled knowingly at the police and cast her eyes upwards.

The grip on Rose's arm tightened. 'Sorry, my love, but no can do. We're on patrol. We need that seat for real villains. In you go. You'll get pneumonia out here.'

He didn't address her as Mrs Bell. That patronizing 'my love' told her that they'd swallowed everything Antonia had said. Blitzed by fear, anger and the cold, she allowed them to steer her into the house. She was through.

Constable Owen was talking to Antonia. 'She lost her handbag and shoes in the tube. We've got a description. I suggest she tries London Transport Lost Property Office just in case.'

Rose felt like a hospital patient being discussed by the staff. She sank into an armchair in the front room beside the fire she'd laid for her romantic evening with Hector. The coal was well alight. She shut her eyes, shut out the world.

Antonia took charge. 'Who's good at making tea? I'd better do something about this poor lamb's feet.'

She was too overpowering for the police. They made excuses and left so fast that Rose heard the front door close and the car being started before her bemused brain grasped that she was alone with the woman who'd tried to murder her.

'Get those stockings off.'

She opened her eyes.

Antonia was standing over her with a bowl in her hands like an angel of mercy. Her voice slipped into a more mellow tone. '. . . or what's left of them. You want to clean up your feet, don't you?' She set the bowl on the floor. 'I had to use the kettle. The boiler's out.'

Bemused and obedient, Rose felt under her skirt and unfastened the tattered stockings and peeled them off. The contact with the warm water was heaven.

'Soap?'

Under the cool inspection of the green eyes, she worked on her feet. The soles were sore and the skin was broken in several places. They felt better for being clean and warm.

She looked up. 'I can't fight any more. Let's get it over with.'

'Mm?' Now Antonia seemed bemused.

'Finishing what you started yesterday evening. Killing me.'

'Killing you, darling? You *are* confused. Why on earth should I want to do that? Oh, I don't deny that I tried to put you to sleep for a few minutes, and I'm sorry it turned into the tussle it did. You certainly pack a punch.'

'Antonia, I'm not that stupid. You came at me like a tigress after blood.'

'Of course. I was so flaming mad that I lashed out and lost control.' She laughed. 'You know me.'

'You're lying. It was planned. You had a pad of chloroform.'

Antonia was ready to justify anything. 'Sweetie, I trusted you and you let me down. Instead of cooking that meal for Hector you threw it away and went to Reggiori's.'

'I was afraid I'd poison him.'

'Obviously.'

'Well, I knew you wanted to get rid of him. I couldn't knowingly poison anybody. That's hideously cruel.'

'You knew damn all. I didn't say anything about poison.'

'You didn't need to say anything. It was obvious.'

'What you're telling me, Rose darling, is that you felt sorry for the poor beggar. Let's put our cards on the table. You developed quite a pash for my old man. I saw the warpaint and the glad rags last night. I never had a cook who wore pearls and French perfume. Is it any wonder I lashed out? Don't get me wrong. It wasn't that I was jealous. It was the deceit. You and I had an understanding.'

'And for that you'd murder me?'

'Not you, darling.'

'For God's sake, Antonia! You tried to chloroform me.'

'Only to put you out for a bit. I couldn't trust you any more, could I? I just meant to give you a whiff and get you out of my hair while I attended to Hector.'

Rose pressed her lips together and glared back, too angry to speak, refusing to be soft-soaped.

'In the event,' Antonia continued in the same breezy manner, 'you ran off into the fog, which saved me some trouble. When Hector came in I was ready for him. And now I need your help with some lifting.'

Rose stared at her.

'The corpse, darling. It's lying in the hall at home. We've got to move it upstairs to the bedroom before we fetch the undertaker. It's got to look as if he died in bed. The face is slightly marked like yours. Not enough to cause comment, fortunately.'

Every muscle tightened. 'This isn't true. You're a liar.'

Antonia sighed. 'I can't deny that, kitten. I did mislead you yesterday. Didn't want you getting in the way. This time Hector really is dead. I slapped the chloroform over his face the minute he stepped through the front door yesterday evening. Put him to sleep and then smothered him with a cushion.' She picked her handbag off a chair and unfastened it. 'Look, I've filled in his name on the death registration certificate. And the date.'

Rose saw the name boldly inked in. A few words written on paper proved nothing and she wanted to say so but her throat had tightened too much for speech. The description of Hector's death in that entrance hall in Park Crescent was horribly credible. Suddenly she wanted Antonia to be lying, desperately wanted her to have invented this grotesque admission of murder, even though it meant another deathtrap had been set for herself. She couldn't cope with the thought of Hector dead.

She'd thought she was beyond the point where anything could hurt her. This extinguished the last hope of any future. She handed back the paper.

Antonia took her silence as satisfaction. 'Get something on your feet and we'll go now. I'll get you some breakfast there. There's nothing here.'

Rose stayed seated. She had just come to her senses. There was a flaw in what was being suggested. 'You don't need my help. You've got Vic to assist you. If there really was a body he could lift it.'

'Vic?' From the pitch of the voice it might have been the Archbishop of Canterbury. 'Vic doesn't know Hector is dead. God, we don't want Vic to find out.'

'Stop playing the innocent, Antonia. He's your lover. I know you've told him everything because I was there in your house yesterday morning when you sent him to check whether Hector was poisoned. Do you understand? I was there. I came early. He didn't see me, but I saw him. He went up to the bedroom and looked inside. And then he went downstairs and used the telephone and I'm certain he was phoning you.'

She treated it casually, walking out of the room and into the kitchen as she spoke. 'You're right about one thing, Rosie dear, he did phone me. Weren't you near enough to listen? Pity. Listen, how can I get it into your head that there wasn't any poison in the damned curry? That meat was perfectly edible and so was everything else.'

Rose dug her fingers into the arms of the chair. 'In that case, why did you give Vic a key and send him to the house?'

'This is gospel truth,' the answer came back from the kitchen. 'He wasn't looking for a corpse. He was trying to find out whether you'd spent the night with Hec.'

Rose frowned.

Antonia came back with a towel that she was twisting between her hands. 'Yes, I sent him round, Rosie. I've been staying with him in Knightsbridge instead of visiting my wretched old Mum in Manchester, as if you hadn't guessed.'

'How much does he know?'

'Vic? Sweet F.A., darling. He thinks all this was a love trap for you and my sneaky little husband, and I must say, I had suspicions of my own when I learned from Hector's own lips that he'd taken you out to dinner.' She let that sink in. 'I'd better confess that it wasn't the total surprise to me that I registered yesterday. That was a little mischief on my part. I wanted to hear it from your own angelic lips. Actually I'd already talked to Hec on the telephone yesterday morning, playing the doting wife, enquiring whether you'd made him a decent curry. He was positively chirpy when he told me he'd taken you to Reggiori's instead. Apart from being bloody annoyed I was curious to know what it amounted to. After all, if you two had given me evidence of adultery I could have divorced him. No need for a funeral. Unluckily for Hector, Vic couldn't find a single brown hair on the pillows.' She let the towel unfurl and tossed it to Rose. 'Pity. You could have saved me no end of bother.'

25

Antonia had left the Bentley round the corner in Charlwood Street. She didn't speak until they were travelling in slow convoy up Vauxhall Bridge Road with the early morning traffic from south of the river.

'Rose.'

'Yes?'

'Why are you doing this?'

'Doing what?'

'Coming back to the house with me. It's only for Hector's sake, isn't it?'

'Does it matter?' Rose stared ahead at the adverts on the back of a bus. She felt weary, but more in control. Before leaving the house she had fitted in a wash and forced herself to eat a slice of bread and Marmite. She was wearing stockings and shoes again and a jumper and skirt. She had also dug out her grey demob overcoat that buttoned at the neck.

Antonia persisted with her point about Hector. 'The fact is, you want to find out for yourself if he's really dead. You don't know whether to believe me.'

'Can you blame me?'

Antonia smirked. 'He cared bugger all about you. You know that, don't you? Women were always making fools of themselves over bloody Hector, wanting to mother him.'

'Who said I wanted to mother him?'

She gave a single, high-pitched laugh. 'If it was sex you wanted, he just wasn't up to it, sweetie, believe me.'

'It takes two.'

'Go to hell,' Antonia snapped back, no longer amused. 'That's bloody good coming from you. It takes two! How was it with Barry, then? Did you satisfy him? You and who else? Was it two or two hundred?'

Rose didn't answer. Her other compelling reason for agreeing to come was that she needed to keep tabs on this murderous woman after two nasty shocks in twenty-four hours. She meant to stick with her now until it was safe to be alone again.

Antonia steered the car through the mews entrance behind Park Crescent and into a garage.

'Come on, then. Come and see for yourself.'

She opened a gate and let them into the yard at the back of the house where the two dustbins stood. Then she unlocked the kitchen door and led the way in. Yesterday's shopping still lay unused on the table.

Rose followed, her skin suddenly so sensitive that she was acutely conscious of every movement of her clothes. Pulses throbbed in her face and neck. She said a silent, desperate prayer that Hector might still be alive.

Antonia crossed the room and hesitated at the door that led to the hall. Rose tensed, sensing that she ought to be ready to defend herself against another sudden attack. Then Antonia spoke over her shoulder. 'Take a long, deep breath, my poppet.'

They stepped into the hall.

Rose took the breath, and held it. And held it longer.

Just inside the front door, where Antonia had said it would be, lay a corpse in a camelhair overcoat like the one Hector had worn to Reggiori's. Dark trousers and brown shoes. Hands still in leather gloves. An ear partly covered by a black woollen scarf. Curly red-gold hair.

'Want to look at the face?' Antonia was standing beside the body preparing to give the shoulder a prod with her foot.

'There's no need.' Rose heard herself say in a flat voice that sounded like someone reading lines without understanding them. She picked up a green porkpie hat that was lying against the skirting board. 'It can't be anyone else.'

Outwardly controlled, she ached from her throat to the pit of her stomach. It wasn't the piercing pain of shock; she had felt increasingly certain from the way Antonia had been behaving that this time she had spoken the truth. No, it was grief that she felt, a bitter, grinding grief for Hector and for the loss of a life that she had known was threatened and she would have saved.

'Feeling strong?' Antonia took off her coat and threw it over a chair. 'Do you need a snifter first or shall we get started?'

'Do you want to move him?'

'I didn't bring you here for tea and biscuits.'

'All right. Let's do it now.' Rose steeled herself. Numb as she felt, she was determined not to give way to panic in front of Antonia. She placed Hector's hat respectfully on a chair and stepped closer.

She wasn't new to the sight of death. She had seen air-raid victims brought out on stretchers from bombed buildings and she had gone through the ordeal of identifying Barry at the mortuary. But this was the first time she had been called upon to touch a corpse.

'You take the legs, then. We'd better get him straight first.'

The body was lying on its side in a bowed attitude with the left leg bent into a near right angle and the other almost straight. His left arm lay along the length of the body and the right was trapped under the head.

It was necessary to bring the legs together to lift them. She moistened her lips and told herself to treat it straightforwardly as a simple, mechanical task. To forget that this had been Hector. Stooping, she took hold of the bent leg above the ankle. She gave a gasp of shock and let go at once. Through the trousers it felt as if the limb were encased in plaster.

Antonia had taken hold of the arm that lay under the head and was trying unsuccessfully to straighten it. 'God, he's as stiff as a board.'

'Is it rigor mortis?'

'It must be.'

'I think I do need that drink.'

'You're not the only one.'

They moved into one of the sitting rooms and Antonia

poured generous brandies into wine glasses. She spilled some and didn't even notice. She had gone very pale.

Rose made an effort to be practical. 'It wears off after a time, I believe.'

'Any idea how long?'

'No.'

'There's no movement at all. It'll be the devil to get upstairs. It's the arms and legs. They're in such awkward positions.'

'Can we wait for it to wear off?'

'And leave him lying in the hall? It could be hours and hours. It only wants someone to knock at the door and we're sunk. Christ Almighty, Rose, why didn't I think of this?'

Rose was incapable of dealing with anyone else's state of panic, least of all Antonia's. The revulsion she'd felt when she handled that hardened limb had taken a grip on her mind.

Antonia stood in the middle of the room with hunched shoulders and folded arms. 'Even if we managed to get him up to the bedroom how would I get him into pyjamas? I'd have to rip them apart to get the arms and legs in. Blast you, Hector!'

'Is it important to have him in pyjamas?'

'*Important*? He's supposed to have died in bed, of cardiac failure. I've written it on the death certificate.'

To Rose there seemed only one feasible course of action, but she wasn't going to suggest it herself. She waited for it to come from Antonia, as it eventually did.

'We'll have to drag him into one of these rooms for the time being and move him later.'

'I don't think I can bear to touch him again.'

'Bloody hell.'

She despised herself for giving way after she had held herself together so well. 'You can say it. I'm a coward.'

Antonia curled her lip and said rather more. 'If you fill your knickers over a little thing like this, I don't like to think about your date with Mr Pierrepoint.'

'Who's that?'

'The hangman.'

It was a telling threat. Rose had a vivid mental picture of herself in the execution chamber. Even in the black hours after Barry's death she had never let her thoughts move on so far as that horrid possibility. She stared at Antonia for some seconds. 'All right. I'll try.'

They went out into the hall again. Rose took a grip of one of the coat sleeves. Shoulder to shoulder they dragged the body to the back room.

'On the sofa.'

'He won't look natural.'

'Shut up and pick up the legs.'

Rose obeyed. She avoided looking directly at the face and as soon as the job was done she ran to the toilet and retched repeatedly.

In the kitchen Antonia made black coffee. When she put the cup in front of Rose there were two pills beside it.

Rose turned them over suspiciously. 'What are these?'

'Benzedrine. I get them on prescription from my doctor. I'm supposed to be slimming. Try them.'

'Not likely.'

'What's up? It's going to be another long night. They'll keep you awake. Give you a marvellous feeling in your head. Didn't you take them in the war?'

Rose took a sip of the coffee and said nothing.

'Oh, for pity's sake!' Antonia snatched up the pills and swallowed them.

They sat without saying anything to each other. Soon the silence became unendurable. Antonia switched on the wireless. Someone was playing a cinema organ. Finally Antonia went out to see if the state of the body had altered. She shook her head when she came back.

'Just the same. I was planning to see the undertaker this morning.'

'You can't have him here yet.'

'I could ask him not to come until late.'

'How do we know when it wears off? It could be hours and hours. Haven't you got a medical book in the house?'

'I never bother with books.'

'You've got a room stacked with them upstairs.' Rose realized as she spoke that she hadn't mentioned going upstairs before. Antonia shot her a look.

Searching for information in some book was better than doing nothing. They went up and eventually found an *Enquire Within Upon Everything* that omitted to mention rigor mortis. Most of the books were in foreign languages.

'Hector could have told us to the minute,' said Antonia with an oddly belated note of pride in her murdered husband. 'He was very well informed on things like that.'

Rose thought what stupid comments people come out with in times of stress.

26

Shortly after three that afternoon they were admitted to the office of Longshot and Greely, Funeral Directors, an oak-panelled or more likely oak-veneered inner room behind a curtained shopfront in Marylebone Road. When Rose was introduced as Antonia's friend and Mr Greely put out his hand, she had to steel herself to make the first human contact since handling Hector. Her sense of touch was more sensitive than ever she had suspected. Actually she would have found Greely's soft handshake obnoxious at any time. Probably he was not much over forty, but his movements were decrepit.

'Park Crescent? I know it like my own house, ladies. That magnificent colonnade. And such commodious houses. Rest assured that any arrangements you should favour us with will meet the highest standards. Longshot and Greely have conducted funerals for some of the great families of London for generations. We shall be honoured to perform this last duty for your dear father.'

'Husband.' Antonia corrected him from under a veil. She had changed into a black fitted coat with frogged fastenings.

'Indeed?' An additional set of furrows appeared on Greely's brow. 'My dear lady, forgive me. One assumed. . . . You appear so young for such a tragic eventuality.'

'It was his heart.'

'Ah.'

'There was a weakness. We'd known of it for years.'

'Even so.'

'Exactly.'

'Was it sudden when it came?'

'Completely. He died at home in the drawing room.'

'Today?'

'Yesterday, about six in the evening.'

'And he is still there? Have no worries, my dear lady. I shall arrange for him to be conveyed to our chapel of rest within the hour. From what you say I assume that there will be no need of an inquest and we can proceed with the arrangements within the next few days. I dare say you are too distressed to discuss such things as yet, but possibly tomorrow. . . .'

'I want to settle it now.' Antonia spoke in a soft, yet decisive voice.

'We shall see to it, provided, of course, that you find our terms satisfactory.'

Rose thought it appropriate to contribute something to the conversation since she was supposed to be the widow's support. 'It will be a very quiet occasion.'

'Cremation,' said Antonia.

'Whatever you wish, ladies. I take it that the deceased – your late husband – expressed a preference for cremation.'

'He wasn't opposed to it.'

'How soon can you arrange it?' asked Rose.

'Ladies, there will be no delay in my firm's arrangements, I assure you. However, the Cremation Regulations do require us to observe certain formalities. Paperwork. Very tedious.'

Antonia opened her bag. 'We brought the registrar's certificate.'

'Yes.' He held it folded in his hand. 'In point of fact, I must give *you* some forms to be completed.'

Antonia opened her bag and took out her fountain pen. 'We'll do it now.'

'I'm afraid not,' said Greely. 'Form A is a declaration that you must make in the presence of a Justice of the Peace or a Commissioner for Oaths.'

'Is there one nearby? If it's only a matter of visiting an office, we'll do it this afternoon.'

'Ah, but as there has been no inquest, I must also let you have forms B and C, the medical certificate forms. Form B must be filled in by the doctor who certified the death and Form C is for another doctor of at least five years standing, who should also see the – em – body. Then all the forms, including this certificate you obtained from the registry have to be sent to the Medical Referee of the London Cremation Company for his written authority.'

There was a petrifying silence.

'I understand your feelings, ladies, believe me. I wish the procedure could be simplified. It is, of course, a safeguard against deaths that happen in suspicious circumstances – not that this remotely applies in your case.'

Rose glanced at Antonia's strained face and then back at Greely. 'What is the procedure for a burial?'

'Oh, much more straightforward.'

Antonia reached a rapid decision. 'We'll have him buried, then. I just can't face all these delays.'

Rose nodded. It was the obvious thing to do. They couldn't run the risk of forging the medical forms as well as the registration certificate. Burial was the answer. It wasn't as if Hector's body contained poison or had any obvious injuries. Even an exhumation wouldn't reveal anything.

Greely seemed encouraged by Antonia's change of mind. 'Then we *can* attend to things at once. Let's make sure that this registration is all in order. Forty-two, was he, poor fellow? No age at all. And I dare say you also have the other piece of paper in your bag?'

Antonia frowned and opened her handbag. 'No, what's that?'

'If you left it at home, it doesn't matter at this stage. Doesn't matter in the least as long as you bring it tomorrow.'

Rose tensed and crossed her legs. 'What is this piece of paper? She gave you the certificate.'

He opened a drawer in his desk and took out a form and held it up briefly for their scrutiny. 'It looks like this. This one relates to a burial last week. The registrar will have issued a similar one with your copy of the registration certificate. You see, I don't actually require the document you handed me. That is for your use. I require the other–' He coughed behind his hand. '–the disposal certificate, as it's known.'

'The what?' Antonia raised her voice in a manner hardly fitting a just-bereaved widow.

'It's the certificate that authorizes me as the funeral director – or whoever you should honour with the arrangements – to conduct the burial. Without it, I am unable to proceed.'

Antonia shot a horrified glance at Rose. 'I didn't bring it with me.'

Greely smiled reassuringly. 'Not to worry. Not to worry at all. It isn't the first time. People get confused, and understandably in the circumstances. Why don't you see if it's at home, and if it isn't, if you've mislaid it, I can apply to the registrar for a duplicate.'

'No, you will not.'

'Oh, there's no extra fee. I'll tell you what I suggest. You ladies go back to the house and see if this elusive little form is lying about somewhere. In the meantime I'll drive over with one of my colleagues to collect – that is to say, take care of – your late husband, and if for any reason the certificate is lost–'

'No.' Antonia cut him off in mid-sentence. She stood up and snatched the registration certificate from his desk. 'I've never been treated with such callous and pettifogging disregard. I came here looking for sympathy and understanding and you talk to me about *disposal*, as if my Hector is unwanted rubbish. After this I couldn't bear to put him in your hands. We'll get someone with a modicum of respect for the departed to do it. Come on, Rose, before I say something I regret.'

'Madam, I apologize most sincerely. I assure you I was merely trying to explain the formalities. Upsetting you like this is the very last thing I wanted.'

Rose wasted no sympathy on him either as she followed Antonia out. 'It's the last you'll hear from us, anyway.'

Out in the street Antonia stood tight-lipped beside the car. Although Rose felt in a state of panic too, she offered to drive. In the WAAF she'd driven everything from staff cars to two-ton lorries.

Antonia's voice was bleak. 'What on earth do we do now?'

'Better go somewhere quiet where we can think. Round the Park.'

Rose started up and swung the Bentley into Baker Street and across Park Road to join the traffic on the Outer Circle. For all she cared now, they could drive round and round Regent's Park until the petrol ran out, a sort of limbo. Hell wasn't far away.

Eventually Antonia spoke in a flat, embittered voice. 'What did he call it?'

'A disposal certificate. God, what a laugh! After all our trouble he didn't need the death certificate at all.'

Antonia was white with shock. 'I'm devastated. Why did I walk out of there? Now that it's too bloody late I can see what we should have done. We should have let him collect the body. He wanted the job. He would have overlooked the wretched form. He could have stretched a point. He kept saying it wasn't important.'

'I don't think so, Antonia. Once he'd seen the body he'd quietly ask the registrar's office for one, and that would be curtains for you and me.'

'It's curtains anyway.'

They passed the Zoo entrance and Gloucester Gate before either spoke again. This time Antonia's anger switched to Rose. 'You knew about this all along, didn't you?'

'What?'

'The bloody disposal certificate. What else? You must have had one for Barry. So why didn't you tell me?'

'Dry up, Antonia! I didn't even look at the wretched forms. I just handed them over to the bank. They acted as executors, so they did everything. For God's sake get it out of your head that I tried to undermine the plan. We wouldn't be in this mess if I could have avoided it and that's the truth.'

The force of this reasoning evidently impressed Antonia, because she took a more positive line. 'Is there any way we can get hold of one of those damned forms?'

'Only from the registry office.'

'By reporting Hector's death, you mean? That's out.

We'd have to get a doctor to look at the body first and write out a certificate.'

'Do you think a doctor could tell what happened?'

'He'd order a post mortem for sure. Perfectly healthy men don't drop dead without some reason.'

'Was Hector fit?'

'He never had a day off work that I can remember.'

'So he never saw a doctor. We could ask *any* doctor to look at him.'

'Duckie, even the most pea-brained, superannuated, gin-sodden GP in the world knows bloody well that sudden death has to be reported to the coroner.'

Rose wasted no more words. Her mind was made up. She spun the wheel and turned sharp left into Albany Street, raced through the gears and stamped on the accelerator.

'Christ! Where the heck are we going?'

'You'll see.'

27

As Rose reversed the car into a space in Lowndes Square she admitted that they wouldn't be working to a plan. In Air Force parlance it was chocks away and let us pray.

The entrance to the Stationery Office depot was manned by a burly ex-serviceman with two rows of ribbons and a seen-it-all-before look. He said nobody was ever allowed inside without an appointment and then stared over their heads as if that were the end of it. Rose kept talking. And when she told him she was Barry Bell's widow it worked like a password. He beamed and grasped her hand. Wing Commander Bell had been a particular pal of his with a wicked sense of humour just like his own and the depot could do with a few more like him.

It was a long time since Rose had found cause to be thankful to Barry.

She explained that she had been asked by Mr Gascoigne to collect some of her husband's things and since she was still not coping very well alone she had brought her friend.

The doorman wrote out a pass for them and ordered a messenger boy to take the two ladies to Gascoigne's office. They were led through swing doors and along a corridor painted in institutional green and cream. A second set of doors opened into a place of a size and scale they were unprepared for, a warehouse as long as the nave of St Paul's, with rank upon rank of metal storage racks where the pews would had been.

Rose's nerve faltered. She glanced Antonia's way and rolled her eyes upwards.

Antonia shook her head and gave the V-sign.

Gascoigne's office was higher than everything else, mounted on struts like a watchtower. They climbed an iron staircase, and had to be let into the office to wait because he wasn't inside. Through windows the length of each wall they could see brown-coated civil servants between the racks collecting packets of stationery and loading them on to hand-trolleys.

While the boy went to look for Gascoigne the two women stared out at the scene. Antonia asked if Barry had been one of the trolley-pushers.

'He must have been.'

'Can't imagine it.'

Rose could, without difficulty. She wasn't a believer in the occult, yet she had a disturbing sense of his presence here. Listening to the doorman she had sharply visualized the wisecracking clever dick who was her husband striding through that entrance with some fresh quip to brighten the day. All along the corridor she had been conscious of him, into the warehouse and up the stairs and now if she turned her head he would be just behind her in one of those brown overalls, grinning all over his face at what had happened to her and what she was desperate enough to be planning now.

Bastard. She still hated him. Soon after they'd married he'd given up bothering to amuse *her*. All the bonhomie was directed at other people.

Antonia said someone was coming.

'Oh, God.'

'He's only a man, darling.'

Gascoigne had come up the stairs in a rush and was breathless. He was in the same dark grey pinstripe he'd worn at the funeral. He held out his hand. 'My dear Mrs Bell, they didn't tell me you were expected this afternoon.'

'They didn't know. We just happened to be passing. This is Mrs Ashton who is helping me attend to things.' Not entirely untruthful. Ashton had been Antonia's maiden name. And they were attending to things.

A small stack of chairs stood in one corner. Gascoigne lifted two out and dusted them with his handkerchief. 'How are you feeling now, Mrs Bell?'

'Not much better, I'm afraid.'

'It's early days.'

'You mentioned some articles of my husband's.'

'Yes, indeed.' He opened a desk and took out a brown envelope. 'Would you care to check them?'

'That's all right.'

He coughed. 'I meant would you be good enough to check them. Perhaps it's fussy of me, but I need a receipt.' He flapped his hand vaguely. 'Bureaucracy, I'm afraid.'

She let the things slide out on to his desk. A Swan fountain pen that she had seen Barry use at home to fill in his football coupon. Two tickets for a dance at the Hammersmith Palais on October 12th – one date loverboy had been unable to keep. Finally a snapshot. She got a jolt as if Barry himself had nudged her. The picture was of a woman holding a child, a boy of eighteen months or so. She turned it over. In a neat, small hand was written, 'To Darling B from Mike and Me'.

She tore it in two and dropped it into the wastepaper basket with the dance tickets and the envelope.

Gascoigne looked shocked. 'I seem to have dragged you here unnecessarily.'

Antonia beamed at him. 'Not at all. The pen will come in useful, if it's only to sign your receipt.' She picked it up and handed it to Rose, who scribbled her signature on the slip of paper Gascoigne had ready.

Gascoigne thanked her. 'Will you have a cup of tea? It's past the time, but I'm sure the ladies downstairs will rise to the occasion. Wing Commander Bell was very popular with them.'

'No doubt.' Rose was choking with bitterness from seeing the photograph. She pressed her hankie to her face and told herself angrily to stay in control. Then she stood up and glanced out of the window at the storage racks. 'What would really please me would be to see exactly where he worked.'

Gascoigne paled. 'That's not possible, I'm sorry to say.'

Antonia chipped in. 'Oh, I say, you can't mean that, Mr Gascoigne. You don't know what a comfort it would be.'

'It's a matter of security.'

'No, darling. Humanity. It's a matter of humanity. What do you think she's going to do – steal a ration book?'

'Goodness, no.'

'Well, then?' She moved closer to Rose and slipped her arms around her and looked appealingly at Gascoigne.

'There are regulations.'

'You're just obeying orders, is that it? That excuse has an ugly ring to it, Mr Gascoigne.'

A flicker of indecision crossed his features.

Rose raised her head from Antonia's shoulder and smiled wanly. 'Please forget that I mentioned it. I wouldn't want you to get into trouble over me.'

He licked his lips. He was a lost man. He scraped his chair and sprang up. 'Look, I think we can bend the rules just this once.'

Downstairs he hurried them past the trolley-pushers to an unoccupied space between the racks. 'As you probably know, this depot was established early in the war, when Churchill realized the havoc that would be caused if the building in Storey's Gate was bombed. Now I think we have more capacity than they do. We handle just about every item of government stationery. I am the despatch officer.'

'You must be kept busy.'

He smiled disdainfully.

Rose turned to one of the stacks. 'What are these?'

'Leaflets about swine fever. Everything along here relates to agriculture. Not much to interest a lady.'

She asked whether the numbers painted in white on the base of the rack were significant and he started telling her about the classification system.

Rose cut in. 'There must be a list of all these numbers somewhere.'

'There is. I'll show you.'

As they followed him to the end of the rack Rose tapped Antonia's arm. 'See you at the car.'

She stood for a minute or so in front of the plan and index displayed on the end wall – long enough to learn that the Registration of Births, Marriages and Deaths section was in Rows GRO1 to 6 and that Form 134/B (Disposal) was stored in GRO6. Gascoigne was running his finger down the list pointing out items that they might have come across as housewives.

Rose sidled around the end of the nearest rack, turned and walked away, up the column towards the far end. As soon as she reckoned Gascoigne wouldn't see her if he turned round she stepped out fast. She relied on Antonia to invent some excuse.

She slowed to pass two people with trolleys. They didn't give her a second look. She could imagine how easy it would be to get into a zombie-like state pushing a trolley up and down these aisles. Whichever one you chose the scene was the same: dark shelves reaching almost to infinity and lit at intervals by lamps with conical shades coated in dust.

The system also made strong demands on one's concentration. She reckoned the racks marked GRO ought to have been about halfway along, but she'd gone three-quarters of the way and still hadn't found them. She stopped, not wanting to panic, yet fearing she was in error. If she retraced her steps she had no certainty of doing any better. Her shoulders went tense and she breathed faster. Couldn't stand still. Had to look as if she knew what she was doing.

She turned and went back the way she had come, along the ends of the rows, checking the code numbers. About the middle she became convinced that she was wasting precious time. None of the GRO numbers was there. She would have noticed the first time.

Then she raised her eyes and saw a set of letters and figures much higher up the rack she was standing beside. Because she'd first noticed the information at eye level she hadn't looked any higher. There was a whole series she'd missed. Encouraged, she moved on and found the rack marked GRO6 just a short way ahead. She reached out and ran her hand along one of the shelves. Now all she had to do was find 134/B (Disposal).

The stationery itself was not on view. It was stored in brown paper packets with the coding written on labels pasted on to the ends. She moved along the rack reading them off.

134/B. She clenched her fist in triumph, or relief.

Her idea was to unwrap the top packet, remove a disposal form and tuck it into her handbag. With some care she prised her fingernail under the fold to separate it without causing a tear.

'Are you looking for something?'

A man had come up behind her.

She gasped and spun round.

'What are you doing, exactly?' He wasn't one of the trolley-pushers. He was in a suit like Gascoigne. An important-looking man with silver hair and a black moustache.

A surge of fear galvanized Rose. A lie sprang readily to her lips. 'I was sent over from Somerset House. They ran out of 134/Bs. Mr Gascoigne told me where to find them.'

'Ah. Gascoigne.'

'Here they are. Good.' She tucked a packet under her arm and set off at as brisk a walk as she dared towards the far end of the warehouse and the exit. She wouldn't stop if he called out. There was such a pounding in her head that she wouldn't hear anyway.

She stared ahead, knowing she was trapped if anyone chose to block her path. It was the recurring nightmare of being chased up a narrow passageway, thinking she could make it to the end and then being met by a leaping tiger. Or, in this case, Gascoigne. But he didn't appear. She turned right and headed for the swing doors without a glance to either side. People were moving about there and she avoided looking at them. Through the doors and into the corridor.

Walk.

It was longer than she remembered. God, she thought, I hope I picked the right doors. And then, oh, no, what am I going to tell the doorman?

He turned to face her as she burst through the doors. 'Everything all right?'

'Yes.' She smacked her hand over the label on the packet. 'I got the things.'

'You seem to have lost your friend.'

‘Oh, she’s following. Got talking to someone. ’Bye, then.’

‘Best of luck.’

She’d already had more of that than she was entitled to expect.

28

Through the rear-view mirror of the Bentley, Rose's eyes were fixed on the farthest pillar in a row of housefronts at one end of Lowndes Square, the point where she would first catch sight of somebody approaching from the Stationery Office Depot. She had the engine running and her hands gripping the wheel.

Please God let it be Antonia, she thought.

Yet how absurd. She was sitting here waiting for the woman who had tried to chloroform her, who would surely have murdered her, whatever she claimed afterwards. A callous, unpredictable killer for whose arrival Rose was praying fervently. She had no illusions about Antonia. The charm was totally resistible now. Remarks that once seemed witty left her cold, yet she couldn't ignore the certainty that she herself was destined for the gallows if Antonia was arrested and persuaded to confess. What a mess! She didn't see any way to untangle herself.

So she waited in the car.

Two more minutes went by. Rose drummed her fingers on the rim of the wheel.

Then Antonia appeared, her fair hair springing against the black velvet collar as she clattered around the corner in her high heels. She flashed a wide smile when their eyes met. Bravado, Rose thought sourly as she leaned across and lifted the lock on the door, but smiled back.

Antonia hauled it open, sank into the seat and swung her legs in.

'Any joy?'

'Behind you.'

Antonia turned, looked at the packet of forms on the back seat and whistled. 'Hell's bells, Rosie, we only needed one.'

'It was easier to take the packet.'

'Five hundred! Gordon Bennett! Are you going into business?' She started to laugh.

Rose joined in the peal of giggles, a frankly hysterical reaction as they shattered the tension.

'You don't do things by halves, ducky!'

Their laughter shrilled at least an octave higher, recalling that hilarious moment – Rose had forgotten the cause of the hilarity – in the Black and White Milk Bar just after they had met in Piccadilly. For a few blissful seconds it blotted out everything that had happened since that afternoon.

Someone had to say something when the laughter died and it was Antonia. 'Ah well, who knows, the extra ones may come in useful.'

'What?' Rose almost swung the car into a taxi she was overtaking.

'In case the pen slips and I mess it up, darling.' She gave a chesty laugh. 'What else?'

This time Rose didn't join in.

As they approached the traffic lights at the top of Sloane Street, she returned to practicalities and suggested they stopped somewhere in Hyde Park. 'If we fill the form in right away, we can get to an undertaker's before they close.' She got a nod from Antonia so she turned right, through the Albert Gate into South Carriage Drive. 'How did you cope with Gascoigne?'

'Told him you'd had trouble with your suspenders.'

'Oh, for God's sake.'

'What's up? It was the perfect thing to say. He went pink and twitchy at the thought and his eyes glazed over, dirty old sod, so I knew what to talk about – stocking-tops, belts, garters, corsets and quivering thighs, forests of them. And how to hitch up your stocking with a sixpence. Oh, and the shortage of elastic. That really got his smutty little mind going. The steam was coming out of his ears by then. He forgot all about his precious coding system and he didn't mention you for ten minutes.'

'How did you get away?'

'With ease. When I'd run out of things to say about

suspenders I passed on the thought that perhaps we ought to find out whether you were all right. We had a look up and down the aisles, by which time I felt sure you must have found the form and cleared off, so I told Gascoigne that you must have got extremely embarrassed and quit the building minus stockings or worse. He had no difficulty visualizing that. I think he found it very believable. We went down to the entrance and the doorman told us you'd left in a hurry. I winked at Gascoigne and followed you.'

Rose stopped the car. The light was already going and they still had to get to an undertaker's. She fished in her handbag for Barry's fountain pen while Antonia ripped the brown paper off the packet of disposal forms.

'Don't bother, darling. I'd better use mine. I filled in the registration form with it.' She took it out and unscrewed the top. 'Can't be too careful.'

Rose wanted her to concentrate. They couldn't afford a mistake in the form-filling, but Antonia continued to talk. 'There's a dear little undertaker called Hopkinson at the top end of Tottenham Court Road. Much nicer than Greely. We can go straight there and hand him this. Then I'll get you to come home with me and see if Hector's any easier to move before they come for him. It *would* look more natural if he was lying in bed. By now he ought to be more pliable, didn't he?'

'I've no idea.'

'I will need your pen after all. There's a short bit here that I'm supposed to fill in as myself. Different ink, you see, and bolder handwriting. No flies on me. What was I about to say? Yes, after you've helped me upstairs with Hector I suggest we shake hands and go our different ways.'

'I'm all for that.'

'Fine, but don't sound so bloody pleased about it, my flower. I'm not looking for gratitude for what I did, but you don't have to treat me like a case of measles. Considering the mess your marriage was in when we met, you haven't come out of it at all badly.' She returned the pen to Rose. 'Do you want to check it? The other part has to be filled in by the undertaker.'

'What?' Rose felt a tightening in her stomach. 'What did you say? Let me see.'

'Part C. Part A is the registrar's bit authorizing the disposal, which I've filled in. Part B is for the informant to complete. That's me, and I've done it. And C is for the undertaker. "Notification of Disposal". Oh my God!' She clapped her hand to her mouth.

Rose quietly studied Part C. 'A person disposing of a body must within ninety-six hours deliver to the registrar this notification as to the date, place and means of the disposal of the body.' She was churning inside, but she spoke mechanically, chanting out the obvious as if she were playing consequences, except that it felt and sounded like the death sentence. 'Who does the undertaker notify? The registrar. And the registrar checks it against his records. And if it's a name that doesn't appear in his records, he wants to know why. When he doesn't get a satisfactory answer he asks the police to investigate.' She paused. 'You know, Antonia, we've had it. This perfect murder is a perfect dud.'

'Bloody hell!' Antonia screwed up the paper and drummed her fists against the dashboard. 'Five hundred sodding forms and we can't use one of them.'

Rose didn't have that much energy left. She turned on the engine and drove out of the Park, into the traffic moving up Park Lane. She was incapable of saying any more. She was blitzed. It was all she could do, all she wanted to do, to perform the mindless functions of controlling the car. It was some kind of link with normality, like hanging out washing the morning after an air raid that had shattered every window in the house.

Mercifully Antonia also went silent.

The street lights were on already. Outside the Dorchester a man was selling evening papers. Rose switched on the headlamps as she swung the Bentley into Oxford Street and the predictable jam. While they were inching towards Oxford Circus the subversive aroma of roast chestnuts wafted from a street corner.

'It's past teatime.'

'Shall we?'

'A bag of chestnuts won't go far.'

They stopped at Yarner's in Langham Place and sat by an upstairs window at one of the glass-topped tables with a pot of tea in front of them. They had a corpse at home to dispose of and they blandly ordered Bismarck Herring sandwiches, buttered crumpets and chocolate cake from the silver-haired waitress in her black dress, pink apron and cap. The imminent prospect of returning to the house without the slightest idea what to do with Hector appalled them both. Tea was a convenient hiatus. They didn't speak, except to place the order and pay the bill. They were long past the point of small talk.

Back in the car, Rose handed across a cigarette and lit one herself. 'It's got to be faced. You can't use an undertaker now.'

'What do you mean – *you*?'

'All right. Slip of the tongue. We're in this together.'

Another half-minute passed.

Antonia said, 'Nobody knows he's dead except you and me.'

'And Mr Greely.'

'That undertaker? He didn't use my name once. He'll forget all about us.'

'Some hopes! I should think you're indelibly fixed in his memory. I can't imagine anyone else has ever changed their mind in a funeral parlour.'

'Greely might remember me, but he didn't meet Hector, did he?'

'You'd better tell me what you're driving at.'

Antonia blew out a thin plume of smoke. Suddenly the bleak look had slipped from her features and was supplanted by an expression Rose had seen before, that afternoon they were standing outside the Ritz – lips pressed together into a secret smile, pleased with itself and scornful of the world, eyes slightly glazed and looking at nothing in particular. 'Hector will just have to disappear.'

Rose frowned.

'Go missing, darling. Plenty do.'

'That's going to take some believing. He wasn't the type.'

'What?'

'Successful businessmen don't go missing. How are you going to account for it?'

'I won't. It's not my job.'

'But you'll have to notify the police.'

'Eventually.'

'And?'

'I'll tell them he didn't come home one night.'

Rose shook her head and sighed. 'It's not much good, Antonia. What are they supposed to think?'

'Anything you bloody well like.' Antonia rattled off a list. 'He fell down a manhole. He lost his memory. He was robbed and pushed into the river. He refused to pay protection money to a gang. He seduced the entire Luton Girls' Choir and fled the country. He got religion and went into–'

Rose cut in. 'For God's sake, Antonia! How will you get rid of the body?'

'*We*, my little helpmate.'

'We, then.'

Antonia waved a dismissive hand. 'Bury him somewhere. Out in the country. A Surrey wood.'

'Have you any idea how hard it is to dig a grave in uncultivated ground?'

'Why? Have you?'

Rose gave her a glare that would have sunk a battleship. 'The newspaper reports always say the victim was found in a shallow grave.'

'What's your suggestion?'

'I don't have one.' Any minute they would be at each other's throats. 'All right. We'll go back to the house.' She succeeded in sounding calm, but her hands shook when she tried fitting the key into the ignition. She didn't know which was worse, the hostility from Antonia or the terror boiling inside herself.

She drove slowly up Portland Place and brought the car round the Devonshire Street turn to the Mews. Antonia got out and ran into the house. Rose pulled out the key of the car and followed.

Antonia's voice hailed her excitedly from the sitting room where they had left the body. 'He's starting to loosen up. I think we can move him tonight.'

Rose thought, what's the point? She remained in the kitchen, sparing herself another sight of the corpse.

Antonia appeared again, radiant with her discovery. Her dead husband might have been a bread-mix from the way she talked about him. 'I'll put some heat in there and he'll be ready in no time.'

Rose looked round for something else to occupy her. The cat had walked in and wanted feeding, so she opened the fridge. Some uncooked meat was in there on a plate. 'Is it safe to feed this to Raffles?'

'What do you mean – safe?'

'Free from poison.'

'For crying out loud, you halfwit. There was never any poison.'

'No poison?'

'Only the chloroform.'

'For Hector?'

'No – for you, stupid.' The barb sprang from Antonia's tongue and she immediately tried to cover it with words. 'The point is, you can feed the bloody cat with perfect safety. I've got to find an electric fire.' She quit the room.

Rose stood rigid. Now she knew. Hector's murder had been an afterthought, one of Antonia's devil-may-care decisions after the murder attempt failed. The whole charade of Antonia going away and Hector requiring cooked meals had been dreamed up to bring Rose herself to the house to be chloroformed and killed.

Why?

How could she have so antagonized Antonia? The worst she was guilty of was an innocent meal out with Hector.

What did Antonia hope to gain by it?

She thought back to Barry's death. That had been casual and coldblooded. Barry had been insufferable, but not to Antonia. She had no grudge against him, yet she had calmly offered to kill him. And kept her promise.

Antonia didn't need a bloodlust or a brainstorm. She murdered with detachment. Yet not without reason. Surely not without reason.

She must have killed Barry because it put Rose under an obligation to her. Something was wanted in return.

The opportunity to steal the death certificate from the registrar? Not just that.

Rose clenched her fists.

My identity.

I assumed all along that she wanted me to square the account by killing Hector, possibly without knowing what I was doing. I was wrong. If she'd wanted Hector dead she'd have done it herself. She didn't need me for that. But if she killed me she could write her own name on the death certificate and 'die'. She'd have my handbag with all my papers and my house keys. She'd become Rose Bell and she'd be free to go to America with Vic and marry him.

And Hector, could he have known about this? Was it possible that he'd gone along with it? Did he know of the plan that evening in Reggiori's?

Rose thought back to what she had heard about the drowning of Hector's first wife. He'd connived at that. Why shouldn't he have also connived at another murder?

The cat mewed.

She took the meat from the fridge and looked for a knife with a good, sharp edge.

29

'Just what are you doing with that knife?'

Antonia stood in the doorway, her right hand gripping the door frame.

Rose looked up. She'd taken it from a drawer containing wooden spoons, tin openers, meat skewers and a selection of knives and cleavers. This had been the obvious one to choose, a long bone-handled carver with a blade that may once have been uniformly wide. Years of sharpening had honed it to a point.

'What I said I would do – cutting up meat for the cat.'

'It shouldn't be used for that.'

'Why not? It's wonderfully sharp.'

'It's the carver.'

'I've finished now.' Calmly Rose picked up the chopping board and used the knife to push the pieces off into the cat's dish. 'That should keep him quiet.' She took the knife to the sink and ran some water over it. She reached for a teacloth and wiped the blade, taking care not to touch the edge, turning it over appreciatively. 'An old knife like this is certainly worth looking after.'

'Why do you say that?'

Rose gave a shrug. 'I wouldn't mind betting it's sharper than anything else you've got.'

For a moment Antonia had looked alarmed. Now she seemed to accept that she'd misinterpreted what she'd seen. She put her hand to her hair and twined one blonde strand around her forefinger and twitched her mouth into an odd, speculative smile. 'There's a hacksaw in the garage.'

Rose frowned. 'What's that got to do with it?'

'I should have thought it was obvious.'

'Well, it isn't to me. What are you suggesting?'

'He'd be easier to bury in pieces.'

Rose dropped the knife in the drawer and slammed it shut.

Antonia carried on in a persuasive voice as if she were suggesting how to pass a diverting evening. 'We could wrap the bits in newspaper and bury them in different places.'

'That's vile. How could you possibly do it?'

'The two of us, ducky.'

Rose's stomach heaved. 'You must be mad even to think of such a horrible thing.'

She got a cold stare. 'Think of something better, then.' Getting no answer, Antonia added, 'Sweetie, we've got a dead man to dispose of. You'd better face up to reality.'

The words hit Rose hard. The thought of butchering any human corpse, let alone Hector's, was too nauseous to contemplate. Yet she was barren of suggestions.

As if to underline the inactivity, Antonia fetched some playing cards from one of the other rooms and started a game of patience on the kitchen table.

'Understand what I said, Rose? You kept your lily white hands clean when I got rid of Barry, but you're as tainted as I am because you asked me to do it. I don't know what goes on inside that mind of yours, but you can't go on looking the other way. Face it, you're a killer, just as I am. If you want to go on living, stop playing Snow White and get some blood on your hands.'

The phone rang.

Their eyes met. Antonia stood up. 'It'll be Vic.'

'Don't answer it.'

'I can talk to Vic.'

'You don't know who it is.'

The bell pealed out its insistent notes.

'For pity's sake, it's only a telephone.' Antonia ran across the hall.

'You're asking for trouble.'

Furious, Rose followed her into the room and stood not a yard away.

'Yes? . . . Speaking, yes.' Antonia switched the receiver to her other ear and turned her back on Rose. Her voice was guarded. This certainly wasn't Vic. 'Really? He left here as usual. . . . No, not yet, but that's nothing unusual. He works all hours, as you know. . . . I see. . . . No, he didn't – but then I didn't enquire. I'm his wife, darling, not his nursemaid. Perhaps he spent the day at that exhibition. . . . Closed? I didn't know that. . . . Well, did he go to Paris, do you think? He had lunch with some Frenchman the other day. . . . God, no, I'd be the last to know. . . . Listen, my dear, it's not the end of the world. Surely the place can survive for a couple of days without him? I'll get him to ring you if he gets in touch. There's nothing more I can do.' She slammed down the phone. 'Bloody woman.'

'His secretary?'

'Fussing over sweet F.A., as usual. What time is it?'

'Just gone nine.'

'A fine time to call me. I've got my suspicions about Hector and that girl.'

'She's got suspicions of her own by the sound of it.'

'Piffle. She doesn't know there's anything wrong.'

'That's beside the point, Antonia. He's been missed at work already. If you're going to play the anxious wife you'll have to call the police damn quick.'

Antonia slid her eyes in the direction of the drawing room where the corpse was lying. 'How can I?'

Rose had no answer. She'd rejected everything Antonia had suggested.

In her mind's eye she stood over Hector's body with a hacksaw, bracing herself to use it. Revolting. Yet it was rapidly coming to that.

No. She'd reached her sticking-point. 'There must be another way of dealing with this. A better way.'

'Well?' Antonia waited with the air of a schoolmistress expecting some glib answer.

Out of sheer desperation Rose talked, casting for ideas as she spoke. 'We take everything out of his pockets that could be used to identify him.'

'We'd have to do that whatever happened.'

'Let me finish. And then we put him in the boot of the car

and drive out and . . . find a bomb site that hasn't been cleared.'

'A bomb site – that's a thought.'

Confidence surged through Rose like a drug. 'We drop him into a hole and cover it with rubble. The chances are that he'll never be found. If he is, they'll think he was looting and had an accident. Or that he was just some tramp using it as a place to sleep.'

Antonia made a fist and feigned a punch. 'Brilliant, Rosie! Let's drink to it.' She fetched two glasses and a bottle of the Burgundy, which she uncorked with one pull of the corkscrew. 'Just one. Got to stay on our feet.'

They touched glasses. Antonia's eyes may have caught some reflected light from the cut glass but it seemed to Rose that they shone with something more than relief. There was a gleam of triumph there. Almost of rapture. It was as if she was looking ahead to some sort of happy-ever-after.

Rose brusquely recalled her to the present. 'Croydon is the place. I come through there when I visit my parents. It's peppered with bomb sites.'

'Croydon?' Antonia spoke the name as if it were Timbuktu. 'We don't need to go that far when you've got a perfectly good site in Pimlico, darling.'

'Where?'

'Christ Almighty, if *you* don't know. . . .'

Rose gazed at her in disbelief. 'You can't mean Oldfield Gardens.'

'You bet I do. It hasn't been cleared, has it?'

'I am not going to bury Hector in Oldfield Gardens.'

Antonia rebuked Rose in a good-natured way. 'Don't be such a sap. It's the ideal place. It's not overlooked.'

'No. I refuse. It's much too near. It would be asking for trouble.'

'That great poster screens it from the road.'

'We're taking him to Croydon.'

Antonia conceded tamely. 'Have it your way if you insist, darling.'

Rose went out to the car. She had remembered the

packet of disposal forms on the back seat. She brought them back to the house, gave them to Antonia and told her to make a fire of them. Antonia took them off to the drawing room, joking that if they helped to raise the temperature a few degrees the afternoon hadn't been a complete waste of time. She was in a better mood now that they'd settled what to do with Hector, and she seemed appreciative of Rose's more positive role.

Some time towards midnight Antonia came back to the kitchen. She'd changed into a sweater and slacks and she'd brought some down for Rose and dumped them on the table, together with a pair of flat shoes.

'You can't climb over bomb sites in heels.'

It was sensible. The things were dark blue in colour, too. Rose changed while Antonia went off to take another look at the body. She could have done with a size smaller in slacks, but the shoes fitted well. She was thankful to get out of her own things for the task ahead. It was like being back in uniform, which had always given her the feeling she was part of something impersonal, at several removes from her real life.

30

Antonia called out breezily that the body was ready to move.

Rose felt the gooseflesh rise again. Resolved to master her nerves, she reached for the wine bottle, poured herself some more and swallowed it at a gulp. 'Coming.'

She joined Antonia in the drawing room. This time she didn't flinch at the sight of the body. She did what Antonia had urged, faced up to reality and forced herself to take in the scene as if it were a waxwork tableau. More colour remained in Hector's features than she would have expected. Perhaps the chloroform had roughened his cheeks. Antonia had already removed some money from the pockets and placed it on a table nearby, together with a wallet, a handkerchief and a set of keys. No one could possibly identify Hector now, she claimed confidently.

'Ready, then?' Rose said. They were acting on her initiative now. She was taking charge.

Antonia nodded. It was almost as if she welcomed the secondary role.

They bent over the body and took a grip. The muscles were noticeably less rigid now. There was some movement at the knees and hips.

Antonia took most of the weight, slotting her hands under the armpits. They stumbled to the door and across the hall, pausing outside the kitchen. In two more stages they lifted him out to the garage. The torso was difficult to get into the car boot, so Rose lifted the legs in first and then supported the small of the back as they heaved him inside.

She shut down the lid and leaned on it.

'How's the time?'

'It must be after midnight. Rose, how long will it take to get there?'

'Getting on for three-quarters of an hour. And then we've got to scout around for a place to leave him.'

'Let's fetch our coats, then.'

At the door on the way out, Antonia gave a girlish shriek of laughter. 'What on earth are you bringing your handbag for?'

'It's got everything in it. My ration book. My identity card.'

'Rosie, you'll be the death of me. We're not going shopping and we don't want to be identified. Leave it behind. All we need is the key of the car.'

'I forgot.' Rose turned and threw the bag on to the kitchen table, annoyed at her own stupidity. To reassert herself she announced that she would do the driving. Antonia didn't object.

Great Portland Street was almost deserted. Only when they approached the Oxford Circus end did they start seeing people in evening clothes standing far out in the road to try and hail one of the few taxis operating at that hour. Some waved at anything on four wheels and shouted their fury at being ignored. A fine drizzle was adding to their discomfort.

Rose switched on the wipers and glanced at the petrol gauge. They had ample. The Bentley fairly purred compared with the RAF staff cars she was used to handling. She took the route through Piccadilly Circus and the Haymarket towards Charing Cross, then followed the river as far as Vauxhall Bridge. At the lights she said she wouldn't mind a cigarette.

Antonia didn't respond.

'I said have you got a fag?'

'What, darling?'

'A cigarette. My handbag is back at the house. Remember?'

Antonia found a packet of her wicked-smelling Abdullahs in the glove compartment.

'Thanks. You were miles away.'

'Mm.'

'Thinking about America?'

'What?'
'America. Princeton, isn't it?'
Antonia tensed beside her. The voice shed its mateyness. 'How do you know about that?'
The lights changed. Rose eased from second into third and they started to cross the bridge. 'Hector told me. Wasn't I supposed to know?'
Antonia started justifying herself rapidly. 'It doesn't matter a damn. I can't go now. I can't get married again, not while Hec is officially missing. It takes years and years before the law will admit that a missing person is dead. I can't marry again, and Vic won't even talk about living together. I thought this country was the last word in prudishness, but it seems they're just as narrow-minded in New Jersey.'
Rose drove on without comment.
Antonia only pressed her case more vigorously. 'Didn't I tell you about this? Believe me, there wasn't any question of trying to keep it from you. I mean, why should I, darling? I introduced you to Vic. God, after what you and I have been through together, we don't need to hide anything from each other.'
Rose had stopped listening. Something bloody underhanded was going on. She'd touched a raw nerve when she mentioned America. Antonia's pacifying gush was more of a threat than outright hostility. All this reassurance couldn't paper over the fact that Vic and his job in Princeton were still paramount in Antonia's plans. It was screamingly obvious that she hadn't given up the idea. She was resolved to go to America with him. How could she, without marrying him?
Stockwell came up, then Brixton. They swung into the Brixton Road. Not much was moving in either direction. It was tempting to take the Bentley up to higher speeds along the wide highway, but she dared not risk it. This was the time of night when police cars lay in wait in side roads.
Heavier rain than they had been through had saturated the road. Each streetlamp stood over its own reflection and each oncoming car appeared to have four headlamps. The

wet tyres rustled and clicked. Don't let it lull you into quiescence, Rose told herself. This is the most dangerous hour of your life.

The first sign for Croydon came up.

Antonia rubbed at the window with her hand. 'Journey's end, my flower.'

Rose drove on. Most of the bombing had been further in, and she had a particular site in mind. A street close to West Croydon Station had been devastated by one of the giant V2 rockets in 1944. The entire area had since been evacuated and fenced round with corrugated iron, but children had ripped down a section of the fence to make their own cycle speedway track where there had been private gardens. Shells of houses stood about waiting for demolition, long since looted of anything worth owning. Clumps of willowherb and yellow ragwort had sprouted where pavements had been.

The turn came up on the left. For a short stretch they drove on the regular road past houses where people slept. The street lighting was sparse. Then the Bentley's headlamps picked out the gap she had remembered in the fence at the far end. There was space enough for the car to pass through, out of sight of the houses. It swayed and rocked across a pitted surface on to the remains of a road until they were forced to stop where a wall had collapsed.

Antonia flung open the door and got out. 'Wonderful, darling!' She stood in the rain with her arms folded, relishing the scene as if it were Epsom Downs on Derby Day. 'Let's go prospecting, shall we? There's a torch on the back seat.'

Rose couldn't understand this boisterousness. Nerves affected people in unexpected ways, but was this a case of nerves? Was the Benzedrine responsible? She switched off the headlamps and shone the torch across the site. Two years' growth of weeds had covered the rubble and made the footing awkward. Antonia was already striding indomitably towards the nearest ruined houses, which were – or had been – semi-detached, the sort that aspiring middle class people owned. Probably they had once been allotted numbers that the owners had replaced with names like *Mon Repos*. They stood roofless and derelict. Rose shone the torch upwards. Where bits of wall jutted out of the debris were traces of floral wallpaper.

The first two houses were impenetrable. Presumably to keep children out, boards had been hammered across the doorways and window spaces and crisscrossed with taut barbed wire. They picked their way around them with the torch until even Antonia's optimism faltered.

'We're wasting our time if they're all like this.'

Rose refused to be beaten. This was her show now. She was no longer passive. She had forced her personality out of its straitjacket and she had a liking for liberty. She pointed the torch behind them, across what had once been the garden. 'What's that, then?'

The small circle of light had stopped on a dark, raised mass.

'Just rubbish.'

Certainly when Rose stepped closer she found a collection of rusting and broken objects that must have been heaped there during the salvage operation. A garden roller without its wooden handle, several dented saucepans, a piece of saturated, threadbare carpet, a wheelbarrow, the frame of a deckchair. She stooped to examine something that gleamed. It was a chromium-plated key-plate.

Antonia came over. 'What have you found?'

'Somebody's front door by the look of it. Help me slide it to one side.'

'What for? Is there something underneath?'

'I don't know. There might be.' Rose had noticed a patch of concrete and a curved piece of corrugated steel that suggested a possibility.

Together they gripped the edge of the door and tried to move it.

'There's too much heavy stuff on top.'

They scrabbled among the rubbish and lifted off a few bricks and a coalbucket filled with china fragments. At the second attempt they succeeded in pulling the door about a yard to one side.

Antonia whistled. 'Nice work, darling!'

They had uncovered three or four steps leading underground to a cavity blocked by more rubbish, the frame of a pushchair and a dustbin lid.

'Who would have known it?' said Antonia.

They had found an Anderson shelter, the fortified hole in the ground that millions of families had installed in their gardens in the first years of the war, consisting of a curved arch of corrugated steel sunk three feet and covered with earth. This one had partially collapsed and was so overgrown as to be barely recognizable.

Together they hauled out the objects that were blocking the entrance. Then they used the torch again. The steel walls had become unclamped at the top and now sagged. The space inside was much reduced.

'It doesn't look very safe.'

'Doesn't need to be,' said Rose.

She picked up a stone and tossed it in. They heard it bounce across the concrete floor. Antonia grabbed the torch and crouched to peer inside. Her voice had a promising echo. 'Darling, it's ideal. His own tomb. We can cover him with rubble and put back the rubbish and no one will ever find him. When they clear the site they'll just bulldoze this. Let's fetch him, shall we? Have you got the keys?'

Rose handed them over as if to a servant. She felt elated at having solved the problem of where to deposit the body. She was entitled to some self-congratulation. She alone had thought of this place and found the shelter. Without her, Antonia wouldn't have stood a chance of getting away with murder. As it was, Hector's body was most unlikely to be found. He would just be listed as a missing person, one of thousands. And the credit for that belonged to her.

Mustn't get over complacent, she thought immediately. The night isn't over yet. She followed Antonia to the car.

Antonia had already turned the key and lifted the boot lid. They reached into the dark interior and hauled out the body and staggered towards the garden containing the shelter. The distance they had to cover was about seventy yards, and the footing was treacherous. Either of them could easily have turned an ankle. As it was, they managed it without a rest, pausing only when they stood by the steps of the shelter. They set the body down with the head and shoulders resting on the door.

'Get some breath back first.' Rose took a seat on the steps.

'As you wish.' Antonia took the torch from her pocket and started shining it over the rubbish around them.

'Looking for something?'

'Nothing in particular.'

Rose didn't believe her. She was capable of anything.

Antonia said, 'Feet first, I reckon.'

'What?'

'When we lift him in, his feet should go first.'

Rose didn't comment. Her eyes were following the beam of the torch. It picked out a set of rusty fire irons lying loose beside the wheelbarrow. Tongs, a shovel and a poker. The beam danced on to something else, coaxing her attention that way. Some instinct made her resist. Instead she turned her gaze back, outside the pool of light, and saw Antonia put her foot against the poker and covertly nudge it closer to the shelter entrance.

'Are you listening, Rose?'

Suddenly the torch was shining full in her face. She stiffened like a rabbit caught in a headlight's glare, except that the paralysing terror struck her a moment before the light. She managed to whisper, 'What?'

'Ready to start?'

Rose put up her arm protectively. 'Stop it. It's dazzling me.'

'Get up, then.'

The beam moved away and the immediate feeling of helplessness passed. Rose had her hand to her eyes and she looked between the fingers to where the poker was lying. She'd expected Antonia to make a grab for it. Not yet, apparently. But she would at the next opportunity. 'If you want his legs to go into the shelter first, you can lift them. I'm not going right inside.'

'Why not?' demanded Antonia. 'You're smaller than I am.'

'I don't like small spaces.'

Antonia lowered the torch and held it out to her. 'Look inside. It's all right. No rats or anything. Get a grip on yourself, you great sissy.'

'That's enough!' Rose sprang up and pushed a warning finger at Antonia's face. 'I could easily walk away and leave you now.'

The tone switched abruptly from scorn to protest. 'But you've refused all along to lift him by the shoulders.'

'Never mind. I'm ready to do it now.'

'Oh, for Christ's sake! Have it your way, ducky, but let's get on with it.'

Antonia dropped the torch and strutted histrionically past Rose to take a grip on Hector's legs. But the bluster didn't succeed as a diversion. Rose kept her eyes on the poker. She watched Antonia locate it with her right foot and glance down and attempt to nudge it out of sight under some thistles. Proof positive that she would launch an attack with it any minute. One or two blows on the skull with that would be death.

Disposing of Hector wasn't enough. Antonia meant to kill again.

Why?

Rose knew why.

It's the same plan as before, only this time she's streamlined it. She means to kill me and take over my identity. She'll bury me here, with Hector's corpse. She's got my handbag at home with my keys, my ration book and my identity card. She can get into my house and find my birth certificate and anything else she needs. She'll use my name to get married to Vic. And then she'll go to America with him.

She will not.

Rose forced herself to stand up, step woodenly across the rubble and take up the position she had said she would, facing Antonia, with the length of Hector's body between them. This was the task that had to be completed, whatever else happened. Neither could manage it alone.

She stooped and slid her hands under the back, between the arms. Then she looked at Antonia, who was dipping to take the weight of the legs. They nodded at each other like two removal men lifting a piece of furniture.

Rose knew that the minute her usefulness was at an end, when Hector's corpse was safely in the shelter, Antonia would attack. She definitely meant to kill.

And if by some chance the bodies of a man and a woman were discovered here later, the woman with an impacted skull, she would be dressed in clothes that had belonged to Antonia. The cunning that had ordered the events of the past few hours was clear.

Rose shuffled forward bearing the main weight of the body, eyes downcast as if she couldn't bear the sight of poor Hector's face. Actually her reason for looking down had more to do with self-interest: she was coming to the place where the poker was lying. She made a performance of stumbling slightly when she reached the thistles. It enabled her to nudge her right foot under the poker and push it at least a couple of feet aside.

Antonia seemed not to have noticed. She was making her way backwards down the three concrete steps, dipping low under the steel roof. She was right inside the shelter as Rose came down the steps. Funny. She obviously felt safe. She'd never considered Rose as a physical threat.

'All right?'

'Yes.'

They lowered their burden to the concrete floor.

Neither added a word. The silence wasn't out of respect for the dead.

Now.

Rose turned and stretched across the concrete to reach for the poker. Her fingertips made contact with the handle. She took a grip, turned back towards the shelter entrance and raised her arm high behind her shoulder.

Antonia was bowing low to come out. There wasn't much light to see her by, but the pale arch of her hair was discernible, and as she lifted her face the eyes appeared colourless. There was an instant when those eyes sighted Rose, a split second of disbelief.

Rose swung the poker and crashed it into the blonde head with more force than she knew she possessed.

Antonia slumped forward, across Hector's body. Probably that first blow killed her, but there was too much bitterness, too much resentment to be contained in one blow. Rose battered Antonia repeatedly about the head. She sobbed as she struck and the sobs kept the rhythm of the blows for some time before she exhausted herself, slowed and stopped.

31

A long silence.

Rose was incapable of telling how long she remained on her knees with her hands over her eyes. Eventually she sensed that the shaking of her body wasn't so much from a sense of shock as from cold. Her coat was saturated. Fine rain still lashed down. She stood up stiffly and looked down at what she had done.

And felt more relieved than regretful.

I am safe from her. Whatever I am guilty of, I am safe from her. She can't hurt me now.

And nor can anyone else if I cover the bodies, bury them under the rubble. Somehow I must raise the strength.

She picked up the torch and trudged up the steps and looked about her. The circle of light travelled over the ground, searching. It stopped at a black area that the weeds had failed to colonize. She went closer and found a folded piece of tarpaulin attached to a length of timber, all that was left of somebody's coalshed. As she bent to take a grip, a large frog hopped out from under the fold, but she didn't recoil. She lifted a corner and disturbed other things that would normally have repelled her, woodlice, beetles and centipedes. She was unmoved. She had a new scale of horrors now. With the aid of a rusty old tyre lever that came to hand, she prised and tore the tarpaulin away from the wood. Then she dragged it across the site to the shelter and down the steps.

Before covering the bodies she knelt and used her sleeve to wipe some smudges from Hector's forehead. His eyes were closed and the pale lashes were damp from the rain. He still had the look of an overgrown cherub. She thought for a moment of that remark Antonia had made about mothering him. But you really fancied me, didn't you, Hec, she thought. Then she drew the tarpaulin gently over his face and tucked it under his shoulder, separating him from the face-down corpse of Antonia with its skullcap of blood.

She got up and set about collecting rubble to bury them with, heaping whatever she could lift into the void and hearing it slap against the tarpaulin. The bulky things that she and Antonia had pulled out, the coal bucket, the pushchair and the dustbin lid, helped fill the space. Some chunks of masonry were too heavy, so she rolled them to the steps and toppled them in. Her hands felt sore and her fingernails were in shreds. Her back ached. Still she toiled, going increasingly far from the shelter in search of debris she could handle.

It began to look less like a shelter entrance as she filled it in. She buried the bottom step and then the next. The broken wheelbarrow went in, and part of a wooden fence. More broken bricks and chunks of plaster followed.

As the level of debris in the shelter rose, so did her spirits. Bone-weary she may have been, but she had outsmarted and destroyed the most dangerous woman she was ever likely to meet.

Antonia is lying under three feet of rubble. This is what would have happened to me, she told herself. Instead, I was brave enough to defy her. I met the challenge. I didn't flinch when it was necessary to kill. She tried to destroy me and got destroyed herself. She tried to steal my life, my name, and make it hers. I didn't let her.

I deserve to get away with this.

She picked up the torch and switched it on again to survey the result of her efforts. After an hour or more of heavy work the surface was level. The shelter entrance was practically indistinguishable from the rest of the site. She found the old door that had been lying over the steps and pushed it back into position.

Dead and gone.

She took a long, sustaining breath and stepped wearily across the garden towards the Bentley. She would drive back to Park Crescent and park the car in its garage in the mews and collect her things. It would be bliss to put on her own clothes again. She'd pick up her handbag and make a parcel of the muddy clothes and drop them somewhere on the way home. She'd be home in Pimlico before dawn.

The car gleamed damply in the torchlight. I wouldn't mind a sleep on the back seat for twenty minutes, she thought. No, that's the sort of stupid thing the old Rose Bell would have done. Can't do that. Antonia wouldn't do that. She'd conquer the fatigue and drive straight back to London, and that's what I shall do. You can only expect to get away with murder if you keep your nerve and master your weaknesses. I was downtrodden and pathetic until a few weeks ago. Not now.

I got rid of Barry and saved myself from Antonia. I came out the winner. The survivor. The merry widow.

I'm stronger, more confident and better off than I have been in the whole of my life. Widow be damned. I'll get a good man, a real catch. See if I don't. What was it Antonia said? With legs like mine I should have heels three inches high.

She had her hand on the car door when a man called out to her.

'Just a minute, miss.'

She turned and looked across the site to the gap in the fence. He was standing there under a streetlamp holding the handlebars of his cycle – a policeman in uniform.

Her heart-rate doubled, but she refused to panic. He doesn't know a thing, she told herself.

His words confirmed it when he wheeled the bike across to her. 'You're out late, miss, or is it early?'

He was under twenty-five, clean-shaven, blue-eyed. Quite a dish, in fact. And the way he was looking at her he might have just asked for a dance.

She laughed.

He took the lamp off the front of his bike and took stock of the Bentley. 'Handsome car. Yours, is it?'

She leaned on the open door with a possessive air. 'Right down to the last rivet, darling. And now you want to know what I'm doing here on a bomb site looking like this. Am I right?'

He grinned.

She had his measure. He was putty. Soon deal with him.

'I let my wretched doggie off the lead and he ran in here and that was the last I saw of him. I've been scrambling in and out of dangerous places calling his name for hours. I hope he's all right.'

'He'll probably find his own way home. They usually do. Do you live nearby, miss?'

'No, in London. That's why I'm so worried.' The lies rolled easily off her tongue.

'It's a long way to bring a dog for a walk.'

'Oh, we only stopped for a wee.' She gave him a smile. 'You know what I mean. I've been to Brighton for the evening and I'm on the way home.'

'You've got your clothes in a state, miss.'

'I know, darling. Isn't it a bore? I can't wait to get out of them and into a nice, hot bath. Imagine it!'

He tilted his head to one side. She watched his eyes. He was young. He gave a half-smile – the sap.

'What's the dog's name?'

Quick – a name for a dog. 'Lucky.' She was away now. 'A cross between a bull terrier and a Bedlington, if you can imagine that. Pink eyes and white woolly hair. If ever a dog was misnamed, it's this one.'

'Well, if I hear anything. . . .'

'You'll make a certain lady very grateful indeed.'

'What's your name, miss?'

A name for a woman this time. 'Um – Princeton. Vicky Princeton. What's yours?'

He slid his finger under the strap of his helmet.

She said, 'Well, you're flesh and blood, sweetie. You must have a name.'

'We use numbers in the police, Miss Princeton.'

She peered at his collar. '109 is it? I'd rather call you Bobby.'

He said ponderously, 'I'd better make a note of your address, in case someone brings in the dog.'

She laughed and said as if she was being propositioned, 'Oh, yes?'

This wasn't all fun and games. He'd taken out his notebook and pencil.

'Well, I'm staying with friends at the moment. It's a pub. The Prince Regent in Lambeth.'

'That's not your own address, then?'

'It's not my own dog.' She was pleased with that witty riposte. 'It belongs to the landlord. If I'm still there, I'll buy you a drink, Bobby.'

'PC 109, if you don't mind.'

She smiled. 'I don't, if you don't.' And if I'd met you anywhere else, you pushover, it wouldn't have to end with me driving off alone into the night, she thought.

He kept rigidly to his official manner. 'I must ask you to move the vehicle, miss. Strictly speaking, you shouldn't have driven it in here.'

'I was on the point of leaving anyway . . . officer.'

She swung back the door and got in. Closed it. Smiled.

Felt in her coat pocket for the keys.

Her pocket was empty. So was the other one. But she had driven the car here.

He tapped on the window. 'Something the matter, miss?'

'My keys – I can't find them.'

As she said it, she remembered Antonia asking for the keys to open the boot when the two of them had gone to fetch Hector's body. Once the lid was up, Antonia must have pocketed them.

The bloody keys were buried with Antonia.

PC 109 opened the door. 'Let me have a look. They've fallen on the floor, I expect. Step out a minute, would you?'

Rose got out. This was dreadful. Maddening. She considered making a run for it while he got on his knees to search. No, she had to brazen this out.

The beam of his lamp probed the interior. 'Could they be in the back, do you think?'

'It's possible, I suppose.'

As she opened the rear door a ball of paper fell out of the car. She knew what it was at once – the disposal form Antonia had filled in with Hector's name and screwed up in disgust when she saw the part that had to be returned to the registrar.

Bloody Antonia!

She stooped to snatch it up.

Too quickly. Too nervously. Antonia would never have moved so fast.

Reacting to her sudden movement, the policeman reached out and grabbed it first.

'What have we got here, then?'

'Give it to me.' Suddenly the old fears flapped and swooped like vultures. This was dreadful, ruinous. She wasn't going to get away with murder. She was only Rose Bell, the luckless Rose.

'I said what have we got here?'

He flashed the lamp at her, dazzling her. The white light had a strange, disorientating effect. It bleached out the bomb site, the Bentley, the policeman, in fact everything that had happened since she had last been blinded by torchlight. She had a horrid conviction that Antonia was still there, pointing the torch, mocking her.

She screamed. A full-throated, terrified scream.

The policeman lowered the lamp and said quite calmly, 'I think I'd better see what all the fuss is about, don't you, miss?'

He started to unfold the ball of paper.